American Medical Association Contact Information

American Medical Association
330 N. Wabash Ave., Chicago, IL 60611   (312) 464-5000
www.ama-assn.org

Membership information
(800) 262-3211   *msc@ama-assn.org*
www.ama-assn.org/go/membership

Adolescent health
(312) 464-5315   *gaps@ama-assn.org*
www.ama-assn.org/go/adolescenthealth

AMA Foundation
(312) 464-4200   *steven.churchill@ama-assn.org*
www.amafoundation.org

Becoming a Physician
becominganmd@ama-assn.org
www.ama-assn.org/go/becominganmd

Continuing medical education
(312) 464-4671   *cme@ama-assn.org*
www.ama-assn.org/go/cme

Council on Ethical and Judicial Affairs
(312) 464-4823   *ceja@ama-assn.org*
www.ama-assn.org/go/ceja

Council on Medical Education
(312) 464-4515   *meded@ama-assn.org*
www.ama-assn.org/go/councilmeded

Council on Science and Public Health
(312) 464-5046   *csaph@ama-assn.org*
www.ama-assn.org/go/csa

Domestic violence
(312) 464-5376   *violence@ama-assn.org*
www.ama-assn.org/go/violence

Find a residency or fellowship
(312) 464-4748   *rfs@ama-assn.org*
www.ama-assn.org/go/rfs

FREIDA Online
(800) 266-3966   *freida@ama-assn.org*
www.ama-assn.org/go/freida

Genetics and molecular medicine
(312) 464-4964   *srt@ama-assn.org*
www.ama-assn.org/go/genetics

GME data requests
(312) 464-4487   *sarah.brotherton@ama-assn.org*

Health disparities
(312) 464-4616   *tanya.lopez@ama-assn.org*
www.ama-assn.org/go/enddisparities

Health literacy
(312) 464-5357   *louella.hung@ama-assn.org*
www.amafoundation.org

Infectious Diseases
(312) 464-4147
www.ama-assn.org/go/infectiousdiseases

Liaison Committee on Medical Education
(312) 464-4690   *barbara.barzansky@ama-assn.org*
www.lcme.org

Medical education books and CDs
(312) 464-4635   *fred.lenhoff@ama-assn.org*
www.ama-assn.org/go/mededproducts

Medical licensure
(312) 464-4635   *fred.lenhoff@ama-assn.org*
www.ama-assn.org/go/licensure

National GME Census
(800) 866-6793   *gmetrack@aamc.org*
www.aamc.org/gmetrack

Physician health
(312) 464-4616   *tanya.lopez@ama-assn.org*
www.ama-assn.org/go/physicianhealth

State-level GME data
(312) 464-4487   *sarah.brotherton@ama-assn.org*

Virtual Mentor
(312) 464-5260   *virtualmentor@ama-assn.org*
www.virtualmentor.org

AMA Sections/Interest Groups; AMA Advocacy

The AMA represents you: Join today

The AMA offers many sections and special groups representing all physicians. All members receive the *Journal of the American Medical Association* and *American Medical News*. To join the AMA, call (800) AMA-3211, access *www.ama-assn.org/go/join*, or complete the enclosed membership form.

Gay, Lesbian, Bisexual and Transgender (GLBT) Issues Advisory Committee
(312) 464-4748   *glbt@ama-assn.org*
www.ama-assn.org/go/glbt

Group Practice Physicians Advisory Committee
(312) 464-4546   *carrie.waller@ama-assn.org*
www.ama-assn.org/go/medicalgroup

International Medical Graduate Section
(312) 464-5678   *img@ama-assn.org*
www.ama-assn.org/go/imgs

Medical Student Section
(312) 464-4746   *mss@ama-assn.org*
www.ama-assn.org/go/mss

Minority Affairs Section
(312) 464-4335   *mas@ama-assn.org*
www.ama-assn.org/go/mas

Organized Medical Staff Section
(312) 464-2461   *omss@ama-assn.org*
www.ama-assn.org/go/omss

Resident and Fellow Section
(312) 464-4748   *rfs@ama-assn.org*
www.ama-assn.org/go/rfs

Section on Medical Schools
(312) 464-4655   *section@ama-assn.org*
www.ama-assn.org/go/sms

Senior Physicians Group
(312) 464-4539   *spg@ama-assn.org*
www.ama-assn.org/go/spg

Women Physicians Congress
(312) 464-4335   *wpc@ama-assn.org*
www.ama-assn.org/go/wpc

Young Physicians Section
(312) 464-4751   *yps@ama-assn.org*
www.ama-assn.org/go/yps

Current AMA Advocacy Efforts

The AMA is aggressively involved in advocacy efforts related to the most vital issues in medicine today, including:

Access to Care
Affordable Care Act
Affordable Care Act State Implementation
AMPAC
American Recovery & Investment Act
Antitrust Reform
Combating Prescription Drug Abuse and Diversion
Delivery and Payment Models
Drug Shortages
Diabetes Prevention
FTC State Engagement
Funding Research and Medical Education
Graduate Medical Education
Health Care Costs
Health Information Technology
Health Insurance Market Reforms
Independent Payment Advisory Board
Managed Care Reform
Medical Liability Reform
Medicare
Medicare: Building a Higher-Performing System
Medicare Patient Empowerment Act
Medicare SGR Transition Principles
Patient Safety and Quality Improvement
Personalized Medicine
Physician Transparency Reports (Sunshine Act)
Practice Management
Private Payer Reform
Protecting the Business of Medicine
Public Health Improvement
Reforming Medicaid
Regulatory Improvements
Scope of Practice
Student Debt
Sustainable Growth Rate
Truth in Advertising
Violence Prevention

Visit *www.ama-assn.org/go/advocacy* to learn more.

Medical Licensure and Medical Education Organizations

Accreditation Council for Graduate Medical Education
(ACGME)
515 N State St, Chicago, IL 60654
(312) 755-5000   (312) 755-7498 Fax
www.acgme.org

American Board of Medical Specialties (ABMS)
222 N LaSalle St, Ste 1500, Chicago, IL 60601
(312) 436-2600
www.abms.org

American Hospital Association (AHA)
One N Franklin, Chicago, IL 60606
(312) 422-3000   (312) 422-4796 Fax
www.aha.org

American Osteopathic Association (AOA)
142 E Ontario St, Chicago, IL 60611-2864
(312) 202-8000   Fax: (312) 202-8200
www.osteopathic.org

Educational Commission for Foreign Medical Graduates
(ECFMG)
3624 Market Street
Philadelphia, PA 19104-2685
(215) 386-5900   (215) 386-9196 Fax
www.ecfmg.org

Federation of Medical Regulatory Authorities of Canada
2283 St Laurent Blvd, Ste 103
Ottawa, ON K1G 5A2
(613) 738-0372   (613) 738-9169 Fax
www.fmrac.ca

Federation of State Medical Boards (FSMB)
400 Fuller Wiser Road, Suite 300, Euless, TX 76039
(817) 868-4000   (817) 868-4099 Fax
www.fsmb.org

The Joint Commission
One Renaissance Blvd
Oakbrook Terrace, IL 60181
(630) 792-5000   (630) 792-5005 Fax
www.jointcommission.org

National Board of Medical Examiners (NBME)
3750 Market St, Philadelphia, PA 19104-3102
(215) 590-9500   (215) 590-9555 Fax
www.nbme.org

National Board of Osteopathic Medical Examiners (NBOME)
8765 W Higgins Rd, Ste 200
Chicago, IL 60631-4174
(773) 714-0622 or (877) 714-0622 (toll-free)
(773) 714-0631 Fax
www.nbome.org

NBOME Executive Offices and Conference Center; National
Center for Clinical Skills Testing (NCCST)
101 West Elm Street
NCCST, Suite 150
Executive Offices, Suite 230
Conshohocken, PA 19428

National Committee for Quality Assurance (NCQA)
1100 13th St, NW
Washington, DC 20056
(202) 955-3500   (202) 955-3599 Fax
www.ncqa.org

National Practitioner Data Bank and
Healthcare Integrity and Protection Data Bank
PO Box 10832
Chantilly, VA 20153-0832
(800) 767-6732
www.npdb-hipdb.com

Royal College of Physicians and Surgeons of Canada
774 Echo Dr
Ottawa, Ontario, K1S 5N8
(800) 668-3740   (613) 730-8830 Fax
http://rcpsc.medical.org

United States Medical Licensing Examination (USMLE)
3750 Market St
Philadelphia, PA 19104-3190
(215) 590-9700   (215) 590-9470 Fax
www.usmle.org

Assessing medical education and career options?

Beginning a residency or practice?

Considering a career change?

Determining whether to relocate or retire?

The AMA wrote the book—in fact, more than a dozen
books—to help you with the ABCs (and even Ds!) of medical
education and practice. See "Helpful Practice Management
Resources From the AMA" on the next page.

Helpful Practice Management Resources from the AMA

Understanding Coding for the Non-coder
Written specifically for non-coders who need to understand
basic concepts and structures of coding, this resource intro-
duces you to the relationship between coding, payment and
documentation and their impact in health care. Gain a better
understanding of code sets and medical insurance elements
with specific examples of real-life application that focuses on
a high-level view of medical coding and how it affects your
payment.
OP077010 (Print book)   EB077010 (E-Book)
$59.95 ($44.95 for AMA members)

Policies and Procedures for a Successful Medical Practice
Customize the basic policies and procedures provided in
Policies and Procedures for a Successful Medical Practice and
add additional policies and procedures to make it "your own".
Learn how to write and create policies and procedures that
you can use to train your employees to do things your way, and
to add professionalism and consistency to your practice.
OP217213 (Print book)   EB217213 (E-Book)
$124.95   (AMA member price: $99.95)

**A Guide to Achieving Meaningful Use: Leverage Your EHR
to Redesign Workflows and Improve Outcomes**
The concept behind the Meaningful Use legislation is much
more than an incentive program; it's a roadmap for clinical
quality improvement and patient-caregiver engagement in the
care decision process. A Guide to Achieving Meaningful Use
provides details on Stages 1 and 2 of Meaningful Use requirements (with early guidance on Stage 3), Meaningful Use gap
analysis guidance and electronic health records (EHRs).
OP178913 (Print book)   EB179713 (E-Book)
$75   (AMA member price: $56)

Handbook for HIPAA-HITECH Security, second edition
Enhance your understanding of HIPAA-HITECH security rule
requirements with this quick reference tool that provides
step-by-step guidance to implement and maintain compliance
with the latest regulations and federal laws in your practice.
This essential guide will help you learn practical and
pragmatic ways to interpret the new regulations and ensure
compliance.
OP320612 (Print book)   EB312512 (E-Book)
$99.95   (AMA member price: $74.95)

HIPAA Plain & Simple: After the Final Rule, third edition
With the recently published final rule for HIPAA, organizations need the latest information and tools to implement
systems to ensure compliance. This essential resource
expands upon the topics of enforcement, the accounting of
disclosures, and contracts with and disclosures to business
associates while providing new content on migrating to operating rules and meaningful use.
OP320712 (Print book)   EB335512 (E-Book)
$79.95   (AMA member price: $59.95)

Starting, Buying, and Owning the Medical Practice
Whether establishing a solo practice, joining a group or pur-
chasing an existing practice, this comprehensive resource
provides in-depth information on the fundamentals of strategic practice management and future planning for the medical
practice. It tackles strategic options, challenges, and alterna-
tives available when determining the most appropriate models
and methods for successful stability and growth.
OP314411 (Print book)   EB312411 (E-book)
$99.95   (AMA member price: $74.95)

**Reimbursement Management: Improving the Success and
Profitability of Your Practice**
Gain an understanding of the entire reimbursement system
and learn how to obtain the fullest reimbursement of claims
possible while avoiding allegations of improper claims. Useful
for both new and seasoned medical practice professionals,
this resource will help increase familiarity with the reimbursement process and build confidence when handling reimbursement issues.
OP091910 (Print book)   EB091910 (E-book)
$79.95   (AMA member price: $59.95)

**EHR Implementation, second edition
A Step-by-Step Guide for the Medical Practice**
This second edition delivers successful implementation strategies that work, and serves as a project management guide to
help consultants, administrators and physicians navigate the
evaluation, selection, negotiation and culture management
transition to an electronic environment. This helpful resource
features field-tested EHR implementation tools, checklists,
decision trees, job descriptions and workflow analyses.
OP322211 $75   (AMA member price: $56)

AMA HIPAA School
Ensure compliance through an online, three-course program
that satisfies HIPAA workforce training requirements. Content
is prepared by nationally recognized HIPAA and EHR experts
and will help your office achieve awareness and understanding, training of privacy and security rules currently required
by the updated HIPAA regulations, satisfy Meaningful Use
Core Measurement 15 regarding privacy and security, and
confidently navigate the complex legislative regulations of
HIPAA and HITECH. Visit ama-assn.org/go/hipaa-compliance
to enroll.
Train one workforce member:
$132   (AMA member price: $99)
Train five workforce members
$399   (AMA member price: $299)

**Call (800) 621-8335 or visit
www.amabookstore.com to order
AMA members may call
(800) 262-3211 to place an order**

Activate your AMA membership today.

Call: (800) 262-3211

Fax: (800) 262-3221

Mail:
American Medical Association
PO Box 4198
Carol Stream, IL 60197-9788

Online:
www.ama-assn.org

Membership categories and dues rates
(Please indicate your membership category below)

Physician

❑ $420 Regular medical practice

❑ $315 Second year in medical practice

❑ $210 First year in medical practice

❑ $280 Military/government service
(If military, please indicate the branch of service in the space provided)

❑ $210 Semi-retired
(65 years of age or older, working 1–20 hours a week)

❑ $84 Fully retired
(Age notwithstanding—working 0 hours)

Resident/fellow

❑ $45 One-year membership

Up to 12.5% multi-year discount available online

Medical student

❑ $20 One-year membership

Up to 17% multi-year discount available online

2014 Membership Application   XMBRSP

YES! I'd like to receive email about AMA advocacy initiatives, news for physicians, and AMA products and services.

My email address is:_____

First name   Middle initial   Last name

Former last name *(if applicable)*

Preferred professional mailing address (❑ Home ❑ Office or ❑ Both)

City   State   ZIP

Office phone   Fax

Medical School   Graduation Year

Date of birth *(to aid in tracking/identification)*   Military branch of service *(if applicable)*

Method of payment *(see rate chart on left)*

❑ **Check** *(Please make your check payable to: American Medical Association)*

❑ Please charge my: ❑ Visa ❑ MasterCard ❑ American Express

Let us remember for you—choose automatic renewal. Select option 1 or 2 below.
(See below for terms and conditions. Automatic renewal does not apply to residents/fellows or medical students.)

❑ 1. Single payment with automatic renewal
❑ 2. Installment payments with automatic renewal
❑ 3. Single payment without automatic renewal

By submitting my credit card information, I authorize AMA to charge my credit card for annual AMA membership dues. I represent that the information I provided is accurate and that I have authority to authorize charges to the designated account for the purpose of paying the amounts due.

Credit card number

Expiration date _____   Security code _____

The security code is the last 4 digits on the back of your credit card. On AMEX cards, it is the 4 digit non-embossed number on the front of the card, above your card number.

Signature _____

Applying for AMA membership:
Membership is contingent upon the American Medical Association's (AMA) acceptance of the membership application. The endorsement, deposit or negotiation of an applicant's check does not guarantee admission into or acceptance of membership by the AMA. Checks received will routinely be deposited without a determination of the propriety of the payment or the applicability of the amount. Applicants who are not admitted to membership will receive a refund from the AMA for the amount submitted.

AMA dues are not deductible as a charitable contribution for federal income tax purposes, but may be partially deducted as a business expense. AMA estimates that 55% of your membership dues are allocable to lobbying activities of the AMA, and therefore are not deductible for income tax purposes.

Dues-paying members are eligible to receive a print copy of *JAMA*. For the 2014 membership year, the allocated cost of $32 for *JAMA* is included in, and not deductible from AMA membership dues. All members receive free online access to *JAMA* and the 9 specialty journals. In addition, all members are eligible to receive *AMA Morning Rounds*.

Conditions of AMA membership and application:
As part of a physician organization committed to strengthening the ethics of medicine, every member pledges to uphold the Principles of Medical Ethics

as interpreted in the Code of Medical Ethics, and to comply with the Bylaws of the American Medical Association and the Rules of the AMA Council on Ethical and Judicial Affairs.

• The AMA Principles and the Code of Medical Ethics can be found at www.ama-assn.org/go/codeofmedicalethics

• The AMA's Bylaws and Rules of the Council on Ethical and Judicial Affairs can be found at www.ama-assn.org/go/ceja

Applicants and members are required to disclose to the AMA Office of General Counsel any violations of the Principles of Medical Ethics or unprofessional conduct including actions taken regarding professional licensure, medical staff privileges, or felony or fraud convictions. Additionally, the Health Care Quality Improvement Act requires professional societies (such as the AMA) to report certain professional review actions, including denial of membership, to the National Practitioner Data Bank.

Terms and conditions for automatic renewal authorization: *Monthly installment payments with automatic renewal:* Installment payments begin the month the membership transaction is made and continue until paid in full by December 31. You will receive a reminder notice each year on or about November 1. Unless you cancel your authorization in

writing by the previous December 1 your designated account will be charged 1/12 of the annual membership dues beginning January of each year.

Annual payment with automatic renewal: Your designated account will be charged immediately for the full amount of your annual membership dues. Thereafter, you will receive a reminder notice each year on or about November 1. Your credit card will then be charged on or about January 1 of each year for AMA membership dues unless you cancel your authorization in writing, by the previous December 1.

Physicians in a membership dues category that will transition at the time of renewal to a higher dues category will see the dues rates below at the time of renewal. The AMA will provide prior written notice of any change in the annual membership dues rate.

• First year in practice: $210
• Second year in practice: $315
• Regular practice: $420

Cancellation of your automatic renewal authorization must be submitted in one of the following ways:

Email: msc@ama-assn.org
Fax: (800) 262-3221
Mail: AMA Member Relations
330 N Wabash Ste 39300
Chicago, IL 60611-5885

AMA
AMERICAN MEDICAL
ASSOCIATION

State Medical Licensure Requirements and Statistics

2014

Executive Vice President, Chief Executive Officer: James L. Madara, MD
Chief Operating Officer: Bernard L. Hengesbaugh
Senior Vice President, Business Products and Services: Robert A. Musacchio, PhD
Vice President, Coding and Reimbursement Products Portfolio: Jay Ahlman
Vice President, Key Accounts, Sales, and Marketing: Ana English
Vice President, Business Operations: Vanessa Hayden
Director, Product Development: Richard W. Newman
Senior Acquisitions Editor: Janet Thron
Manager, Book and Product Development and Production: Nancy Baker
Senior Developmental Editor: Michael Ryder
Production Specialist: Meghan Anderson
Director, Key Account Management: Joann Skiba
Director, Channel Programs and Marketing Operations: Erin Kalitowski
Director, Product Marketing: Karen Christensen-Araujo
Marketing Manager: Lori Hollacher

Internet address: www.ama-assn.org

Additional copies of this book may be ordered by calling (800) 621-8335 or from the secure AMA Web
site at www.amastore.com. Refer to product number OP399014.

Comments or Inquires:
Fred Donini-Lenhoff
Director, Section on Medical Schools
330 N. Wabash Ave.
Chicago, IL 60611
(312) 464-4635

Email: fred.lenhoff@ama-assn.org

www.ama-assn.org/go/licensure

ISBN 978-1-60359-897-2
BP15:10/13

Contents

Tables

Foreword

State Medical Licensure Requirements and Statistics, 2014, presents current information and statistics on medical licensure in the United States and possessions. Data were obtained from a number of sources, including state boards of medical examiners, the Federation of State Medical Boards, National Board of Medical Examiners, National Board of Osteopathic Medical Examiners, Educational Commission for Foreign Medical Graduates, the United States Medical Licensing Examination Secretariat, and others.

Licensure data and policies in this publication were compiled from the AMA's Medical Licensure Survey, which was sent in June 2013 to all 54 composite and 14 osteopathic boards of medical examiners in the United States. Although every effort was made to collect and record accurate data for each board, users of this book should note that the boards meet frequently and, as a result, their licensure and examination policies are modified regularly. It is therefore recommended that the state licensing boards (see Appendixes A and B) be contacted for the most up-to-date information.

Boards in the following jurisdictions did not provide updates to the AMA in 2013 via the licensure survey:

- Connecticut
- Guam
- Illinois
- Maine DO
- Missouri
- New Mexico DO
- New York
- Puerto Rico
- Tennessee DO
- Utah DO
- Vermont DO
- Virgin Islands

For more information

The AMA offers Internet information on medical licensure through its Medical Licensure Online website (*www.ama-assn.org/go/licensure*). The site includes information from this book and *Licensing and Credentialing: What Physicians Need to Know*, as well as links to state and national licensing organizations.

Acknowledgments

The editor would like to thank the personnel of the state medical and osteopathic licensing agencies who provided statistics and licensing requirements for this publication. Acknowledgments are also due to the following individuals and organizations for their assistance

- Accreditation Council for Continuing Medical Education
  Kate Regnier, MA, MBA, Deputy Chief Executive and Chief Operating Officer
  Tamar Hosansky, Director of Communications

- Accreditation Council for Graduate Medical Education
  Thomas J. Nasca, M.D., MACP, Chief Executive Officer

- Administrators in Medicine
  Barbara Neuman, Executive Director

- Robert D. Aronson, Managing Attorney
  Aronson & Associates, P.A.

- Department of the Navy
  Stazy Godlewski, Risk and Quality Management
  Becky Boyrie, CPMSM, Acting Director and Manager, Navy Medical Staff Services, Centralized Credentials & Privileging Directorate

- Educational Commission for Foreign Medical Graduates
  William C. Kelly, MS, Acting Vice President for Operations
  Elizabeth M. Ingraham, Director of Communications
  Leslie Young, Administrative Manager, Publications
  Samuel M. Young, Manager, Communications

- Federation of Medical Regulatory Authorities of Canada
  Fleur-Ange Lefebvre, Executive Director

- Federation of State Medical Boards of the United States
  Drew Carlson, Director of Communications

- US Dept. of Health and Human Services, Health Resources and Services Administration
  Ernia Hughes, Acting Director, Division of Practitioner Data Banks
  David B. Kirby, JD, Editor, Division of Practitioner Data Banks

- The Joint Commission
  Mark R. Chassin, MD, President
  Elizabeth Eaken Zhani, Media Relations Manager

- National Board of Medical Examiners and United States Medical Licensing Examination Secretariat
  Susan Deitch, Office of Communications
  Amy Buono, Program Officer, USMLE

- National Board of Osteopathic Medical Examiners
  Laura G. Barrett, Director for Communications

We would also like to acknowledge the contributions of the following AMA staff:

- Division of Survey and Data Resources
  Monica Quiroz, Mark Long, Susan Montrimas, Derek Smart, and Maria Vasquez
- Medical Education
  Gretchen Kenagy, PhD
- Continuing Physician Professional Development
  Mary Kelly

Fred Donini-Lenhoff, Editor

Susan Skochelak, MD, MPH, Group Vice President, Medical Education

Chapter 1

Licensure Policies and Regulations of State Medical/Osteopathic Boards

Administration of the United States Medical Licensing Examination Steps 1 and 2

All states require a written examination for initial licensure: generally, for MDs, the three-step United States Medical Licensing Examination (USMLE), which has replaced the Federation Licensing Examination (FLEX) and the national board examination of the National Board of Medical Examiners (NBME). Osteopathic physicians take the three-level Comprehensive Osteopathic Medical Licensure Examination (COMLEX-USA) of the National Board of Osteopathic Medical Examiners (NBOME), as described on page 11.

In 1990, the Federation of State Medical Boards (FSMB) and the National Board of Medical Examiners (NBME) established the United States Medical Licensing Examination (USMLE), a single examination for assessment of US and international medical school students or graduates seeking initial licensure by US licensing jurisdictions. The USMLE replaced the Federation Licensing Examination (FLEX) and the certification examination of the NBME, as well as the Foreign Medical Graduate Examination in the Medical Sciences (FMGEMS), which was formerly used by the Educational Commission for Foreign Medical Graduates (ECFMG) for certification purposes.

The USMLE is a single examination program with three steps. Each step is complementary to the others; no step can stand alone in the assessment of readiness for medical licensure. Additional information on the USMLE appears in Chapter 3.

About half of boards do not place any limits on the number of times a candidate for licensure may take USMLE Step 1 and do not place limits on taking Step 2. About one third of boards do not limit the amount of time in which a candidate for licensure must pass Steps 1 or 2; most of the boards with such time limits have specified a seven-year time period (Table 1).

Administration of the United States Medical Licensing Examination Step 3

(See the first two paragraphs on page 1 for general information on the USMLE.)

Many states require US or Canadian medical school graduates to have from six to 12 months of accredited US or Canadian GME to take USMLE Step 3. In some states, graduates of foreign medical schools are required to have completed more GME (as much as three years in several states). A number of states do not require completion of GME to take Step 3 or require only that a physician taking the examination be enrolled in a GME program (Table 2).

Nearly all medical licensing authorities require completion of Steps 1, 2, and 3 within a seven-year period, or 10 years for those in MD/PhD or similar dual-degree programs, although a number of states may make exceptions in the event of extenuating circumstances (Table 3). The seven-year period begins when the medical student or graduate first passes Step 1 or Step 2. Some states allow 10 years for completion of all three steps or do not impose a time limit for completion. Many states limit the number of attempts allowed to pass each step (particularly Step 3) and require additional education, training, or experience after a given number of failed attempts.

For 2013, the fee for the Step 3 examination is $780. Additional information on the USMLE is in Chapter 3.

Additional Notes for Specific Licensing Jurisdictions

Alabama—If an applicant fails to achieve a passing score on Step 3 in three administrations, the Board may approve one additional attempt to pass Step 3 after *demonstration by the applicant of additional education, experience, or training acceptable to the Board.* In addition, Steps 1, 2, and 3 must be passed within a total of ten attempts.

Applicants who are "dual degree candidates" (see definition, below) must achieve a passing score on Step 3 within three administrations and complete Steps 1, 2, and 3 within a 10-year period, beginning when the applicant initially passes his or her first step. (*Note:* The board may approve, at its discretion, an additional five years of eligibility for dual-degree candidates.) The Board does not accept scores from a retaking of a previously passed step of the USMLE.

For purposes of the USMLE, "dual degree candidates" are defined as applicants who are:

- Pursuing an MD or DO degree and PhD degree in an institution or program accredited by the Liaison Committee on Medical Education and a regional university accrediting body; and

- A student in good standing, enrolled in the institution or program; and

- Pursuing PhD studies in a field of biological sciences tested in the USMLE Step 1 content, including, but not limited to, anatomy, biochemistry, physiology, microbiology, pharmacology, pathology, genetics, neuroscience, and molecular biology.

Arizona—There is no time limit for USMLE Step 3 completion for applicants who hold a license in another jurisdiction (licensure by endorsement); for initial licensure, the seven-year limit applies.

Minnesota—Four attempts for Steps 1 and 2 are allowed if the physician holds a license in another state and is board certified by the ABMS, AOA, RCPSC, or CFPC.

North Carolina—Any applicant who has not completed a USMLE step within three attempts must be certified or recertified within the past 10 years by a specialty board approved by the American Board of Medical Specialties, American Osteopathic Association, CCFP, FRCP, or FRCS.

North Dakota—An exception to the three-attempt limit for Steps 1 and 2 may be allowed for a physician who has a valid license in another state, has practiced at least 10 years, has no disciplinary actions imposed by another board, is certified by a board of the ABMS or the RCPSC, and meets the requirement regarding the time limit for examination attempts.

Ohio—Any applicant who has not passed a USMLE step within three attempts must meet the following requirements to be eligible for licensure: (1) Successfully complete an additional year of GME in addition to that required for licensure. Such education shall be completed subsequent to the final step that has been failed more than three times; and (2) Retake the testing sequence.

Any applicant who has not completed the required steps within the 10-year time period, and has not failed any step more than three times, must (1) Retake the appropriate steps to bring the testing sequence within the required 10-year time period; or (2) Demonstrate good cause, as determined by the board, for not having passed all three steps within the 10-year period.

Oregon—A waiver is allowed of the three-attempt limit for USMLE Step 3 (1 year approved GME after third failed attempt before fourth and final attempt) for applicants who are ABMS certified.

A waiver of the seven-year time limit for completion of USMLE Steps 1, 2, and 3 is allowed for applicants who are ABMS certified, have participated in a combined MD/PhD or DO/PhD program, suffered from a documented significant health condition that by its severity would necessarily cause delay to an applicant's medical study, or have completed continuous GME equivalent to an MD/PhD or DO/PhD program.

Tennessee—The board may grant an extension of the seven-year limit for completing the USMLE to an applicant who is licensed in good standing in at least three other jurisdictions and who has otherwise met the requirements for licensure.

Texas—Single degree candidates must pass all examination steps within seven years. The timeframe is expanded to ten calendar years if the applicant is (1) ABMS or AOA Bureau of Osteopathic Specialists board certified, or (2) has been issued a faculty temporary license in Texas, has practiced under that permit for at least 12 months, and has been recommended for licensure by the institution at which the faculty temporary license was used. MD/PhD graduates must pass all steps within two years of completing the GME required for licensure in Texas. The timeframe is expanded to within 10 years of completing the GME required for licensure in Texas if the applicant (1) is ABMS or AOA Bureau of Osteopathic Specialists board certified, or (2) has been issued a faculty temporary license in Texas, has practiced under that permit for at least 12 months, and has been recommended for licensure by the institution at which the faculty temporary license was used.

The time frame to complete the exam sequence is waived for applicants who agree to practice solely and indefinitely in an MUA or HPSA and have been licensed in good standing in another state for 5 years.

In addition, all Texas applicants have three attempts to pass each step, with a few exceptions. Applicants who qualify for the exceptions either held a PIT permit on 9/1/2005 or have been licensed in good standing in another state for five years. Exceptions to the three-attempt limit are a fourth attempt on one step only, or up to six attempts on one step only if the applicant is ABMS or AOA board certified and completes, in Texas, an additional two years of GME beyond what is required.

Virgin Islands—The USMLE is not administered; the Special Purpose Examination (SPEX) is used to evaluate physicians' knowledge.

Washington—All applicants who graduated from medical school after 1993, whether within the United States or internationally, are required to pass the USMLE to qualify for licensure.

Table 1
Administration of the US Medical Licensing Examination Steps 1 and 2

	Number of Times Candidates for Licensure May Take USMLE Step 1	Number of Times Candidates for Licensure May Take USMLE Step 2	Amount of Time Within Which Steps 1 and 2 of USMLE Must Be Passed
Alabama	No limit	No limit	No limit
Alaska	2	2	7 yrs
Arizona*	No limit	No limit	No limit
Arkansas	3	3	7 yrs
California	No limit	No limit	No limit
Colorado	No limit	No limit	7 yrs (all 3 steps)
Connecticut	No limit	No limit	No limit
Delaware	6	6	7 yrs (all 3 steps)
DC	No limit	No limit	7 yrs (all 3 steps); 10 yrs for MD/PhDs
Florida	No limit	No limit	No limit
Georgia	No limit	No limit	7 yrs (all 3 steps); 9 yrs for MD/PhDs
Guam	Not applicable	Not applicable	Not applicable
Hawaii	No limit	No limit	No limit
Idaho	2	2	7 yrs (all 3 steps)
Illinois	5	5	7 yrs (all 3 steps)
Indiana	3	3	10 yrs (all 3 steps)
Iowa	6	6	10 yrs (all 3 steps)
Kansas	No limit	No limit	10 yrs (all 3 steps)
Kentucky	4	4	No limit
Louisiana	No limit	4	No limit
Maine	No limit	No limit	7 yrs (all 3 steps)
Maryland	No limit	No limit	10 yrs (all 3 steps)
Massachusetts	No limit	No limit	7 yrs (all 3 steps)
Michigan	No limit	No limit	No limit
Minnesota*	3	3	5 yrs or before end of training (Step 2)
Mississippi	No limit	No limit	No limit
Missouri	3	3	7 yrs (all 3 steps)
Montana	No limit	No limit	7 yrs (all 3 steps)
Nebraska	4	4	10 yrs (all 3 steps)
Nevada	No limit	No limit	7 yrs (all 3 steps and 9 total attempts); no more than 3 attempts on Step 3. (10 yrs for MD/PhD programs)
New Hampshire	3	3	No limit
New Jersey	No limit	No limit	7 yrs (all 3 steps)
New Mexico	6	6	7 yrs (all 3 steps)
New York	No limit	No limit	No limit
North Carolina	3	3	No limit
North Dakota*	3	3	7 yrs (all 3 steps)

(continued on next page)

Table 1 (continued)
Administration of the US Medical Licensing Examination Steps 1 and 2

	Number of Times Candidates for Licensure May Take USMLE Step 1	Number of Times Candidates for Licensure May Take USMLE Step 2	Amount of Time Within Which Steps 1 and 2 of USMLE Must Be Passed
Ohio*	4	4	10 yrs (all 3 steps); no more than 3 failures of any step
Oklahoma	3	3	10 yrs (all 3 steps)
Oregon*	No limit	No limit	7 yrs (all 3 steps)
Pennsylvania	No limit	No limit	No limit
Puerto Rico	No limit	No limit	7 yrs
Rhode Island	3	3	7 yrs
South Carolina	3	3	10 yrs (all 3 steps)
South Dakota	3	3	7 yrs (all 3 steps); 10 yrs for MD/PhDs; no more than two failures of any step
Tennessee	No limit	No limit	No limit
Texas*	3	3	7 calendar yrs (all 3 steps); 2 years after required GME for MD/PhDs; time frame waived if practicing in an MUA or HPSA
Utah	3	3	7 yrs (10 yrs for MD/PhD programs)
Vermont	No limit	No limit	No limit
Virgin Islands	Not applicable	Not applicable	Not applicable
Virginia	No limit	No limit	10 yrs (all 3 steps)
Washington	No limit	No limit	No limit
West Virginia	No limit	No limit	10 yrs
Wisconsin	3	3	10 yrs (all 3 steps)
Wyoming	No limit	No limit	7 yrs (all 3 steps)

* Refer to introductory text to this table for more information on this state's regulations.

Note: All information should be verified with the licensing board; licenses based on endorsement are granted to those physicians meeting all state requirements.

Table 2
Administration of the US Medical Licensing Examination Step 3: Graduate Medical Education Requirements

	Amount of Accredited US or Canadian GME Required to Take USMLE Step 3	
	Graduates of US/Canadian Medical Schools	International Medical Graduates
Alabama	None (but must be enrolled in GME program)	2 yrs (must be enrolled in third yr of GME program)
Alaska	1 yr	1 yr
Arizona	6 mos	6 mos
Arkansas	None	None
California	None	None
Colorado	1 yr	3 yrs
Connecticut	None	None
Delaware	None	None
DC	6 mos	3 yrs
Florida	None	None
Georgia	1 yr	1-3 yrs
Guam	2 yrs	2 yrs
Hawaii	None (must be enrolled in first yr of GME program)	1 yr (and must be enrolled in second yr of GME program)
Idaho	9 mos	2 yrs, 9 mos
Illinois	1 yr	1 yr
Indiana	1 yr	2 yrs
Iowa	7 mos (or enrollment in approved GME program)	7 mos (or enrollment in approved GME program)
Kansas	1 yr (or enrollment in GME program in Kansas)	3 yrs (2 yrs in ACGME-accredited program plus 1 other yr), or enrolled in GME program
Kentucky	1 yr	1 yr
Louisiana	None (but must be enrolled in GME program)	None (but must be enrolled in GME program)
Maine	1 yr	1 yr (plus ECFMG certificate)
Maryland	None	None
Massachusetts	1 yr	1 yr
Michigan	6 mos	6 mos
Minnesota	None (but must be enrolled in GME program)	None (but must be enrolled in GME program)
Mississippi	1 yr	1 yr
Missouri	1 yr	3 yrs
Montana	1 yr	1 yr (plus ECFMG)
Nebraska	None	None
Nevada	None	None
New Hampshire	None (but must be enrolled in GME program)	None (but must be enrolled in GME program)
New Jersey	1 yr	1 yr
New Mexico	None	None
New York	None	None
North Carolina	None	None
North Dakota	6 mos	1 yr
Ohio	9 mos	9 mos
Oklahoma	None	None

(continued on next page)

Table 2 (continued)
Administration of the US Medical Licensing Examination Step 3: Graduate Medical Education Requirements

	Amount of Accredited US or Canadian GME Required to Take USMLE Step 3	
	Graduates of US/Canadian Medical Schools	International Medical Graduates
Oregon	None (but must be enrolled in GME program)	None (but must be enrolled in GME program)
Pennsylvania	None	None
Puerto Rico	None	None
Rhode Island	1 yr	1 yr
South Carolina	1 yr	3 yrs
South Dakota	None	None
Tennessee	1 yr	1 yr
Texas	None	None
Utah	None	None (must be ECFMG-certified)
Vermont	7 mos	7 mos
Virgin Islands	Not applicable	Not applicable
Virginia	None	None
Washington	1 yr (or enrolled in GME program)	1 yr (or enrolled in GME program)
West Virginia	None	None
Wisconsin	1 yr	1 yr
Wyoming	1 yr	1 yr

Abbreviations

USMLE—United States Medical Licensing Examination
ECFMG—Educational Commission for Foreign Medical Graduates
GME—graduate medical education

Note: *All information should be verified with the licensing board; medical licenses are granted to those physicians meeting all state requirements—at the discretion of the board.*

Table 3
Administration of the US Medical Licensing Examination Step 3: Time Limits for Completion

	Number of Times Candidates for Licensure May Take USMLE Step 3	Requirements to Repeat Step 3 if Not Passed in Designated Number of Attempts	Time Limit for Completion of All Steps of USMLE	Time Limit for MD/PhD or Dual-Degree Candidates	Time Limit May be Waived in Event of Extenuating Circumstances
Alabama*	3	Further education or training	7 yrs	10 yrs	Yes (if ABMS or AOA certified)
Alaska	2		7 yrs		No
Arizona*	No limit		7 yrs (initial applicants only)		No
Arkansas	3		7 yrs	10 yrs	Yes
California	4	Minimum of 4 years continuous licensure in another state and ABMS cert. may be considered	10 yrs		Yes
Colorado	No limit		7 yrs	10 yrs	Yes
Connecticut	No limit		7 yrs		No
Delaware	6		7 yrs		No
DC	No limit	After 3 failed attempts, 1 additional yr ACGME- or AOA-approved GME	7 yrs	10 yrs	Yes
Florida	No limit		No limit		—
Georgia	3	1 yr of additional Board-approved training	7 yrs	9 yrs	Yes
Guam	No limit		7 yrs		No
Hawaii	No limit		7 yrs	7 yrs	No
Idaho	2	Remedial training; may be required to be interviewed, evaluated, or examined by the Board	7 yrs	10 yrs	Yes
Illinois	5	Further education, experience, or remedial training	7 yrs		Yes
Indiana	3		10 yrs	10 yrs	Yes
Iowa	3	After 3 failed attempts, 3 yrs of progressive GME required	10 yrs (If not, ABMS or AOA board certification required)	10 yrs	Yes
Kansas	3	After 3 failed attempts, must appear before Board for approval to take a fourth or subsequent attempt	10 yrs		Yes
Kentucky	4		No limit		No
Louisiana	4		10 yrs		Yes
Maine	3	After 3 failed attempts, applicant may request waiver	7 yrs		Yes
Maryland	No limit		10 yrs	10 yrs	No
Massachusetts	3		7 yrs		Yes
Michigan	No limit	After 5 yrs from first attempt, additional GME in Board-approved program in-state	No limit		—
Minnesota	3 (4 if currently licensed in another state and specialty board certified)		Within 5 yrs of passing Step 2 or by end of training		Yes (medical illness)

(continued on next page)

Table 3 (continued)
Administration of the US Medical Licensing Examination Step 3: Time Limits for Completion

	Number of Times Candidates for Licensure May Take USMLE Step 3	Requirements to Repeat Step 3 if Not Passed in Designated Number of Attempts	Time Limit for Completion of All Steps of USMLE	Time Limit for MD/PhD or Dual-Degree Candidates	Time Limit May be Waived in Event of Extenuating Circumstances
Mississippi	3	After 3 failed attempts, 1 additional yr ACGME- or AOA-approved GME	7 yrs		Yes
Missouri	3		7 yrs		No
Montana	3		7 yrs	Exception may be granted	Yes
Nebraska	4		10 yrs		No
Nevada	3		7 yrs (all 3 steps and 9 total attempts)	10 yrs	Yes (if ABMS certified)
New Hampshire	3	Further education, training, or experience	No limit		—
New Jersey	5	Further education, training, or experience	7 yrs (if not passed, must repeat entire sequence)		Yes
New Mexico	6 (within 7 yrs of first pass)		7 yrs	10 yrs	Yes
New York	No limit		No limit		—
North Carolina	3		No limit		—
North Dakota	3		7 yrs	Exception may be granted	No
Ohio*	4	Further training, retake entire sequence	10 yrs	10 yrs	Yes
Oklahoma	3		10 yrs	10 yrs	No
Oregon*	4	After 3 failed attempts, 1 yr of GME required before 4th attempt	7 yrs	Exception may be granted	Yes (see note)
Pennsylvania	6		No limit		—
Puerto Rico	No limit		7 yrs		
Rhode Island	3		7 yrs		Yes
South Carolina	3		10 yrs		No
South Dakota	3		7 yrs	10 yrs	Yes (if ABMS certified)
Tennessee*	No limit		7 yrs		Yes (see note)
Texas*	3		7 yrs	2 years after required GME	Yes
Utah	3	Remedial training	7 yrs	10 yrs	No
Vermont	3		7 yrs	10 yrs	No
Virgin Islands*	Not applicable		Not applicable		No
Virginia	No limit		10 yrs		Yes (if ABMS certified)
Washington*	3	Remedial training	7 yrs	10 yrs	Yes

Table 3 (continued)

Administration of the US Medical Licensing Examination Step 3: Time Limits for Completion

	Number of Times Candidates for Licensure May Take USMLE Step 3	Requirements to Repeat Step 3 if Not Passed in Designated Number of Attempts	Time Limit for Completion of All Steps of USMLE	Time Limit for MD/PhD or Dual-Degree Candidates	Time Limit May be Waived in Event of Extenuating Circumstances
West Virginia*	No limit		10 yrs	10 yrs	No
Wisconsin	3	Must reapply for license and present evidence of further education or training	10 yrs	12 yrs	No
Wyoming	No limit	1 additional year of training or other assessment, training, or evaluation program(s)	7 yrs	8 yrs	No

Abbreviations

ABMS—American Board of Medical Specialties
ACGME—Accreditation Council for Graduate Medical Education
AOA—American Osteopathic Association
USMLE—United States Medical Licensing Examination
GME—graduate medical education

* Refer to introductory text to this table for more information on this state's regulations.

Note: *All information should be verified with the licensing board; medical licenses are granted to those physicians meeting all state requirements—at the discretion of the board.*

Administration of the Comprehensive Osteopathic Medical Licensing Examination: Time Limits for Completion

Osteopathic Physicians (DOs) take the three-level Comprehensive Osteopathic Medical Licensure Examination (COMLEX-USA) of the National Board of Osteopathic Medical Examiners (NBOME).

A candidate is eligible to take the COMLEX-USA Level 3 examination if he or she meets the following requirements:

1. Passed the COMLEX-USA Level 1, COMLEX-USA Level 2-CE and Level 2-PE examinations as determined by the NBOME; and

2. Graduated from an osteopathic medical school accredited by the American Osteopathic Association's Commission on Osteopathic College Accreditation (AOA COCA) with an earned DO degree, and the NBOME has received confirmation from the Office of the Dean of the candidate's college/school of matriculation or a verified copy of his or her diploma from an accredited osteopathic medical school.

Notwithstanding the foregoing, a candidate who graduated from an accredited college of osteopathic medicine before January 1, 2005 and successfully completed COMLEX-USA Level 2-CE before June 30, 2005 is exempt from the requirement of passing COMLEX-USA Level 2-PE as a condition of eligibility to take COMLEX-USA Level 3.

The majority of medical and osteopathic boards do not place a limit on the number of attempts to pass COMLEX-USA that a candidate for licensure may undertake, nor do they place a time limit for passage of all three Levels of COMLEX-USA (Table 4).

Additional Notes for Specific Licensing Jurisdictions

North Carolina—Any applicant who has not completed a COMLEX level within three attempts must be certified or recertified within the past 10 years by a a specialty board approved by the American Board of Medical Specialties, American Osteopathic Association, CCFP, FRCP, or FRCS.

Oregon—Three attempts for COMLEX-USA Level 3, plus one year graduate medical training (waiver of 1 year of training plus fourth attempt if AOA certified); seven years to complete USMLE or COMLEX-USA (possible waiver for dual degree candidates; individuals with personal illness; those with current certification by AOA; or those who have completed graduate training equivalent to number of years to a dual degree program).

Table 4
Administration of the Comprehensive Osteopathic Medical Licensing Examination: Time Limits for Completion

	Number of Times Candidates for Licensure May Take COMLEX	Time Limit for Completion of All Steps of COMLEX
Alabama	No limit	No limit
Alaska	2 attempts per Level	7 yrs
Arizona DO	No limit	No limit
Arkansas	3 attempts per Level	7 yrs
California DO	No limit	No limit
Colorado		
Connecticut	No limit	No limit
Delaware	No limit	No limit
DC	No limit	7 yrs; 10 yrs for DO/PhD candidates
Florida DO	No limit	No limit
Georgia	3 attempts	No limit
Guam		
Hawaii	No limit	No limit
Idaho	No limit	No limit
Illinois	5 attempts total	No limit
Indiana	5 attempts per Level	7 yrs
Iowa	6 attempts for Levels 1 and 2; 3 attempts for Level 3	10 yrs
Kansas	3 attempts for Level 3	10 yrs
Kentucky	4 attempts per Level	10 yrs
Louisiana	4 attempts at Levels 2 or 3	10 yrs
Maine DO	No limit	No limit
Maryland	No limit	10 yrs
Massachusetts	3 attempts for Level 3; 1 yr of GME before 4th attempt	7 yrs
Michigan DO	No limit	No limit
Minnesota	6 attempts	No limit
Mississippi	No limit	No limit
Missouri	3 attempts	No limit
Montana	No limit	No limit
Nebraska	4 attempts per Level	10 yrs
Nevada DO	No limit	No limit
New Hampshire	3 attempts	No limit
New Jersey	5 attempts	7 yrs
New Mexico DO	No limit	No limit
New York	No limit	No limit
North Carolina*	3 attempts per Level	No limit
North Dakota	3 attempts per Level	7 yrs
Ohio	4 attempts per Level	10 yrs
Oklahoma DO	No limit	No limit

(continued on next page)

Table 4
Administration of the Comprehensive Osteopathic Medical Licensing Examination: Time Limits for Completion

	Number of Times Candidates for Licensure May Take COMLEX	Time Limit for Completion of All Steps of COMLEX
Oregon*	3 attempts for Level 3, plus 1 yr GME for 4th attempt	7 yrs
Pennsylvania DO	No limit	No limit
Puerto Rico		
Rhode Island	3 attempts per Level	
South Carolina	3 attempts per Level (4 with ABMS/AOA certification)	10 yrs
South Dakota	3 attempts per Level	7 yrs
Tennessee DO	No limit	No limit
Texas	3 attempts per Level	7 yrs (2 years past required GME for DO/PhD applicants)
Utah DO	3 attempts per Level	7 yrs (10 yrs for DO/PhD candidates)
Vermont DO		7 yrs
Virginia	No limit	No limit
Washington DO	No limit	No limit
West Virginia DO	No limit	No limit
Wisconsin		
Wyoming	7 attempts	7 yrs (8 yrs for DO/PhD candidates)

Endorsement Policies for Physicians Holding an Initial License

Endorsement is the process through which a state issues an unrestricted license to practice medicine to an individual who holds a valid and unrestricted license in another jurisdiction. Licensure endorsement, previously referred to as "reciprocity," is generally based on documentation of successfully completing approved examinations, authentication of required core documents, and completion of any additional requirements assessing the applicant's fitness to practice medicine in the new jurisdiction. Each state has strict endorsement requirements.

A few boards require that a license be endorsed within a certain period after examination (usually 10 years). In most of these states, the Special Purpose Examination (SPEX) is required if the time limit is not met (Table 5).

The Comprehensive Osteopathic Medical Variable-Purpose Examination (COMVEX) is a post-licensure examination for osteopathic physicians who require reevaluation after initial licensure; for more information, see www.nbome.org/comvex.asp.

Nearly all medical boards will accept or consider for endorsement the NBME certificate or the United States Medical Licensing Examination (USMLE), except for those jurisdictions that do not accept endorsements. A number of osteopathic boards do not accept USMLE for licensure by endorsement.

The majority of state medical boards require some or all candidates for licensure endorsement to appear for an interview; a few also require some or all candidates to appear for an oral examination (Table 6).

Additional Notes for Specific Licensing Jurisdictions

Idaho—Each applicant must pass an examination acceptable to the Board, within the time period recommended by the examination authority, which thoroughly tests the applicant's fitness to practice medicine. If the applicant fails to pass the examination on two separate occasions, the applicant may be required to be interviewed, evaluated, or examined by the Board.

Maryland—Licensure by endorsement is not available; the information in Table 5 reflects the requirements for any applicant for initial medical licensure, whether or not another state has issued a license to the applicant.

SPEX is required if an applicant's licensure application was completed more than 15 years ago, the applicant has not maintained uninterrupted licensure in the US, and the applicant has not been certified or recertified by a specialty board within the past 10 years.

Oregon—SPEX may be waived if an applicant (1) was ABMS certified or recertified within 10 years of date of applying for an Oregon license, or (2) completed an accredited one-year residency or a board-approved clinical fellowship, or (3) obtained continuing medical education to the Board's satisfaction.

Table 5
Endorsement Policies for Physicians Holding an Initial License

	Time Limit for Endorsement After Exam	Requirements If Time Limit Not Met	Credential(s) Also Accepted (in Addition to USMLE, NBME)						Notes
			LMCC	NBOME	SBE	COMLEX	FLEX	ABMS	
Alabama	10 yrs	SPEX, ABMS	Yes	Yes		Yes	Yes		
Alaska	None		Yes	Yes					
Arizona	None		Yes						
Arizona DO	None			Yes		Yes			
Arkansas	None		Yes						
California	None		Yes						
California DO	None			Yes		Yes			
Colorado	None		Yes						LMCC for graduates of US or Canadian medical schools only
Connecticut	None		Yes	Yes	Yes				
Delaware	None		Yes	Yes	Yes	Yes	Yes		
DC	None		Yes	Yes	Yes	Yes	Yes		
Florida	None								
Florida DO	None			Yes	Yes	Yes			Endorsement not available
Georgia	None		Yes	Yes		Yes			
Guam	10 yrs	SPEX		Yes					
Hawaii	None								
Hawaii DO	None		Yes						
Idaho*	5 yrs	SPEX	Yes	Yes	Yes	Yes			LMCC for graduates of US or Canadian medical schools only
Illinois	None		Yes	Yes					
Indiana	None		Yes						
Iowa	None		Yes	Yes	Yes	Yes	Yes		
Kansas	None		Yes	Yes	Yes	Yes	Yes		SBE (pre 1972)
Kentucky	None		Yes	Yes		Yes			
Louisiana	10 yrs	SPEX, ABMS			Yes				SPEX may be waived if applicant was certified or recertified by a writtene exam through an ABMS board within 10 years of application date
Maine	None		Yes		Yes		Yes		Also accepts General Medical Council (UK)
Maine DO	None	SPEX		Yes					
Maryland*	15 yrs	SPEX	Yes	Yes		Yes	Yes	Yes*	ABMS is considered.
Massachusetts	None	Current evaluation	Yes	Yes	Yes	Yes	Yes		SBE (prior to 6/19/70)
Michigan	None		Yes		Yes				SBE (pre-FLEX)
Michigan DO	None			Yes	Yes				
Minnesota	10 yrs	SPEX, ABMS	Yes	Yes	Yes	Yes	Yes		SPEX may be waived if applicant is certified by an ABMS board, an AOA specialty board, or a Canadian specialty board
Mississippi	10 yrs	SPEX, ABMS	Yes	Yes	Yes				LMCC for graduates of US or Canadian medical schools only; SBE (pre-1973); SPEX may be waived if applicant was certified or recertified by an ABMS board within 10 yrs of application
Missouri	None		Yes	Yes					
Montana	None		Yes	Yes	Yes	Yes			
Nebraska	None		Yes	Yes	Yes	Yes	Yes		
Nevada	None		Yes						
Nevada DO	10 yrs	ABMS, COMVEX, SPEX		Yes		Yes			

(continued on next page)

Table 5 (continued)
Endorsement Policies for Physicians Holding an Initial License

	Time Limit for Endorsement After Exam	Requirements If Time Limit Not Met	Credential(s) Also Accepted (in Addition to USMLE, NBME)						Notes
			LMCC	NBOME	SBE	COMLEX	FLEX	ABMS	
New Hampshire	None	Exam, interview, proof of clinical competence, etc	Yes	Yes		Yes	Yes	Yes	
New Jersey	None		Yes					Yes	LMCC w/ABMS SBE; ABMS w/SBE
New Mexico	None		Yes		Yes		Yes		FLEX before 1974
New Mexico DO				Yes		Yes	Yes		
New York	None		Yes					Yes	LMCC (with a valid Canadian provincial license), foreign license
North Carolina	10 yrs	Training, SPEX, CFPC, FRCS, ABMS CAQ	Yes	Yes	Yes	Yes	Yes		CFPC (Certificant of the College of Family Physicians), FRCS (Fellowship of the Royal College of Surgeons), ABMS CAQ (Certificate of Added Qualification)
North Dakota	None		Yes	Yes	Yes	Yes	Yes		
Ohio	None		Yes						Professional experience in US or abroad
Oklahoma	None		Yes						
Oklahoma DO				Yes					
Oregon*	10 yrs	SPEX	Yes	Yes	Yes	Yes	Yes	Yes	
Pennsylvania	None		Yes						
Pennsylvania DO	None			Yes	Yes	Yes	Yes		
Puerto Rico	None								
Rhode Island	None		Yes	Yes					
South Carolina	10 yrs	SPEX	Yes	Yes	Yes	Yes	Yes	Yes	SBE w/ABMS
South Dakota	None		Yes	Yes	Yes	Yes	Yes		
Tennessee	None		Yes					Yes	
Tennessee DO				Yes					
Texas	—	—	—						Endorsement is not offered. All applicants must meet requirements for initial licensure
Utah	None	Retake exams	Yes		Yes				LMCC for graduates of US or Canadian medical schools only
Vermont	None		Yes		Yes		Yes		
Vermont DO				Yes	Yes				SBE (pre-FLEX)
Virgin Islands									No reciprocity or endorsement; all licensure candidates must sit for complete SPEX exam.
Virginia	None		Yes	Yes	Yes	Yes	Yes		Before 1970: SBE, with ABMS
Washington	None		Yes						LMCC after 1969
Washington DO				Yes	Yes				SBE (pre-FLEX)
West Virginia	None		Yes		Yes				
West Virginia DO				Yes	Yes	Yes			SBE (pre-FLEX)
Wisconsin	None		Yes						LMCC after 1978
Wyoming	None		Yes	Yes	Yes	Yes	Yes		

Abbreviations

ABMS—certification from a member board of the American Board of Medical Specialties

COMLEX-USA—Comprehensive Osteopathic Medical Licensure Examination

COMVEX—Comprehensive Osteopathic Medical Variable-Purpose Examination

FLEX—Federation Licensing Examination

LMCC—certification by the Licentiate of the Medical Council of Canada

NBME—certificate of the National Board of Medical Examiners

NBOME—certificate from the National Board of Osteopathic Medical Examiners

SBE—state board examination

SPEX—Special Purpose Examination

USMLE—United States Medical Licensing Examination

* Refer to introductory text to this table for more information on this state's regulations.

Note: All information should be verified with the licensing board; licenses based on endorsement are granted to those physicians meeting all state requirements.

Table 6
Licensure Endorsement: Requirements for Candidates' Appearance Before the Board

	Candidates Who Must Appear...	...for Oral Examination	...for Interview	Notes
Alabama	Some		X	
Alaska	Some		X	
Arizona	Some			
Arizona DO	Some		X	
Arkansas	Some		X	
California	None			
California DO	None			
Colorado	None			
Connecticut	None			
Delaware	Some		X	Interviews are waived by Board president.
DC	None			
Florida	Some		X	
Florida DO	Some		X	Endorsement not available.
Georgia	Some		X	
Guam	Some		X	
Hawaii	None			
Hawaii DO	None			
Idaho	Some		X	
Illinois	Some		X	
Indiana	Some		X	
Iowa	Some		X	
Kansas	Some		X	At board discretion, candidates for licensure endorsement must appear before the Board.
Kentucky	Some			
Louisiana	Some		X	At board discretion, candidates for licensure endorsement must appear before the Board.
Maine	Some		X	
Maine DO	Some		X	
Maryland	—			Endorsement is not offered. All applicants must meet requirements for initial licensure.
Massachusetts	Some		X	
Michigan	None			
Michigan DO	None			
Minnesota	Some		X	
Mississippi	All		X	
Missouri	Some		X	
Montana	Some		X	
Nebraska	None			
Nevada	Some		X	
Nevada DO	Some		X	
New	None			
New Jersey	Some		X	
New Mexico	Some		X	

(continued on next page)

Table 6 (continued)
Licensure Endorsement: Requirements for Candidates' Appearance Before the Board

	Candidates Who Must Appear...	...for Oral Examination	...for Interview	Notes
New Mexico DO	All		X	
New York	None			
North Carolina	Some		X	
North Dakota	Some		X	
Ohio	None			
Oklahoma	Some		X	
Oklahoma DO	Some		X	
Oregon	Some		X	
Pennsylvania	None			
Pennsylvania DO	None			
Puerto Rico	None			
Rhode Island	Some		X	
South Carolina	All		X	
South Dakota	Some		X	
Tennessee	Some		X	
Tennessee DO	Some		X	
Texas	—			Endorsement is not offered. All applicants must meet requirements for initial licensure.
Utah	Some		X	
Vermont	None			
Vermont DO	None			
Virgin Islands	—			No reciprocity or endorsement; all licensure candidates must sit for complete SPEX exam.
Virginia	Some		X	
Washington	None			
Washington DO	None			
West Virginia	Some		X	At board's discretion.
West Virginia DO	All		X	
Wisconsin	Some	X	X	Oral exam/interview is discretionary. Expedited endorsement of applicants with an active license in MN.
Wyoming	Some	X	X	

Licensure Policies Related to the Federation Licensing Examination (FLEX)

Policies of state licensing boards for endorsement of medical/osteopathic licensing examinations taken before and after the development of the Federation Licensing Examination (FLEX) vary from state to state (Table 7). Each state board created its own licensing examination before FLEX, which may partially explain the sizable variation in endorsement policies from one state to another. Some boards will endorse scores on state licensing board examinations in use prior to the development of FLEX; these scores may be endorsed in connection with a passing score on the Special Purpose Examination (SPEX). Endorsement of a certificate of the National Board of Medical Examiners (NBME) or of an examination refers to issuance of a license based on an acceptable score on the NBME or the state's board exam.

Additional Notes for Specific Licensing Jurisdictions

Iowa—Applicants who took old (pre-1985) FLEX must provide evidence of at least two of the following: (1) certification under seal that the applicant passed FLEX with a FWA of 75% or better, as determined by the state medical licensing authority, in no more than two sittings; (2) verification under seal of medical licensure in the state that administered the examination; (3) evidence of current certification by an American specialty board approved or recognized by the Council of Medical Education of the AMA or the ABMS or AOA.

Mississippi—FLEX scores obtained at different sittings cannot be combined. An exemption may be granted to the requirement for a FWA of 75% on FLEX if the applicant has completed an approved GME program and is ABMS or AOA board certified.

Table 7
Licensure Policies Related to the Federation Licensing Examination (FLEX)

	Exceptions to 75 FWA on 3-part FLEX	Must Pass 3-Part (Pre-1985) FLEX in One Sitting	Must Pass 2-Part (1985-93) FLEX in One Sitting	Notes
Alabama	None	No	No	
Alaska	None	No	No	
Arizona	None	Yes	No	
Arizona DO	None	No	No	
Arkansas	None	Yes	No	
California	None	Yes	No	
California DO	None	No	No	
Colorado	None	Yes	No	
Connecticut	See note	No	No	Before June 1985: 75 on day 3 of FLEX to combine best scores (within 7 years); FLEX-Weighted Average (FWA) truncated
Delaware	None	No	No	
DC	None	Yes	No	
Florida	None	Yes	No	
Florida DO	NA	NA	NA	
Georgia	None	Yes	No	
Guam	None	Yes	Yes	
Hawaii	None	No	No	
Hawaii DO	None	No	No	
Idaho	See note	Yes	No	FLEX scores obtained at different sittings cannot be combined
Illinois	None	No	No	Applicant had to have passed all three parts of the pre-1985 FLEX in the same state
Indiana	Split scores okay	No	No	
Iowa*	See note	No	No	
Kansas	None	Yes	No	
Kentucky	None	Yes	No	
Louisiana	None	Yes	No	
Maine	None	No	No	
Maine DO	None	No	No	
Maryland	None	Yes	No	
Massachusetts	None	Yes	Yes	
Michigan	None	No	No	
Michigan DO	NA	NA	NA	
Minnesota	None	Yes*	No*	Five tries allowed for passing Pre-1985 FLEX; three tries for passing 2-Part FLEX
Mississippi*	See note	Yes	No	
Missouri	None	Yes	No	
Montana	None	No	No	
Nebraska	None	Yes	No	
Nevada	None	No	No	
Nevada DO	None	No	No	
New Hampshire	None	No	No	
New Jersey	Before Jan 1981: 74.5 FWA	No	No	
New Mexico	None	No	No	

(continued on next page)

Table 7 (continued)
Licensure Policies Related to the Federation Licensing Examination (FLEX)

	Exceptions to 75 FWA on 3-part FLEX	Must Pass 3-Part (Pre-1985) FLEX in One Sitting	Must Pass 2-Part (1985-93) FLEX in One Sitting	Notes
New Mexico DO	None	No	No	
New York	None	No*	No*	All three parts must have been passed within five-year period
North Carolina	None	No	No	
North Dakota	None	Yes	No	
Ohio*	72 (see note)	Yes	No	A score of 72 is acceptable if the exam was taken during the first two years of a state's administration and was accepted as passing by state
Oklahoma	None	Yes	No	
Oklahoma DO	NA			
Oregon	None	Yes	No	
Pennsylvania	None	No	No	
Pennsylvania DO	None	No	No	
Puerto Rico	None	Yes	Yes	
Rhode Island	None	No	No	
South Carolina	None	Yes	No	
South Dakota	None	Yes	Yes	
Tennessee	None	Yes	Yes	
Tennessee DO	None	No	No	
Texas	None	Yes	No	Endorsement is not offered. All applicants must meet requirements for initial licensure. Responses shown are for applicants using FLEX to obtain initial licensure in Texas.
Utah	None	No	No	
Vermont	None	Yes	Yes	
Vermont DO	None	No	No	
Virgin Islands	—	—	—	
Virginia	None	No*	Yes	(Unless taken before June 1976)
Washington	None	No	No	
Washington DO	None	No	No	
West Virginia	None	Yes	No	
West Virginia DO	NA	NA	NA	
Wisconsin	None	Yes	No	
Wyoming	None	Yes	No	

Abbreviations

FWA—Federation Licensing Examination (FLEX) Weighted Average, which applied to the pre-1985 three-part FLEX and gave greater weight to parts 2 and 3; all states currently require a minimum passing score of 75 on each component of the post-1985 two-part FLEX.

ABMS—certification from a member board of the American Board of Medical Specialties

CAQ—Certificate of Added Qualification

CFPC—College of Family Physicians of Canada

COMLEX—Comprehensive Osteopathic Medical Licensure Examination

COMVEX—Comprehensive Osteopathic Medical Variable-Purpose Examination

FLEX—Federation Licensing Examination

FRCS—Fellowship of the Royal College of Surgeons

IMG—international medical graduate

LMCC—certification by the Licentiate of the Medical Council of Canada

NBME—certificate of the National Board of Medical Examiners

NBOME—certificate from the National Board of Osteopathic Medical Examiners

SBE—state board examination

SPEX—Special Purpose Examination

USMLE—United States Medical Licensing Examination

* Refer to introductory text to this table for more information on this state's regulations.

Note: *All information should be verified with the licensing board; licenses based on endorsement are granted to those physicians meeting all state requirements.*

Additional Requirements for Endorsement of Licenses Held by International Medical Graduates (IMGs)

In all states, international medical graduates (IMGs) seeking licensure by endorsement must meet the same requirements as US graduates (listed in Table 5), in addition to the requirements shown in Table 8.

Nearly all states require that IMGs seeking licensure by endorsement hold a certificate from the Educational Commission for Foreign Medical Graduates (ECFMG). In lieu of holding that certificate, a candidate for licensure in North Dakota, for example, may have passed a certification examination of an American Board of Medical Specialties (ABMS) board.

About half of the boards require IMG candidates to have graduated from a state-approved foreign medical school; several boards also maintain and use a list of approved/unapproved foreign medical schools for decisions on initial licensure (see Table 12, column 3). A number of boards require two or three years of US or Canadian GME, and a majority of jurisdictions also may require an interview or oral examination prior to endorsement.

Note: Physicians who graduated via the Fifth Pathway are not required to have an ECFMG certificate. For more information on the Fifth Pathway, see page 34.

Additional Notes for Specific Licensing Jurisdictions

California—Four years' licensure required for IMGs, in addition to two years of ACGME-accredited training (or one year of ACGME-accredited training plus ABMS, or one year of ACGME-accredited training plus the Special Purpose Examination [SPEX]).

Florida—Rules on clinical clerkships for IMGs adopted by the Florida Board before October 1986 do not apply to any graduate who had already completed a clinical clerkship or who had begun a clinical clerkship, as long as the clerkship was completed within three years.

Illinois—Candidate must have completed a six-year postsecondary course of study, comprising two academic years of liberal arts instruction, two academic years in basic sciences, and two academic years in clinical sciences, while enrolled in the medical school that conferred the degree.

Iowa—Requirement for graduation from a state-approved medical school is waived if candidate (1) passed SPEX or state science examination, (2) completed three years of GME in an ACGME-accredited residency program, or (3) held a permanent license to practice without restrictions in a US jurisdiction for at least five years.

Maryland—In addition to two years of ACGME- or Royal College of Physicians and Surgeons of Canada (RCPSC)-accredited GME, one year of GME required if candidate failed any part of an examination three times; no more than three failures permitted (exceptions may apply).

Minnesota—SPEX is required if candidate took initial licensing exam more than 10 years ago, unless candidate is currently ABMS, AOA, or Canadian medical specialty board certified.

North Dakota—The ECFMG certificate requirement is waived for holders of the Fifth Pathway and for graduates of medical schools in Canada, England, Scotland, Ireland, Australia, or New Zealand. The requirement may be waived, by unanimous vote of the Board, for holders of ABMS certification.

The requirement for 30 months of US/Canadian GME is waived if the candidate holds an ABMS board certificate or has passed SPEX and (1) has successfully completed one year of state-approved GME in the US or Canada (or three years of GME in the United Kingdom), (2) has other professional experience and training equivalent to GME years two and three, and (3) meets all other licensing requirements.

Oregon—Candidate must have graduated from a foreign school that provided instruction equivalent to a US medical school and is considered equivalent if accredited by an accrediting organization acceptable to the Board or recognized by civil authorities of the country in which the school is located as an acceptable education program. Medical school must be chartered in country in which it is located; candidate must attend four full terms of eight months each term, with physical on-site attendance. The four full terms may be waived for candidates with ABMS certificates who have substantially complied with attendance requirements. Candidate must be ECFMG certified.

Rhode Island—Candidate must have obtained supervised clinical training in the US as part of the medical school curriculum in a hospital affiliated with an LCME-accredited medical school or an ACGME-accredited residency.

Table 8
Additional Requirements for Endorsement of Licenses Held by International Medical Graduates (IMGs)
IMGs must also meet all the requirements for endorsement listed in Table 5

	Must Have ECFMG Certificate	Must Have Graduated From State-approved Foreign Medical School (cf Table 12, Column 3)	Must Appear for...		Amount of Accredited US or Canadian GME Required	Notes
			Interview	Possible Interview		
Alabama	Yes	Yes			3 yrs	SPEX (if no ABMS or SBE within 10 yrs)
Alaska	Yes	Yes		Yes	3 yrs	
Arizona	Yes	No			3 yrs	
Arkansas	Yes	Yes			3 yrs	
California*	Yes	Yes			2 yrs	
Colorado	Yes	Yes			3 yrs	Foreign med school must be board-approved, on case-by-case basis, if applicant is not board certified
Connecticut	Yes	Yes			2 yrs	Foreign med school must have been listed with the World Health Organization in 1970 (or by individual review)
Delaware	Yes	No		Yes	3 yrs	
DC	Yes	No			3 yrs	
Florida*	Yes	No		Yes	2 yrs	
Georgia	Yes	Yes		Yes	1 yr	3 yrs required if graduate of school not on California list
Guam	Yes	No		Yes	3 yrs	
Hawaii	Yes	No			2 yrs	
Idaho	Yes	Yes		Yes	3 yrs	Unapproved medical school graduates must meet additional requirements
Illinois*	Yes	No		Yes	2 yrs	
Indiana	Yes	No		Yes	2 yrs	Foreign medical school must be listed with FAIMER or CA
Iowa*	Yes	No		Yes	2 yrs	2 yrs of US/Canadian GME required as of 7/1/06
Kansas	Yes	No		Yes	2 yrs	Foreign med school must have been in existence 15 yrs
Kentucky	Yes	Yes		Yes	2 yrs	
Louisiana	Yes	Yes		Yes	3 yrs	
Maine	Yes	Yes		Yes	3 yrs	Foreign medical school must be listed with ECFMG
Maryland^	Yes	No			2 yrs	
Massachusetts	Yes	No		Yes	3 yrs	
Michigan	Yes	No			2 yrs	
Minnesota*	Yes	Yes	Yes		2 yrs	ABMS or SPEX required if >10 yrs since licensure exam
Mississippi	Yes	Yes	Yes		3 yrs	1 yr if ABMS- or AOA-certified
Missouri	Yes	Yes		Yes	3 yrs	
Montana	Yes	Yes		Yes	3 yrs	
Nebraska	Yes	No			3 yrs	
Nevada	Yes	Yes		Yes	3 yrs	
New Hampshire	Yes	No			2 yrs	
New Jersey	Yes	No		Yes	2 yrs	2 yrs, and under contract for completion of 3rd year
New Mexico	Yes	Yes		Yes	2 yrs	Must be board certified in ABMS-recognized specialty and have practiced for past 3 yrs in US/Canada
New York	Yes	No			3 yrs	
North Carolina	Yes	No		Yes	3 yrs	Accept passing ECFMG exam together with completion of Fifth Pathway program

(continued on next page)

Table 8 (continued)
Additional Requirements for Endorsement of Licenses Held by International Medical Graduates (IMGs)
IMGs must also meet all the requirements for endorsement listed in Table 5

	Must Have ECFMG Certificate	Must Have Graduated From State-approved Foreign Medical School (cf Table 12, Column 3)	Must Appear for...		Amount of Accredited US or Canadian GME Required	Notes
			Interview	Possible Interview		
North Dakota*	Yes	Yes		Yes	30 mos	
Ohio	Yes	No			2 yrs	
Oklahoma	Yes	Yes			2 yrs	Must have graduated from Board-approved medical school
Oregon*	Yes	Yes			3 yrs	
Pennsylvania	Yes	No		Yes	3 yrs	Foreign medical school must be listed with ECFMG
Puerto Rico	Yes	Yes			1 yr	
Rhode Island*	Yes	Yes		Yes	3 yrs	1 yr of advanced standing recognized if granted by ABMS
South Carolina	Yes	No	Yes		3 yrs	For Fifth Pathway candidates or ABMS/AOA certification
South Dakota	Yes	Yes		Yes	3 yrs	Must complete a residency program in the US or Canada
Tennessee	Yes	Yes		Yes	3 yrs	
Texas	—	—	—	—	—	Endorsement is not offered. All applicants must meet requirements for initial licensure.
Utah	Yes	No		Yes	2 yrs	
Vermont	Yes	Yes			3 yrs	
Virginia	Yes	No		Yes	2 yrs	Licensure in another state can replace ECFMG certification
Washington	Yes	No			2 yrs	
West Virginia	No	No			3 yrs	3 yrs GME, or 1 yr plus ABMS certification
Wisconsin	Yes	No			1 yr	Possible oral exam
Wyoming	Yes	No			2 yrs*	1 yr if ABMS or certified by an ABMS or AOA board, or continually licensed in good standing in one or more states for past 5 yrs

Abbreviations

ABMS—American Board of Medical Specialties

AOA—American Osteopathic Association

ECFMG—Educational Commission for Foreign Medical Graduates

GME—Graduate medical education

SBE—state board examination

SPEX—Special Purpose Examination

USMLE—United States Medical Licensing Examination

* Refer to introductory text to this table for more information on this state's regulations.

Note: *All information should be verified with the licensing board; licenses based on endorsement are granted to those physicians meeting all state requirements.*

Policies About the Special Purpose Examination (SPEX) and Comprehensive Osteopathic Medical Variable-Purpose Examination (COMVEX)

The Special Purpose Examination (SPEX), a one-day, computer-administered examination with approximately 420 multiple-choice questions, assesses knowledge required of all physicians, regardless of specialty. SPEX is used to assess physicians who have held a valid, unrestricted license in a US or Canadian jurisdiction who are:

- Required by the state medical board to demonstrate current medical knowledge
- Seeking endorsement licensure some years beyond initial examination
- Seeking license reinstatement after a period of professional inactivity

The Comprehensive Osteopathic Medical Variable-Purpose Examination (COMVEX) is a post-licensure examination for osteopathic physicians who require reevaluation after initial licensure. COMVEX may be used in a number of situations, including but not limited to the following:

- An osteopathic physician originally licensed through an examination devoid of osteopathic content is now applying for a license in a state that requires that an osteopathic physician take an osteopathic examination
- An osteopathic physician is applying for licensure in a state that imposes a time limit (e.g., completing examination within a 10-year period), and the candidate has not been tested by a licensing board or a certifying board within that time frame
- An osteopathic physician is requesting a reinstatement of a license following a career interruption
- A tenured osteopathic physician needs to demonstrate basic osteopathic medical competence

Most jurisdictions use SPEX or COMVEX to assess current competence or if a candidate has not taken a written licensure exam or the American Board of Medical Specialties (ABMS) board certification exam within a specified number of years. Jurisdictions also recognize board certification exams offered by the American Osteopathic Association. In approximately half of jurisdictions, SPEX or COMVEX scores are valid for an unlimited length of time (Table 9).

For more information on physician reentry to practice, see Table 25.

Additional Notes for Specific Licensing Jurisdictions

Alaska—SPEX is required to restore a retired license.

Florida—SPEX is offered only to candidates who have actively practiced medicine for at least 10 years after obtaining a valid license in a jurisdiction or a combination of jurisdictions in the United States or Canada and who meet Florida's licensure requirements.

Hawaii—SPEX may be required if physician took a state licensing exam.

Maryland—SPEX required if active licensure was interrupted during last 10 years and if physician has not passed written licensure exam within last 15 years and ABMS board certification exam within last 10 years.

New York—SPEX required if state board exam taken before 1968.

North Dakota—SPEX (or ABMS board certification) is required if candidate is being considered for the following exception: If the candidate has not completed 30 months of GME but has met all other licensing requirements and has successfully completed one year of US or Canadian GME in a board-approved program, and if the board finds that the candidate has other professional experience and training substantially equivalent to the second and third years of GME, then the candidate may be eligible for licensure.

Oregon—SPEX required if no training or ABMS/AOA certification within the past 10 years, or if practice ceased for 12 months or more immediately prior to applying without subsequent 1 year training, ABMS, or AOA certification or CME.

Texas—If an applicant has not passed a monitored examination within 10 years preceding date of application, the applicant is required to pass SPEX or a monitored specialty board certification or recertification exam. SPEX scores accepted from other licensing jurisdictions if candidate passed with score of 75 or higher, within 3 attempts.

Vermont DO—SPEX or COMVEX, or both, may be required to reinstate an expired license.

Virgin Islands—SPEX required to obtain licensure.

West Virginia DO—COMVEX may be required.

Table 9
Policies About the Special Purpose Examination (SPEX) and Comprehensive Osteopathic Medical Variable-Purpose Examination (COMVEX)

	SPEX or COMVEX May Be Required...	...By Board Order	... To Restore License After Disciplinary Action	...If not Practicing for Several Years	...to Assess Current Competence	...if no Written Licensure Exam or Board Certification Exam Taken Within	...Determined on Individual Basis	SPEX/ COMVEX Scores Valid for	SPEX/COMVEX Scores Accepted From Other Jurisdictions
Alabama	Yes	X	X	X	X	10 yrs		10 yrs	Yes
Alaska*	Yes				X			No limit	Optional
Arizona	Yes	X			X			10 yrs	Yes
Arizona DO	Yes	X	X	X	X	7 yrs		7 yrs	
Arkansas	Yes	X			X				Yes
California	Yes	X			X	10 yrs		10 yrs	Yes
California DO	Yes	X	X		X			No limit	No
Colorado	Yes	X			X				Yes
Connecticut	Yes				X				Yes
Delaware	Yes			X	X		X		
DC	Yes	X		X	X				Yes
Florida*	Yes				X			No limit	Yes
Florida DO	Yes	X	X	X	X		X		Yes
Georgia	Yes	X		X	X				Yes
Guam	Yes	X			X	10 yrs		No limit	Yes
Hawaii*	Yes	X						No limit	Yes
Hawaii DO	No								
Idaho	Yes	X			X			No limit	Yes
Illinois	Yes		X	X	X			No limit	Yes
Indiana	Yes	X	X	X	X			No limit	Yes
Iowa	Yes			X	X			No limit	Yes
Kansas	Yes	X			X			No limit	Yes
Kentucky	Yes	X			X			No limit	No
Louisiana	Yes				X	10 yrs		10 yrs	Yes
Maine	Yes			More than 1 yr	X			No limit	No
Maine DO	Yes	X		More than 1 yr	X			No limit	No
Maryland*	Yes		X	X	X	15 yrs (licensure)	X	No limit	Yes
Massachusetts	Yes								No
Michigan	Yes	X			X				Yes
Michigan DO	Yes	X			X				Yes
Minnesota	Yes	X	X	X	X	10 yrs	X	No limit	Yes
Mississippi	Yes		X		X		X	10 yrs	Yes
Missouri	Yes		X		X			No limit	Yes
Montana	Yes			X (2 yrs)	X			No limit	Yes
Nebraska	Yes						X		Yes
Nevada	Yes				X		X	10 yrs	Yes
Nevada DO	Yes	X			X		X	10 yrs	Yes
New Hampshire	Yes	X							No
New Jersey	No								No

(continued on next page)

Table 9 (continued)
Policies About the Special Purpose Examination (SPEX) and Comprehensive Osteopathic Medical Variable-Purpose Examination (COMVEX)

	SPEX or COMVEX May Be Required	...By Board Order	... To Restore License After Disciplinary Action	...If not Practicing for Several Years	...to Assess Current Competence	...if no Written Licensure Exam or Board Certification Exam Taken Within	...Determined on Individual Basis	SPEX/ COMVEX Scores Valid for	SPEX/COMVEX Scores Accepted From Other Jurisdictions
New Mexico	Yes		X	X	X			Not defined	Yes
New Mexico DO	Yes						X	Not defined	
New York*	Yes				X		X	No limit	Yes
North Carolina	Yes				X	10 yrs	X	10 yrs	Yes
North Dakota*	Yes				X			No limit	Yes
Ohio	Yes	X	X	X (2 yrs)	X			No limit	Yes
Oklahoma	Yes	X	X	X	X		X		Yes
Oklahoma DO	Yes				X				
Oregon*	Yes	X	X	X (1 yr)	X	10 yrs		10 yrs	Yes
Pennsylvania	Yes		X	X	X				Yes
Pennsylvania DO	Yes		X		X				Yes
Puerto Rico	No								Yes
Rhode Island	No								No
South Carolina	Yes		X	X	X	10 yrs		10 yrs	No
South Dakota	No								No
Tennessee	Yes		X	More than 5 yrs	X			No limit	Yes
Tennessee DO	No								
Texas*	Yes	X	X	X	X	10 yrs		10 yrs	Yes
Utah	Yes		X	X	X			Not defined	Yes
Vermont	Yes			X					No
Vermont DO*	Yes			More than 1 yr					
Virgin Islands*	Yes				X			No limit	No
Virginia	Yes	X	X	X	X			No limit	No
Washington	Yes		X	More than 2 yrs	X		X	No limit	Yes
Washington DO	Yes				X		X	No limit	No
West Virginia	Yes				X			No limit	Yes
West Virginia DO*	Yes				X				Yes
Wisconsin	Yes				X		X	No limit	Yes
Wyoming	Yes	X	X	X	X		X	No limit	Yes

Abbreviations
ABMS—American Board of Medical Specialties
COMVEX—Comprehensive Osteopathic Medical Variable-Purpose Examination
SPEX—Special Purpose Examination

* Refer to introductory text to this table for more on this state's regulations.
Note: *All information should be verified with the licensing board; medical licenses are granted to those physicians meeting all state requirements—at the discretion of the board.*

Initial Licensure of US Medical/Osteopathic School Graduates

All states require a written examination for initial licensure: generally, for MDs, the three-step United States Medical Licensing Examination (USMLE), which has replaced the Federation Licensing Examination (FLEX) and the national board examination of the National Board of Medical Examiners (NBME). Osteopathic physicians take the three-level Comprehensive Osteopathic Medical Licensure Examination (COMLEX) of the National Board of Osteopathic Medical Examiners (NBOME).

To be eligible to take USMLE Step 3, more than half of the state medical boards require graduates of US medical schools to have completed at least one year of graduate medical education (GME) (Table 10). Slightly less than half of boards do not require completion of any GME to take USMLE Step 3 (although in some cases a candidate must be enrolled in a GME program).

A candidate is eligible to take the COMLEX Level 3 examination if he or she meets the following requirements:

1. Passed the COMLEX Level 1, COMLEX Level 2-CE and Level 2-PE examinations as determined by the NBOME; and

2. Graduated from an osteopathic medical school accredited by the American Osteopathic Association's Commission on Osteopathic College Accreditation (AOA COCA) with an earned DO degree, and the NBOME has received confirmation from the Office of the Dean of the candidate's college/school of matriculation or a verified copy of his or her diploma from an accredited osteopathic medical school.

Notwithstanding the foregoing, a candidate who graduated from an accredited college of osteopathic medicine before January 1, 2005 and successfully completed COMLEX Level 2-CE before June 30, 2005 is exempt from the requirement of passing COMLEX Level 2-PE as a condition of eligibility to take COMLEX Level 3.

All medical and osteopathic boards require completion of at least one year of GME before issuing a full, unrestricted license.

Additional Notes for Specific Licensing Jurisdictions

West Virginia DO—Either AOA- or ACGME-accredited first-year training is accepted. Those candidates who complete an ACGME-accredited first year need to have also completed 40 hours of AOA Category 1A credit in Osteopathic Manipulative Management and Treatment.

Table 10
Initial Licensure of US Medical/Osteopathic School Graduates

	Amount of Accredited US or Canadian GME Required	
	...to Take USMLE Step 3 or COMLEX Level 3	...for Licensure
Alabama	None (must be enrolled in GME program)	1 yr
Alaska	1 yr	2 yrs (1 yr if completed medical school before Jan. 1995)
Arizona	6 mos	1 yr
Arizona DO	6 mos of a 1-yr AOA- or ACGME-accredited program	1 yr AOA- or ACGME-accredited GME
Arkansas	None	1 yr
California	None	1 yr (including 4 mos general medicine)
California DO	None	1 yr AOA- or ACGME-accredited GME, including at least 4 mos general medicine (unless applicant completed 1 yr of GME before July 1, 1990)
Colorado	1 yr	1 yr
Connecticut	None	2 yrs
Delaware	1 yr	1 yr
DC	6 mos	1 yr
Florida	None	1 yr
Florida DO	6 mos of a 1-yr AOA- or ACGME-accredited program	1 yr AOA-approved rotating internship
Georgia	1 yr	1 yr
Guam	2 yrs	
Hawaii	None (must be enrolled in 1st yr of GME prgm)	1 yr
Hawaii DO	None	1 yr AOA- or ACGME-accredited GME
Idaho	9 mos	1 yr
Illinois	1 yr	2 yrs (1 yr if entered GME before Jan. 1988)
Indiana	1 yr (6 mos may be waived)	1 yr
Iowa	7 mos (or enrollment in board-approved program)	1 yr AOA-, ACGME-, RCPSC-, CFPC-accredited GME
Kansas	1 yr (or enrollment in GME program in Kansas)	1 yr
Kentucky	1 yr	2 yrs
Louisiana	None	1 yr allopathic GME
Maine	1 yr	3 yrs (for those graduating after 7/1/2004)
Maine DO	1-yr AOA- or ACGME-accredited program	1 yr AOA- or ACGME-accredited GME
Maryland	None	1 yr
Massachusetts	1 yr	2 yrs
Michigan	6 mos	2 yrs
Michigan DO	None	1 yr AOA-approved GME
Minnesota	None (must be enrolled in GME program)	1 yr
Mississippi	1 yr	1 yr
Missouri	1 yr	1 yr
Montana	1 yr	2 yrs
Nebraska	None	1 yr
Nevada	None	3 yrs
Nevada DO	6 mos of a 1-yr AOA- or ACGME-accredited program	3 yrs in AOA- or ACGME-accredited program (grads after 1995)
New Hampshire	None (but must be enrolled in GME program)	2 yrs

(continued on next page)

Table 10 (continued)
Initial Licensure of US Medical/Osteopathic School Graduates

	Amount of Accredited US or Canadian GME Required	
	...to Take USMLE Step 3 or COMLEX Level 3	...for Licensure
New Jersey	1 yr	2 yrs, and contract for yr 3, if graduated after July 1, 2003; 1 yr if graduated before July 1, 2003
New Mexico	1 yr	2 yrs
New Mexico DO	6 mos of a 1-yr AOA- or ACGME-accredited program	1 yr
New York	None	1 yr
North Carolina	None	1 yr
North Dakota	6 mos of a 1-yr ACGME- or AOA-accredited program	1 yr
Ohio	9 mos	1 yr
Oklahoma	None	1 yr
Oklahoma DO	6 mos of a 1-yr AOA- or ACGME-accredited program	1 yr AOA-approved rotating internship or equivalent
Oregon	None (must be enrolled in GME program)	1 yr
Pennsylvania	None	2 yrs (1 yr if GME in US before July 1987)
Pennsylvania DO	6 mos of a 1-yr AOA- or ACGME-accredited program	1 yr AOA-approved rotating internship
Puerto Rico	None	1 yr
Rhode Island	1 yr	2 yrs
South Carolina	1 yr	1 yr
South Dakota	None	Completion of residency program
Tennessee	1 yr	1 yr
Tennessee DO	6 mos of a 1-yr AOA- or ACGME-accredited program	1-yr AOA-approved or ACGME-accredited GME
Texas	None	1 yr
Utah	None	2 yrs
Vermont	7 mos	1 yr (Canadian GME accepted if program accredited by RCPSC or CFPC)
Vermont DO	6 mos of a 1-yr AOA- or ACGME-accredited program	1 yr AOA-approved rotating internship or 3-yr AOA- or ACGME-accredited GME program
Virgin Islands	USMLE not offered	1 yr
Virginia	None	1 yr
Washington	1 yr (or enrolled in GME program)	2 yrs (1 yr if completed medical school before July 28, 1985)
Washington DO	6 mos of a 1-yr AOA- or ACGME-accredited program Category I AOA CME hours with 10 hours in OMT	1 yr AOA-approved or ACGME-accredited GME, or additional 40 hours
West Virginia	None	1 yr
West Virginia DO*	6 mos of a 1-yr AOA- or ACGME-accredited program	1 yr AOA-approved or ACGME-accredited GME
Wisconsin	1 yr	1 yr
Wyoming	1 yr in good standing in one or more states for past 5 yrs	2 yrs (1 yr if certified by ABMS or AOA board, or continually licensed

Abbreviations

ACGME—Accreditation Council for Graduate Medical Education

AOA—American Osteopathic Association

CFPC—College of Family Physicians of Canada

COMLEX—Comprehensive Osteopathic Medical Licensure Examination

GME—graduate medical education

RCPSC—Royal College of Physicians and Surgeons of Canada

USMLE—United States Medical Licensing Examination

** Refer to introductory text to this table for more on this state's regulations.

Note: All information should be verified with the licensing board;
medical licenses are granted to those physicians meeting all
state requirements—at the discretion of the board.

Initial Licensure of Canadian Citizens Who Are Graduates of Accredited Canadian Medical Schools

When considering applications for licensure, all state medical boards consider Canadian citizens who have graduated from an accredited Canadian medical school on the same basis as graduates of accredited US medical schools (Table 11).

The majority of licensing boards endorse the Licentiate of the Medical Council of Canada (LMCC) as evidence of passing an acceptable licensing examination (applicants must also pass all other board requirements for licensure).

Nearly all licensing boards accept Canadian graduate medical education (GME) as equivalent to GME in a US program accredited by the Accreditation Council for Graduate Medical Education (ACGME). These rules do not uniformly apply to international medical graduates, who should refer to Table 12.

Table 11
Initial Licensure of Canadian Citizens Who Are Graduates of Accredited Canadian Medical Schools

	LMCC Approved for Licensure by Endorsement	GME in Accredited Canadian Programs Accepted as Equivalent to ACGME-accredited GME in the United States	Notes
Alabama	Yes	Yes	
Alaska	Yes	Yes	
Arizona	Yes	Yes	
Arkansas	Yes	Yes	
California	Yes	Yes	Accepted if completed in RCPSC-accredited program in Canada
Colorado	Yes	Yes	
Connecticut	Yes	Yes	
Delaware	Yes	Yes	
DC	Yes	Yes	
Florida	No	Yes	
Georgia	Yes	Yes	
Guam	No	No	
Hawaii	No	Yes	
Idaho	Yes	Yes	
Illinois	Yes	Yes	
Indiana	Yes	Yes	
Iowa	Yes	Yes	LMCC must be endorsed by provincial licensing board
Kansas	Yes	No	
Kentucky	Yes	Yes	
Louisiana	No	Yes	
Maine	Yes	Yes	LMCC, subject to board approval
Maryland	Yes	Yes	LMCC (although applicants are not licensed by endorsement)
Massachusetts	Yes	Yes	
Michigan	Yes	Yes	
Minnesota	Yes	Yes	
Mississippi	Yes	Yes	
Missouri	Yes	Yes	Only if medical school graduate of Canadian medical school
Montana	Yes	Yes	
Nebraska	Yes	Yes	
Nevada	Yes	Yes	
New Hampshire	Yes	Yes	
New Jersey	No	Yes	LMCC considered *only* if applicant is licensed in US jurisdiction
New Mexico	Yes	Yes	
New York	Yes	Yes	LMCC considered *only* if applicant has valid provincial license
North Carolina	Yes	Yes	
North Dakota	Yes	Yes	
Ohio	Yes	Yes	1 yr of GME or its equivalent required

(continued on next page)

Table 11 (continued)
Initial Licensure of Canadian Citizens Who Are Graduates of Accredited Canadian Medical Schools

	LMCC Approved for Licensure by Endorsement	GME in Accredited Canadian Programs Accepted as Equivalent to ACGME-accredited GME in the United States	Notes
Oklahoma	Yes	Yes	
Oregon	Yes	Yes	
Pennsylvania	Yes	Yes	Must have received LMCC after 5/70 and in English
Puerto Rico	No	Yes	LMCC considered *only* if applicant is licensed in US jurisdiction
Rhode Island	Yes	Yes	
South Carolina	Yes	Yes	
South Dakota	Yes	Yes	All applicants must meet all requirements for initial licensure
Tennessee	Yes	Yes	
Texas	—	Yes	Endorsement is not offered. All applicants must meet requirements for initial licensure
Utah	Yes	Yes	
Vermont	Yes	Yes	
Virgin Islands	No	No	
Virginia	Yes	Yes	
Washington	Yes	Yes	Must have received LMCC after 12/69
West Virginia	Yes	Yes	
Wisconsin	Yes	Yes	Must have received LMCC after 1/1/78
Wyoming	Yes	Yes	

Abbreviations

ACGME Accreditation Council for Graduate Medical Education

GME—graduate medical education

LMCC—certification by the Licentiate of the Medical Council of Canada

Note: *All information should be verified with the licensing board; licenses based on endorsement are granted to those physicians meeting all state requirements.*

Initial Licensure of International Medical Graduates (IMGs)

All international medical graduates (IMGs) must hold a certificate from the Educational Commission for Foreign Medical Graduates (ECFMG) examination before taking Step 3 of the United States Medical Licensing Examination (USMLE). (For more information on the ECFMG certificate, see Chapter 3.)

Less than half of boards maintain and/or use a list of approved/unapproved foreign medical schools for initial licensure decisions; several states use the list of schools from the California board (Table 12). In addition, about half of the boards require IMG candidates for endorsement of licensure to have graduated from a state-approved foreign medical school (see Table 8, column 3).

Two thirds of boards will endorse for licensure the Licentiate of the Medical Council of Canada (LMCC) when held by an IMG.

Slightly less than half of state boards allow IMGs to take USMLE Step 3 before they have had GME in a US or Canadian hospital or community medical center (although some of these states require that a candidate be enrolled in a GME program). All states, however, require at least one year of GME for licensure, and about half of states require three years. Candidates are not awarded a license until they undertake the required GME in the United States and meet other board requirements (e.g., an ECFMG certificate, personal interview, payment of fees).

Fifth Pathway

In 1971, the AMA established the Fifth Pathway, a program for US citizens studying abroad at foreign medical schools. The program requires that participants have:

1. Completed, in an accredited US college or university, undergraduate premedical work of a quality acceptable for matriculation in an accredited US medical school, evaluated by measures such as college grade point average and scores on the Medical College Admission Test.

2. Studied medicine in a foreign medical school located outside the United States, including Puerto Rico, and Canada that is listed in the *International Medical Education Directory*, available on the ECFMG website at www.ecfmg.org and developed and maintained by the Foundation for Advancement of International Medical Education and Research (FAIMER^SM), a nonprofit foundation of the ECFMG.

3. Completed all formal requirements for a diploma of the foreign medical school except internship and/or social service. (Those who have completed all the formal graduation requirements of the foreign medical school, including internship and/or social service, and are consequently eligible to apply for ECFMG certification, are not eligible for the Fifth Pathway program.)

If the aforementioned criteria are met, the candidate may substitute the Fifth Pathway program for internship and/or social service in the foreign country. After receiving a Fifth Pathway certificate from an accredited US medical school, these US citizens are eligible to enter the first year of GME in the United States.

In nearly all jurisdictions, individuals who hold Fifth Pathway certificates (but not the ECFMG certificate) are eligible for licensure. Fifth Pathway certificate holders must pass Steps 1 and 2 of the USMLE before entering a GME program accredited by the Accreditation Council for Graduate Medical Education (ACGME).

Note: As of June 30, 2009, through action of the AMA Council on Medical Education, the Fifth Pathway has been discontinued. The Council no longer supports the Fifth Pathway as a mechanism for eligibility to enter the first year of ACGME-accredited graduate medical education programs. The AMA will continue to maintain record of former graduates of Fifth Pathway programs, but will no longer add records of individuals completing a year of supervised clinical education at an LCME-accredited medical school in the United States after July 1, 2009, although entrants beginning in January 2009 will be included.

Additional Notes for Specific Licensing Jurisdictions

California—The state maintains lists of both recognized and disapproved schools, available at:
    www.mbc.ca.gov/applicant/schools_recognized.html
    www.mbc.ca.gov/applicant/schools_unapproved.html

The board may determine that an applicant who acquired medical education at a foreign medical school that is not recognized or has been previously disapproved by the board is eligible for licensure is the applicant meets certain criteria.

Florida—ECFMG certificate required for licensure if a candidate is not a graduate of a foreign medical school approved by the Florida Board of Medicine (none has yet been approved).

Idaho—No list of approved foreign medical schools is maintained, but for IMGs applying for licensure, such schools must have been in existence for at least 15 years prior to the date of application for Idaho licensure.

Kansas—Licensure applicants must have graduated from a school approved by the Board. If the school has not been approved by the Board, an applicant may still be eligible for a license if the school has not been disapproved and has been in operation (date instruction started) for at least 15 years.

Schools approved by the Board are:

1. All schools accredited by the Liaison Committee for Medical Eduction (LCME)
2. Universidad Autonoma de Guadalajara, Mexico
3. Aga Khan, Pakistan
4. American University of the Caribbean, St. Maarten (prior to 1995 this school was located in Montserrat)
5. SABA University, Netherlands (for graduates who matriculated at the school from and after January 1, 2002)
6. Ziauddin Medical School (temporarily approved from 7-1-08 through 6-30-11 for postgraduate permits only)
7. Kamineni Institute of Medical Sciences (temporarily approved from 7-1-08 through 6-30-12 for postgraduate permits only)

Schools unapproved (neither approved or disapproved) by the Board are:

1. SABA University, Netherlands (for graduates who matriculated at the school before 2002)

Applicants from any school disapproved by the Board are not eligible for licensure. The schools are:

1. UTESA (Universidad Tecnologica De Santiago), Santo Domingo in the Dominican Republic
2. UNIREMHOS - (University of Eugenio Marie De Hostos), Santo Domingo in the Dominican Republic - closed 1998

3. St. Matthew's University, British West Indies
4. Universidad C.E.T.E.C., Santo Domingo, Dominican Republic - closed 1984
5. Universidad C.I.F.A.S. Escuela de Medicina, Santo Domingo, Dominican Republic - closed 1984
6. Universidad Mundial Dominicana Escuela de Medicina (World University), Santo Domingo, Dominican Republic - closed 1991
7. Spartan Health Sciences University School of Medicine, Vieux Fort, Saint Lucia
8. University of Health Sciences Antigua School of Medicine, St. John's, Antigua and Barbuda
9. Unversidad Federico henriquez y Carvajal (UFHEC), Santo Domingo, Dominican Republic - closed 1998
10. Kigezi International School of Medicine, Cambridge, England and Kabale, Uganda

For more information, see:
www.kshha.org/medicalschoolsapprovedunapproved.html

Maine—GME taken in Canada or the British Isles (accredited by a national body deemed equivalent to ACGME) may be considered qualifying on an individual basis.

Maryland—In addition to two years of ACGME- or Royal College of Physicians and Surgeons of Canada (RCPSC)-accredited GME required for licensure, one year of GME required if a candidate failed any part of an examination three times; no more than three failures permitted.

Mississippi—ABMS board certification is required of candidates who completed the Fifth Pathway.

Nevada—Effective October 1, 2011, the amount of GME required of IMGs for licensure is at least 24 months, along with a commitment in writing to the Board for completion of the program. Upon proof of satisfactory completion of the program, licensure is granted by the Board within 60 days after the scheduled completion of the program.

New Jersey—An individual's educational experience must meet certain eligibility requirements.

North Carolina—Less than three years of GME may be accepted if applicant is certified by an ABMS or AOA specialty board or holds the CCFP, FRCP, or FRCS.

North Dakota—Thirty months of US or Canadian GME is required for licensure; if a candidate has not completed 30 months of GME but has met all other licensing requirements and has completed one year of GME in the United States or Canada in a board-approved program, and if the board finds that the candidate has other professional experience and training substantially equivalent to the second and third years of GME, the candidate may be deemed eligible for licensure (upon passing SPEX or ABMS board certification).

Oregon—IMG candidates for licensure must have completed at least three years of progressive GME in no more than two specialties in US or Canadian hospitals accredited for such training.

Pennsylvania—The board will grant unrestricted license by endorsement to a candidate who does not meet standard requirements if the candidate has achieved cumulative qualifications that are endorsed by the board as being equivalent to the standard license requirements.

South Carolina—ABMS/AOA board certification required for candidates who completed the Fifth Pathway.

South Dakota—No list of approved/unapproved foreign medical schools is maintained; decisions made on a case-by-case basis.

Texas—Canadian graduates of LCME-accredited schools are considered equivalent to US graduates for educational and post-graduate training requirements.

Table 12
Initial Licensure of International Medical Graduates (IMGs)

	Accepts Fifth Pathway	Maintains/ Uses List of Approved Foreign Med Schools	Endorses Canadian Certificate (LMCC) Held by an IMG	Amount of Accredited US or Canadian GME Required	
				...to Take USMLE Step 3	...for Licensure
Alabama	Yes	Yes	Yes	2 yrs (must be in 3rd yr of GME)	3 yrs
Alaska	Yes	Yes (CA list)	Yes	1 yr	3 yrs
Arizona	Yes	No	Yes	6 mos	3 yrs
Arkansas	Yes	Yes	Yes	None	3 yrs (1 if currently enrolled in prgm at U of Arkansas for Med Sci)
California*	Yes	Yes	Yes	None	2 yrs (including 4 mos general med)
Colorado	Yes	Yes	No	3 yrs	3 yrs
Connecticut	Yes	Yes (WHO)	Yes	None	2 yrs
Delaware	Yes	No	No	1 yr	3 yrs
DC	Yes	No	Yes	6 mos	3 yrs
Florida*	Yes	No	No	None	2 yrs
Georgia	Yes	Yes (CA list)	Yes	1-3 yrs	1 yr if graduate of school on CA list 3 yrs if graduate of school not on list
Guam	No	No	No	2 yrs	3 yrs
Hawaii	Yes	No	No	1 yr (must be in 2nd yr of pgm)	2 yrs
Idaho*	Yes	No	No	2 yrs, 9 mos	3 yrs
Illinois	Yes	No	Yes	1 yr	2 yrs (1 yr if entered GME post-1988)
Indiana	Yes	Yes (CA list)	Yes	2 yrs	2 yrs
Iowa	Yes	No	Yes (with valid Canadian provincial license and fulfillment of all other licensure requirements)	7 mos (or enrollment in GME prgm approved by board at time of application for Step 3)	2 yrs AOA-, ACGME-, RCPSC-, or CFPC-accredited GME
Kansas*	Yes	Yes	Yes	3 yrs (2 yrs in ACGME accredited program plus 1 other yr)	3 yrs (2 yrs in ACGME-accredited program plus 1 other yr)
Kentucky	Yes	No	Yes	1 yr	2 yrs
Louisiana	Yes	Yes (WHO, IMED)	No	None (must be in GME program)	3 yrs (Fifth Pathway may be counted as 1 yr of required GME)
Maine*	Yes	Yes (IMED)	Yes	1 yr	3 yrs
Maryland*	Yes	No	Yes	None	2 yrs ACGME- or RCPSC-accredited GME (as of Oct. 1, 2000)
Massachusetts	Yes	No	Yes	1 yr	3 yrs
Michigan	Yes	No	Yes (with valid Canadian license)	6 mos	2 yrs
Minnesota	Yes	Yes (IMED)	Yes	None (must be in GME program)	2 yrs
Mississippi*	Yes	No	No	1 yr	3 yrs (or 1 yr plus ABMS certification)
Missouri	Yes	No	No	3 yrs	3 yrs
Montana	Yes	Yes	No	1 yr (plus ECFMG)	3 yrs (or ABMS/AOA certification)
Nebraska	Yes	No	Yes	None	3 yrs
Nevada*	Yes	No	Yes	None	2 yrs and attestation of completion of residency program
New Hampshire	Yes	No	Yes	None (must be in GME program)	2 yrs
New Jersey*	Yes	Yes (FAIMER)	No	1 yr	2 yrs, and contract for yr 3, if graduated from med school after July 1, 2003; 1 yr if completed before July 1, 1985

(continued on next page)

Table 12 (continued)
Initial Licensure of International Medical Graduates (IMGs)

	Accepts Fifth Pathway	Maintains/ Uses List of Approved Foreign Med Schools	Endorses Canadian Certificate (LMCC) Held by an IMG	Amount of Accredited US or Canadian GME Required	
				...to Take USMLE Step 3	...for Licensure
New Mexico	Yes	Yes (CA list)	No	1 yr	2 yrs
New York	Yes	No	Yes (with valid Canadian provincial license and fulfillment of all other licensure requirements)	None	3 yrs
North Carolina*	Yes	No	Yes	None	3 yrs
North Dakota*	Yes	Yes (CA list)	Yes	1 yr (none if enrolled in-state)	30 mos
Ohio	Yes	No	Yes	9 mos	2 yrs (through the 2nd-yr level)
Oklahoma	Yes	No	Yes	None	2 yrs
Oregon*	Yes	No	Yes	None (must be in GME program)	3 yrs
Pennsylvania*	Yes	No	Yes (if passed after 5/70 and in English)	None	3 yrs (1 yr if GME taken in US before July 1987)
Puerto Rico	Yes		Yes	None	1 yr
Rhode Island	Yes	Yes (WHO)	Yes (with valid Canadian provincial license and fulfillment of all other licensure requirements)	1 yr	3 yrs
South Carolina*	Yes	No	Yes	3 yrs	3 yrs
South Dakota*	No	No	Yes	None	Completion of residency in the US or Canada (1 yr if GME taken in US before July 1987)
Tennessee	Yes	Yes	Yes	1 yr	3 yrs
Texas*	Yes	Yes	No (but accepts LMCC examination as licensing examination)	None	2 yrs
Utah	No	No	No	None	2 yrs
Vermont	Yes	Yes (CA list)	Yes	7 mos	3 yrs
Virgin Islands	No	No	No	Not applicable	1 yr US GME
Virginia	Yes	No	Yes	None	2 yrs
Washington	Yes	No	Yes (if passed after 12/69)	1 yr (or enrollment in GME program)	2 yrs (1 yr if medical school completed before July 28, 1985)
West Virginia	Yes	No	Yes	None	3 yrs (or 1 yr plus ABMS cert.)
Wisconsin	Yes	No	Yes (if passed after 12/77)	1 yr	1 yr
Wyoming	Yes	No	Yes	1 yr	2 yrs (1 yr if ABMS/AOA cert., or continually licensed in one or more states for past 5 yrs

Abbreviations

ABMS—American Board of Medical Specialties
ACGME—Accreditation Council for Graduate Medical Education
AOA—American Osteopathic Association
CFPC—College of Family Physicians of Canada
ECFMG—Educational Commission for Foreign Medical Graduates
GME—graduate medical education
IMED—International Medical Education Directory
IMG—international medical graduate
LMCC—Licentiate of the Medical Council of Canada
RCPSC—Royal College of Physicians and Surgeons of Canada
USMLE—United States Medical Licensing Examination
WHO—World Health Organization

* Refer to introductory text to this table for more information on this state's regulations.

Note: All information should be verified with the licensing board; licenses are granted to those physicians meeting all state requirements—at the discretion of the board.

Medical Student Clerkship Regulations

For purposes of this publication, a clerkship is defined as clinical education provided to medical students. Nine states evaluate clinical clerkships in connection with an application for licensure (Table 13). In most states, clerkships for US medical students must take place in hospitals affiliated with medical schools accredited by the Liaison Committee on Medical Education (LCME). A number of states have special rules that apply to students of non-LCME-accredited medical schools in the Caribbean, the majority of which complete their clinical clerkships in US hospitals and teaching institutions.

For example, Texas (as noted below) requires that the clerkship(s) must be performed in a hospital or teaching institution sponsoring or participating in a graduate medical education (GME) program accredited, at the time the applicant performed the clerkship, by the Accreditation Council for Graduate Medical Education (ACGME), American Osteopathic Association (AOA), or the board in the *same subject* (e.g., the *exact same specialty or subspecialty*). Required core (or fundamental) clinical clerkships are:

- Internal medicine
- Obstetrics-gynecology
- Pediatrics
- Psychiatry
- Family medicine
- Surgery

Seven boards regulate clerkships provided in their states to students of foreign medical schools (including US citizens studying medicine in foreign schools). For purposes of licensure, eight states accept only those clerkships completed in hospital departments with ACGME-accredited programs.

Additional Notes for Specific Licensing Jurisdictions

Florida—Rules on clinical clerkships for international medical graduates adopted by the Florida Board before October 1986 do not apply to any graduate who had already completed a clinical clerkship or who had begun a clinical clerkship, as long as the clerkship was completed within three years.

A foreign medical school must be registered with the Florida Department of Education for its students to perform clinical clerkships in Florida.

Illinois—Students who complete a core clerkship rotation in a clinical teaching facility that was formally affiliated or under contract with the medical college which conferred their degree must submit a copy of each affiliation agreement between the medical college and each clinical teaching facility. Further, the affiliation agreement must be substantiated by submission of an evaluation form completed by the supervising physician for each core clerkship rotation completed.

Michigan—The medical education program must have included clinical science rotations in internal medicine, general surgery, pediatrics, obstetrics-gynecology, and psychiatry, all completed in at a teaching hospital (defined as a hospital that offers a residency program in the same content area of the clerkship).

New Jersey—For students from foreign medical schools who complete clinical clerkships in the US, the core clerkships (internal medicine, obstetrics-gynecology, pediatrics, psychiatry, and surgery) must be completed (minimum of 4 weeks in each) at facilities with an ACGME- or AOA-accredited residency program in the specific specialty.

Texas—All rotations performed in the US by medical school students must be (1) as a student in an accredited medical or osteopathic school or (2) in a hospital of teaching institution sponsoring or participating in a GME program accredited by the ACGME, the AOA, or the board *in the same specialty or subspecialty* as the medical or osteopathic medical education rotation. *The only exception* is for applicants who are certified by the ABMS or the AOA Bureau of Osteopathic Specialists.

Table 13
Medical Student Clerkship Regulations

	Evaluates Clinical Clerkships of Licensure Applicants	Clerkships for Students of Foreign Medical Schools		Notes
		Regulates Clerkships Provided by Hospitals	Accepts Clerkships Only in Hospital Departments with ACGME-accredited Programs	
Alabama				
Alaska				
Arizona				
Arkansas				
California	Yes	Yes	Yes	Clerkships must total at least 72 weeks, with at least 40 weeks of instruction in core clinical courses of surgery (minimum of 8 weeks of instruction), medicine (8 weeks), pediatrics (6 weeks), obstetrics-gynecology (6 weeks), family medicine (4 weeks), and psychiatry (4 weeks)
Colorado				
Connecticut				
Delaware				
DC				
Florida*	Yes	Yes	Yes	
Georgia				
Guam				
Hawaii				
Idaho				
Illinois*				
Indiana				
Iowa				
Kansas				
Kentucky				
Louisiana				
Maine				
Maryland				
Massachusetts	Yes	Yes	Yes	Clinical study in the US must be in hospitals with ACGME-accredited programs in the area of the clinical study
Michigan*				
Minnesota				
Mississippi				
Missouri				
Montana				
Nebraska				
Nevada				IMGs may be required to provide additional or specific criteria for evaluation
New Hampshire				
New Jersey*	Yes	Yes	Yes	
New Mexico				

(continued on next page)

Table 13 (continued)
Medical Student Clerkship Regulations

	Evaluates Clinical Clerkships of Licensure Applicants	Clerkships for Students of Foreign Medical Schools		Notes
		Regulates Clerkships Provided by Hospitals	Accepts Clerkships Only in Hospital Departments with ACGME-accredited Programs	
New York		Yes	Yes	Applicants who completed one or more clinical clerkships in a country other than where their medical school is located must complete Form 2CC, "Certification of Approved Clinical Clerkship"
North Carolina				
North Dakota				
Ohio				
Oklahoma	Yes			If graduated from foreign med school after July 1, 2003, clerkships done in the US must have been in hospitals accredited by appropriate body, such as the ACGME
Oregon	Yes	Yes	Yes	Clerkships must be completed in institutions that conduct residency programs in the subject of the clerkship that are approved by the ACGME, CMA, RCPSC, or AOA; evaluation of clerkships not required if applicant qualifies for expedited endorsement
Pennsylvania				
Puerto Rico	Yes	Yes		
Rhode Island				
South Carolina				
South Dakota				
Tennessee				
Texas*	Yes	No	Yes	See note
Utah				
Vermont				
Virgin Islands				
Virginia	Yes		Yes	All core rotations completed in the US must be in an ACGME-accredited teaching hospital offering an accredited residecny program in the same specialty in which the clinical training is received
Washington				
West Virginia				
Wisconsin				
Wyoming				

* Refer to introductory text to this table for more information on this state's regulations.

Abbreviations

ACGME—Accreditation Council for Graduate Medical Education

AOA—American Osteopathic Association

CMA—Canadian Medical Association

RCPSC—Royal College of Physicians and Surgeons of Canada

Note: *All information should be verified with the licensing board; medical licenses are granted to those physicians meeting all state requirements—at the discretion of the board.*

Additional Policies Concerning International Medical Graduates (IMGs)

A number of state medical boards have additional graduate medical education (GME) and specialty certificate policies for international medical graduates (IMGs) (Table 14). Fifteen states have requirements for appointment to GME programs other than requiring an Educational Commission for Foreign Medical Graduates (ECFMG) certificate or a limited license.

A small number of boards state that GME completed in foreign countries other than Canada may be considered for credit toward a license. Specialty certificates of foreign boards, such as the Royal College of Physicians in the United Kingdom, may be accepted for credit toward a license in a select states as well.

Additional Notes for Specific Licensing Jurisdictions

Kansas—Additional requirements, if applicant is not a graduate of an accredited medical school in the US: (1) Three years postgraduate training approved by the Board; (2) Medical school in operation for at least 15 years, the graduates of which have been licensed in another state(s) that has standards similar to Kansas; (3) Meet all other requirements for taking the examination for licensure [65-2873(c)(2)].

Maine—The board may accept GME completed in England, Scotland, and Ireland for credit toward a license if it is accepted by the specialty board as meeting board eligibility in the United States and the Maine board is notified via certified letter.

Pennsylvania—IMGs seeking appointment to a GME program need a passing score on United States Medical Licensing Examination (USMLE) Steps 1 and 2, or National Board of Medical Examiners (NBME) Parts I and II or Federation Licensing Examination (FLEX) Component 1, for graduate year 2 medical education; for graduate year 3 and beyond, all parts of USMLE (or NBME or FLEX) are required.

Wisconsin—Temporary educational permit is required of IMGs for a second year of GME (and beyond), unless IMG has a permanent license. Board may accept training in lieu of GME by waiver.

Table 14
Additional Policies Concerning International Medical Graduates (IMGs)

	Has State Board Requirements for Appointment to GME Program Other Than ECFMG Certificate or Limited License	May Accept GME Completed in Foreign Countries Other Than Canada for Credit Toward License	May Accept Specialty Certificates of Foreign Boards (e.g., Royal College of Physicians of the United Kingdom) for Credit Toward a License
Alabama			
Alaska	Yes (residency permit required)		
Arizona	Yes (residency permit required)		
Arkansas	No	No	No
California	Yes (Postgraduate Training Authorization Letter [PTAL] required)	No	No
Colorado			
Connecticut	Yes (residency permit required)	Yes	Yes
Delaware	Yes (residency permit required)	No	No
DC			
Florida			
Georgia			
Guam			
Hawaii			
Idaho			
Illinois			
Indiana			
Iowa			
Kansas*	Yes (residency permit required)		
Kentucky	Yes (residency permit required for 2nd yr)		
Louisiana	Yes (passage of FLEX/NBME/USMLE)		
Maine*		Yes	Yes
Maryland			
Massachusetts	Yes (passage of FLEX/NBME/USMLE)		
Michigan	Yes (certification of medical education)		
Minnesota	Yes (residency intern permit required)		
Mississippi			
Missouri	Yes		
Montana			
Nebraska		Yes	
Nevada	Yes	No	No
New Hampshire			
New Jersey	Yes (residency intern permit required)		
New Mexico			
New York		Yes	Yes
North Carolina			
North Dakota			Yes
Ohio		Yes	Yes
Oklahoma		Yes	Yes
Oregon	No	No	No
Pennsylvania*	Yes		Yes
Puerto Rico			

(continued on next page)

Table 14 (continued)
Additional Policies Concerning International Medical Graduates (IMGs)

	Has State Board Requirements for Appointment to GME Program Other Than ECFMG Certificate or Limited License	May Accept GME Completed in Foreign Countries Other Than Canada for Credit Toward License	May Accept Specialty Certificates of Foreign Boards (e.g., Royal College of Physicians of the United Kingdom) for Credit Toward a License
Rhode Island		Yes (UK only)	Yes; may accept certificates of boards in England, Scotland, and Ireland
South Carolina		No	No
South Dakota		No	No
Tennessee			Yes; specialty board must be AMA-recognized
Texas		No	
Utah			
Vermont	Yes		Yes; specialty board must be recognized by ABMS, RCPSC, or CFPC
Virgin Islands			
Virginia	Yes	No	No
Washington			
West Virginia			
Wisconsin*			No
Wyoming		No	At board's discretion

Abbreviations

ABMS—American Board of Medical Specialties

ACGME—Accreditation Council for Graduate Medical Education

ECFMG—Educational Commission for Foreign Medical Graduates

CFPC—College of Family Physicians of Canada

FLEX—Federation Licensing Examination

GME—graduate medical education

NBME—certificate of the National Board of Medical Examiners

RCPSC—Royal College of Physicians and Surgeons of Canada

USMLE—United States Medical Licensing Examination

* Refer to introductory text to this table for more information on this state's regulations.

Note: *All information should be verified with the licensing board; medical licenses are granted to those physicians meeting all state requirements—at the discretion of the board.*

Additional Policies Concerning Doctors of Osteopathic Medicine (DOs)

A number of state medical boards have additional graduate medical education (GME) policies for doctors of osteopathic medicine (DOs), as shown in Table 15. Most medical boards accept GME accredited by the Accreditation Council for Graduate Medical Education (ACGME) for licensure of osteopathic medical graduates.

Osteopathic postdoctoral training programs are recognized throughout the United States in federal and state laws, rules, and regulations. As the only accrediting agency for osteopathic medical education, the American Osteopathic Association (AOA) reviews and approves all training standards, establishes general policy, and reviews and approves all postdoctoral training programs. See the AOA website for more information: www.osteopathic.org/inside-aoa/accreditation/postdoctoral-training-approval.

Table 15
Additional Policies Concerning Doctors of Osteopathic Medicine (DOs)

	ACGME-Accredited GME Accepted for Licensure of Osteopathic Physicians	State Osteopathic Board Handles Licensure
Alabama	Yes	
Alaska	Yes	
Arizona	Yes	Yes
Arkansas	Yes	
California		Yes
Colorado	Yes	
Connecticut	Yes	
Delaware	Yes	
DC	Yes	
Florida	Yes (if AOA-accredited)	Yes
Georgia	Yes	
Guam		
Hawaii	Yes	
Idaho	Yes	
Illinois	Yes	
Indiana	Yes	
Iowa	Yes	
Kansas	Yes	
Kentucky	Yes	
Louisiana	Yes	
Maine	Yes	Yes
Maryland	Yes	
Massachusetts	Yes	
Michigan	Yes (if AOA accredited)	Yes
Minnesota	Yes	
Mississippi	Yes	
Missouri	Yes	
Montana	Yes	
Nebraska	Yes	
Nevada		Yes
New Hampshire	Yes	
New Jersey	Yes	
New Mexico		Yes
New York	Yes	
North Carolina	Yes	
North Dakota	Yes	
Ohio	Yes	
Oklahoma		Yes
Oregon	Yes	
Pennsylvania		Yes
Puerto Rico		

(continued on next page)

Table 15 (continued)
Additional Policies Concerning Doctors of Osteopathic Medicine (DOs)

	ACGME-Accredited GME Accepted for Licensure of Osteopathic Physicians	State Osteopathic Board Handles Licensure
Rhode Island	Yes	
South Carolina	Yes	
South Dakota	Yes	
Tennessee		Yes
Texas	Yes	
Utah	Yes	Yes
Vermont		Yes
Virgin Islands		
Virginia	Yes	
Washington	Yes	Yes
West Virginia	Yes	Yes
Wisconsin	Yes	
Wyoming	Yes	

Abbreviations

ACGME—Accreditation Council for Graduate Medical Education
GME—graduate medical education

* Refer to introductory text to this table for more information on this state's regulations.

Note: *All information should be verified with the licensing board; medical licenses are granted to those physicians meeting all state requirements—at the discretion of the board.*

Accredited Subspecialties and Nonaccredited Fellowships That Satisfy Graduate Medical Education Requirements for Licensure

Both the AMA and the Accreditation Council for Graduate Medical Education (ACGME) define a residency as graduate medical education (GME) that takes place in any of the medical specialties with ACGME Program Requirements (e.g., internal medicine, pediatrics, surgery, etc.). Beginning in 2000, the ACGME has used the term *fellowship* to denote GME in ACGME-accredited subspecialty programs (e.g., cardiovascular disease, hand surgery, rheumatology) that is beyond the requirements for eligibility for first board certification in the discipline.

All state medical boards accept residency education in specialty programs accredited by the ACGME as satisfying their GME requirements for licensure. In addition, nearly all jurisdictions accept residency education in subspecialty programs accredited by ACGME as satisfying their GME requirements for licensure (Table 16).

A few boards accept clinical fellowships not accredited by ACGME, and some boards may accept research fellowships not accredited by ACGME to satisfy the GME requirement for licensure.

For more information on the ACGME, see Chapter 6.

Additional Notes for Specific Licensing Jurisdictions

Washington—Clinical fellowships not accredited by the ACGME are accepted if the program allows the physician to sit for the specialty board examination in that field.

Table 16
Accredited Subspecialties and Nonaccredited Fellowships That Satisfy Graduate Medical Education Requirements for Licensure

	Accepts Subspecialty GME Accredited by ACGME	Accepts Clinical Fellowships *Not* Accredited by ACGME	Accepts Research Fellowships *Not* Accredited by ACGME
Alabama	Yes		
Alaska	Yes		
Arizona	Yes		
Arkansas	No		
California MD and DO	Yes		
Colorado	Yes		
Connecticut	Yes		
Delaware	Yes		
DC	Yes	Yes (with board approval)	Yes (with board approval)
Florida	Yes		
Florida DO	Yes (only if AOA-accredited)		
Georgia	Yes	Yes (with board approval)	
Guam	Yes		
Hawaii	Yes	Yes (with board approval)	Yes (with board approval)
Idaho	Yes		
Illinois	Yes		
Indiana	Yes		
Iowa	Yes		
Kansas	Yes		
Kentucky	Yes		
Louisiana	Yes		
Maine	Yes		
Maryland	Yes	Yes (with board approval)	
Massachusetts	Yes		
Michigan	Yes		
Michigan DO	Yes (only if AOA-accredited)		
Minnesota	Yes		
Mississippi	Yes		
Missouri	Yes	Yes	
Montana	Yes		
Nebraska	Yes		
Nevada	Yes		
New Hampshire	Yes		
New Jersey	Yes		
New Mexico	Yes		
New York	Yes	Yes	Yes
North Carolina	Yes	Yes (with board approval)	Yes (with board approval)
North Dakota	Yes		
Ohio	Yes	Yes (with board approval)	Yes (with board approval)
Oklahoma	Yes		
Oregon	Yes		
Pennsylvania	Yes		
Puerto Rico	No		
Rhode Island	Yes	Yes (with board approval)	
South Carolina	Yes		

(continued on next page)

Table 16 (continued)
Accredited Subspecialties and Nonaccredited Fellowships That Satisfy Graduate Medical Education Requirements for Licensure

	Accepts Subspecialty GME Accredited by ACGME	Accepts Clinical Fellowships *Not* Accredited by ACGME	Accepts Research Fellowships *Not* Accredited by ACGME
South Dakota	Yes		
Tennessee	Yes		
Texas	Yes	Yes (if board-approved)	
Utah	Yes	Yes (if combined with an ACGME-accredited program)	
Vermont	Yes		
Virgin Islands	Yes		
Virginia	Yes		
Washington MD and DO	Yes	Yes (see note)	
West Virginia	Yes		
Wisconsin	Yes		
Wyoming	Yes		

Abbreviations

ACGME—Accreditation Council for Graduate Medical Education
AOA—American Osteopathic Association
GME—graduate medical education

Note: *All information should be verified with licensing board; medical licenses are granted to those physicians meeting all state requirements—at the discretion of the board.*

Licensure Requirement Exemptions for Eminent Physicians and Medical School Faculty

Less than half of boards license physicians through recognition of eminence in medical education or medical practice (Table 17). For example, Maryland, one of the jurisdictions that licenses physicians through this mechanism, defines "conceded eminence and authority in the profession" as "significant teaching, research, and achievement in a field of medicine recognized by the Board" (see www.mbp.state.md.us/forms/concede.pdf).

In Maryland, applicants seeking licensure by eminence must meet at least three of the following qualifications:

1. *Within 10 years before the application, have published original results of clinical research in a medical journal listed in the Index Medicus or in an equivalent scholarly publication, and have submitted these articles to the Board in English or in a foreign language with verifiable, certified translations in English;*

2. *Have held an appointment at a medical school approved by the LCME or at any medical school listed in the World Health Organization directory at the level of associate or full professor, or its equivalent, for at least five years;*

3. *Within 10 years before the application, have developed a treatment modality, surgical technique, or other verified original contribution to the field of medicine, which is attested to by the dean of a school of medicine in the state or by the director of the National Institutes of Health;*

4. *Have actively practiced medicine cumulatively for 15 years, which may include up to five years sabbatical during which the applicant was involved in research; and*

5. *Be a member in good standing of a board of the American Board of Medical Specialties or other equivalent specialty board.*

Physicians appointed to a medical school faculty are excused from the graduate medical education (GME) requirement for limited licensure in 18 states and from the examination requirement for limited licensure or teaching certification in 18 states. These faculty appointees would, however, receive a limited license or similar credential.

Table 17
Licensure Requirement Exemptions for Eminent Physicians and Medical School Faculty

	License Physicians Through Recognition of Eminence in Medical Education or Practice	Physicians Appointed to a Medical Faculty Are Excused From...		Notes/Comments
		...the GME Requirement for Limited Licensure	...the Examination Requirement for Limited Licensure	
Alabama		Yes	Yes	
Alaska				
Arizona				
Arkansas	Yes	Yes	Yes	IMGs not eligible for licensure may be granted an education license for practice of medicine only within the clinical and educational programs of the University of Arkansas for Medical Sciences. This license is valid for one year from date of issue and requires annual approval to renew.
California DO	Yes	Yes	Yes	
California MD	Yes	Yes	Yes	Physicians appointed to a medical faculty are eligible for a special license or certificate, and they may practice only at the designated medical school or formally affiliated teaching hospital/institution.
Colorado	Yes	Yes	Yes	Distinguished foreign physicians are invited to serve on faculty.
Connecticut		Yes	Yes	
Delaware				
DC	Yes			
Florida		Yes	Yes	Physicians appointed to a medical faculty are eligible for a special license, with which they may practice only at the designated facility/institution.
Georgia		Yes	Yes	Physicians appointed to a medical faculty are excused from the GME requirement for limited licensure for teaching only.
Guam				
Hawaii				
Idaho				
Illinois				
Indiana				
Iowa	Yes	Yes	Yes	Physicians appointed to a medical faculty are eligible for a special license, with which they may practice only at the designated facility/institution. Time spent on a special license can be applied to the GME requirements for permanent licensure.
Kansas	Yes (limited)			Visiting professor tempoarry license (65-28,100); Visiting clinical professor license (65-28, 124).
Kentucky	Yes	Yes	Yes	Physicians appointed to a medical faculty are eligible for a special license, with which they may practice only at the designated facility/institution.
Louisiana	Yes	Yes	Yes	A physician licensed through recognition of eminence in medical education must be approved as a tenured professor or associate/assistant professor by a Louisiana medical school. Limited to that institution only; void if leaves or is terminated from that facility.
Maine				
Maryland	Yes	Yes	Yes	
Massachusetts				
Michigan (MD and DO)	Yes (limited)	Yes	Yes	Physicians appointed to a medical faculty are eligible for a special license, with which they may practice only at the designated facility/institution.
Minnesota				

(continued on next page)

Table 17 (continued)
Licensure Requirement Exemptions for Eminent Physicians and Medical School Faculty

	License Physicians Through Recognition of Eminence in Medical Education or Practice	Physicians Appointed to a Medical Faculty Are Excused From...		Notes/Comments
		...the GME Requirement for Limited Licensure	...the Examination Requirement for Limited Licensure	
Mississippi				
Missouri	Yes		Yes	
Montana	Yes			An IMG seeking a restricted license must have published in an English-language, peer-reviewed medical journal.
Nebraska				
Nevada				
New Hampshire	Yes			A courtesy license for educational purposes is provided to eminent physicians under limited circumstances.
New Jersey				
New Mexico				
New York				
North Carolina	Yes	Yes	Yes	Also excused from ECFMG certification requirement. Must have 1 yr of ACGME-accredited training or its equivalent (as determined by the Board).
North Dakota				
Ohio	Yes	Yes	Yes	Physicians appointed to a medical faculty are eligible for a clinical research faculty certificate, with which they may practice only at the school or teaching hospitals affiliated with the school. This certificate is valid 3 yrs and may be renewed. Selected candidates may be eligible for a certificate of conceded eminence.
Oklahoma				
Oregon	Yes	N.A.		IMGs not eligible for licensure may be granted a Limited License, Medical Faculty (LL,MF) if appointed to a full-time medical school faculty position under direction of the department head. LL,MF may be granted and renewed for a total of 4 yrs, during which applicant must pass the USMLE or have passed FLEX or the National Boards. The physician would then be eligible for licensure. Postgraduate training requirement waived by 4 years of practice in another jurisdiction under license similar to Boards LL, MF.
Pennsylvania DO				
Pennsylvania MD	Yes	Yes		Physicians appointed to a medical faculty are eligible for a visiting medical faculty certificate, with which they may practice only at the school or teaching hospitals affiliated with the school. This nonrenewable certificate is valid 1 yr or duration of the appointment, whichever is shorter.
Puerto Rico				
Rhode Island	Yes	Yes	Yes	Distinguished foreign physicians recommended by the medical school dean may serve on faculty; academic limited registration may be renewed for a maximum of 5 yrs.
South Carolina				
South Dakota				
Tennessee		Yes	Yes	
Texas	Yes	See note	See note	Several types of limited licenses, with different requirements.
Utah		No	No	
Vermont		No		

(continued on next page)

Table 17 (continued)
Licensure Requirement Exemptions for Eminent Physicians and Medical School Faculty

| | License Physicians Through Recognition of Eminence in Medical Education or Practice | Physicians Appointed to a Medical Faculty Are Excused From... | | Notes/Comments |
		...the GME Requirement for Limited Licensure	...the Examination Requirement for Limited Licensure	
Virgin Islands				
Virginia	No	Yes	Yes	
Washington				
West Virginia		Yes	Yes	
Wisconsin				Visiting professor license offered for IMGs invited to serve on the academic staff of a medical school in Wisconsin.
Wyoming				

Abbreviations

ACGME—Accreditation Council for Graduate Medical Education

FLEX—Federation Licensing Examination

GME—graduate medical education

IMG—international medical graduate

USMLE—United States Medical Licensing Examination

Note: *All information should be verified with licensing board; medical licenses are granted to those physicians meeting all state requirements—at the discretion of the board.*

Teaching (Visiting Professor) Licenses

About two thirds of jurisdictions issue teaching (visiting professor) licenses, with fees ranging up to $400 (Table 18).

These permits are granted for various periods of time; for example, the Arizona MD board offers a teaching license valid for one year, which may be renewed for up to four years; California awards renewable certificates of registration for one to three years; Illinois offers visiting professor permits valid for up to two years; Oregon offers a one-year limited license for either visiting professors or medical faculty that can be renewed for one additional year or three additional years, respectively.

Awarding of these licenses may be contingent on certain requirements, depending on the given jurisdiction. For example, Washington state requires (1) a letter of nomination by the dean of the University of Washington medical school or CEO of a hospital or other appropriate health care facility and (2) proof of current licensure in another state or country. Some boards require that practice be limited to the school or institution, or require that the physician have a license in another jurisdiction.

Table 18
Teaching (Visiting Professor) Licenses

	Teaching (Visiting Professor) License Granted	Time License Valid for	License Can Be Renewed?	Practice Limited to School/ Institution?	License in Another Jurisdiction Required?	Notes
Alabama	Yes					
Alaska						
Arizona	Yes, $250	1 yr	Yes up to 4 yrs			Teaching license within Board-approved medical school or GME program. Education teaching permit is also available; granted for 5 days, $100.
Arizona DO	Yes, $318	2 yrs	Yes	Yes	No	Education teaching permit, granted for 5 days, $106.
Arkansas						
California	Yes	1-3 yrs	Yes	Yes	Yes	Certificate of registration awarded for 1 to 3 yrs to physicians who do not immediately meet licensure requirements and who have been offered full-time teaching positions in a medical school. Biennially renewable faculty permits awarded to academically eminent physicians for whom the medical school has assumed direct responsibility.
California DO						
Colorado	Yes, $100					
Connecticut	Yes, $0					
Delaware	No					
DC						Affiliated-With License; contact Board for more info.
Florida	Yes, $100	180 days	Yes up to 5 yrs	Yes	Yes	No more than three physicians per year per institution may hold the certificate.
Florida DO	Yes	2 yrs	No	Yes	Yes	
Georgia	Yes	2 yrs	1 yr (at Board's discretion)	Yes	Yes	Teacher's license for faculty of Board-approved medical college or affiliated clinics
Guam						
Hawaii						
Hawaii DO						
Idaho						
Illinois	Yes	2 yrs				Visiting professor permit for faculty appointments in a medical or osteopathic school. Visiting physician permits for up to 180 days issued for studying, demonstrating, or performing a specific subject or technique in medical/ osteopathic schools; hospitals; or other facilities.
Indiana	Yes, $100	1 yr	No	Yes		Visiting professor license granted to an institution for a specific physician to whom it has granted a visiting faculty appointment. Institution must certify the physician's qualifications.
Iowa	Yes					Special license or temporary license, depending on applicant's qualifications and the teaching activity in Iowa.
Kansas	Yes, $25 or $150					Visiting professor tempoarry license $25 (65-28,100); Visiting clinical professor license $150 (65-28, 124).
Kentucky	Yes, $300					
Louisiana	Yes					License valid for specific period of time.
Maine	Yes, $0					
Maine DO	Yes, $50					
Maryland	Yes, $300	1 yr				Limited license for graduate teaching.

(continued on next page)

Table 18 (continued)
Teaching (Visiting Professor) Licenses

	Teaching (Visiting Professor) License Granted	Time License Valid for	License Can Be Renewed?	Practice Limited to School/ Institution?	License in Another Jurisdiction Required?	Notes
Massachusetts	Yes, $250					Temporary registration issued to physicians holding a temporary faculty appointment at a Massachusetts medical school, are substituting temporarily for a fully licensed Massachusetts physician, or are enrolled in a CME course that requires Massachusetts licensure.
Michigan	Yes, $170					For teaching/research appointment at approved educational program.
Michigan DO	Yes, $170	1 yr	Yes (10x)	Yes		For teaching/research appointment at approved educational program.
Minnesota						
Mississippi						
Missouri	Yes					
Montana						
Nebraska	Yes	1 yr	Yes	Yes		Temporary visiting faculty permits for medical school faculty.
Nevada						
Nevada DO	Yes, $200	6 mos.				
New Hampshire	Yes, $75			Yes	Yes	
New Jersey						
New Mexico	Yes, $100					
New Mexico DO						
New York						
North Carolina	Yes		Yes	Yes	Yes	Special purpose license for teaching purposes.
North Dakota						
Ohio	Yes, $375	3 yrs	Yes	Yes	Yes	Clinical research faculty certificate
Oklahoma						
Oklahoma DO						
Oregon	Yes, $185	1 yr	Yes; 1 or 3 yrs	Yes	No	Limited license (LL) Visiting Professor (VP) and Medical Faculty (MF). LL-VP for 1-yr teaching position; may be renewed for 1 additional yr. LL-MF for full-time faculty position offered by the dean of the medical school and may be renewed for 3 additional yrs.
Pennsylvania	Yes	3 yrs		Yes		Institutional license for teaching and/or practice of medicine in a medical college, affiliate, or community hospital. Temporary license allows for teaching medicine and surgery or participating in a medical procedure necessary for the well-being of a specific patient.
Pennsylvania DO						
Puerto Rico	Yes					
Rhode Island	Yes, $150					
South Carolina						
South Dakota						Teaching or visiting professor licenses, permits, or certificates are not issued.
Tennessee	Yes, $50					
Tennessee DO						
Texas	Yes, $167			Yes	No	Issued for no more than 24 months, in no less than 31-day increments. May not be renewed past 24 months.
Utah						

(continued on next page)

Table 18 (continued)
Teaching (Visiting Professor) Licenses

	Teaching (Visiting Professor) License Granted	Time License Valid for	License Can Be Renewed?	Practice Limited to School/ Institution?	License in Another Jurisdiction Required?	Notes
Vermont						
Vermont DO						
Virgin Islands	Yes					
Virginia	Yes, $55	1 yr	Yes	Yes	No	Limited license for fellowship and teaching positions.
Washington	Yes	1 yr	Yes	Yes	Yes	Teaching/research limited license for teaching (visiting professor); letter of nomination by dean of the University of Washington medical school or CEO of a hospital or other appropriate health care facility is required.
Washington DO						
West Virginia	Yes, $150					Limited medical school faculty license.
West Virginia DO						
Wisconsin	Yes, $216	2 yrs				Teaching license is $216 total: $141 plus $75 for state law exam.
Wyoming						

Abbreviations

CME—continuing medical education

GME—graduate medical education

Note: *All information should be verified with licensing board; medical licenses are granted to those physicians meeting all state requirements—at the discretion of the board.*

Initial Licensure Fees and Requirements

The National Board of Medical Examiners (NBME) administers United States Medical Licensing Examination (USMLE) Steps 1 and 2 to students and graduates of US and Canadian medical schools at test centers established by the NBME; application materials are usually available at these medical schools. The Educational Commission for Foreign Medical Graduates (ECFMG) administers USMLE Steps 1 and 2 to students and graduates of foreign medical schools; application materials are available only through the ECFMG.

Administration of USMLE Step 3 is the responsibility of the individual medical licensing jurisdictions. Step 3 application materials for physicians who have successfully completed Steps 1 and 2 are available from the medical licensing authorities or the Federation of State Medical Boards (FSMB), which administers the examination for all jurisdictions, except Florida, Guam, and the Virgin Islands. For more information on USMLE Step 3, call (800) USMLE XM—(800) 876-5396. Although the FSMB administers the examination, in some jurisdictions physicians apply for the examination directly via the state board rather than through the FSMB.

The fee for 2013 for USMLE Step 3 is $780 (with some exceptions in certain states).

For osteopathic physicians, the National Board of Osteopathic Medical Examiners (NBOME) administers its computer-based cognitive examinations (COMLEX-USA Level 1, Level 2 Cognitive Evaluation and Level 3) at hundreds of professional test sites throughout the United States and Canada. The NBOME's COMLEX-USA Level 2-Performance Evaluation, the clinical skills component of the COMLEX-USA series, is administered at the NBOME's National Center for Clinical Skills Testing in Conshohocken, PA, near Philadelphia. The current COMLEX-USA Level 3 fee is $750.

In addition to these USMLE and COMLEX-USA examination fees, most jurisdictions charge processing, application, and administrative fees (Table 19).

Additional Notes for Specific Licensing Jurisdictions

California—Initial licensure includes $442 processing fee, $49 fingerprinting fee, $25 mandatory loan repayment fee, and $783 licensing fee. Fingerprint fee does not include the fingerprint rolling fee.

New Jersey—Criminal History Background Check is payable to the fingerprinting service and differs for out-of-state submission of fingerprint cards ($70.25) and in-state digital exams ($66.30).

Ohio—The Federation Credentials Verification Service (FCVS) is required of all physicians applying for Ohio licensure by either examination or endorsement. The applicable FCVS fee is in addition to the application fee paid to the medical board. Criminal background check fees are additional.

Texas—Initial applications are for licensure (not identified as examination or endorsement). The application fee is $1,002 and does not include any examination fees or criminal history check fees.

Washington MD and DO—These fees are nonrefundable:

- Impaired physician program fee on each application and for each year of the renewal period—$35 (MD), $25 (DO)
- University of Washington library fee per application or renewal—$25 (MD and DO)
- Late fee—$262 (MD), $250 (DO)
- Reissue expired license fee—$262 (MD), $250 (DO)

Table 19
Initial Licensure Fees and Requirements *(Not including USMLE or NBOME examination fees)*

	Application to:		Licensure Application Fees	Fingerprint Fee	Criminal Background Check Fee	Initial Licensure Cost	Notes
	FSMB	NBOME					
Alabama			$250		$65	$315	$20 for application packet
Alaska	Yes		500			500	
Arizona	Yes		500			500	
Arizona DO		Yes	400			400	USMLE accepted
Arkansas	Yes		400		38.50	438.50	$100 fee
California	Yes		442	$49		1,299	
California DO		Yes	200	49		249	
Colorado	Yes		—			—	
Connecticut	Yes		565			565	
Delaware	Yes		331	59		390	
DC	No		805		50	855	Additional fees may apply
Florida	Yes		500			500	
Florida DO			655			855	Fingerprint fee paid to external vendor
Georgia	Yes		500			500	
Guam	Yes		400			400	
Hawaii	Yes		290			290	
Hawaii DO		Yes	400			400	
Idaho	Yes		500			500	
Illinois	No		396			396	
Indiana	Yes		250		39.45	289.45	
Iowa	Yes		450	55		505	
Kansas	Yes	Yes	300	50		350	$9.50 to obtain NPDB report
Kentucky	Yes		300		36.50	336.50	Background includes fingerprint fee; FCVS required
Louisiana	Yes		382	42.50		424.50	
Maine	Yes		700			700	Added charge for FCVS
Maine DO		Yes	350			350	
Maryland	Yes		790			790	$790 for US graduates, $890 for IMGs
Massachusetts	Yes		600			600	
Michigan	Yes		150	62.75		212.75	
Michigan DO		Yes	150	62.75		212.75	
Minnesota	Yes		200			200	
Mississippi	Yes		600			600	
Missouri	No		300			300	
Montana	Yes		325			325	
Nebraska	No		300	38		338	
Nevada	Yes		600		75	675	
Nevada DO		Yes	600	70		670	Background check includes fingerprint fee
New Hampshire	Yes		300	51.50		351.50	Background check includes fingerprint fee
New Jersey*	Yes		325	66.30, 70.25*		391.30, 395.25	See note
New Mexico	Yes		400	36		436	
New Mexico DO		Yes	300			300	
New York	Yes*		735			735	Application to FSMB for IMGs

(continued on next page)

Table 19 (continued)
Initial Licensure Fees and Requirements *(Not including USMLE or NBOME examination fees)*

	Application to:		Licensure Application Fees	Fingerprint Fee	Criminal Background Check Fee	Initial Licensure Cost	Notes
	FSMB	NBOME					
North Carolina	Yes		350	38		388	$9.50 for NPDB/HIPDB query
North Dakota	Yes		200			200	
Ohio*	Yes		335*			335	
Oklahoma	Yes		500			500	
Oklahoma DO		Yes	575			575	
Oregon	Yes		375		52	427	
Pennsylvania	Yes		35			35	
Pennsylvania DO		Yes	215			215	
Puerto Rico	No		0			0	
Rhode Island	Yes		1,290			1,290	$1,290 fee includes $200 for Controlled Substance registration
South Carolina	Yes		0			0	
South Dakota	Yes		200		43.25	243.25	
Tennessee	Yes		400			400	
Tennessee DO		Yes	400			400	
Texas*	Yes	Yes	1,002	41.45		1,104.45	Texas Medical Jurisprudence Exam ($61)
Utah	Yes		200			200	
Utah DO		Yes	200			200	
Vermont			2,000			2,000	
Vermont DO		Yes	500			500	
Virginia	Yes		302			302	
Washington*	Yes		500	35.25		535.25	
Washington DO*		Yes	625			625	$25 for substance abuse monitoring prgm
West Virginia	Yes		400			400	$50 for physician health program (included in $400 fee)
West Virginia DO		Yes	400			400	
Wisconsin	No		150			150	Initial $15 contract fee for USMLE Exam
Wyoming	Yes		600			600	All applicants considered for temporary license, well-qualified applicants receive temporary license pending completion of application file and final approval by the Board

Abbreviations

COMLEX—Comprehensive Osteopathic Medical Licensure Examination

FCVS—Federation Credentials Verification Service

FSMB—Federation of State Medical Boards

NBOME—National Board of Osteopathic Medical Examiners

USMLE—United States Medical Licensing Examination

* Refer to introductory text to this table for more information on this state's regulations.

Note: All information should be verified with the licensing board; medical licenses are granted to those physicians meeting all state requirements—at the discretion of the board.

Licensure Endorsement and Reregistration Fees, Intervals, and Requirements

Fees for licensure by endorsement, *including processing, application, and administrative fees*, average close to $400.

The majority of boards require physicians licensed in the state to reregister (or renew) their licenses every one or two years, with a handful of jurisdictions on a three-year reregistration interval. The average reregistration fee is around $360, or $220 when averaged by year (Table 20). Many states offer reduced fees for reregistration of inactive licenses (see Table 24 for more information).

Completion of a specified number of hours of continuing medical education (CME) is required for reregistration by most boards. See Table 21 for more information.

Additional Notes for Specific Licensing Jurisdictions

California—Endorsement fee includes a $442 processing fee, $49 fingerprinting fee (not including fingerprint rolling fee), $25 mandatory loan repayment fee, and $783 licensing fee. Licensure reregistration fee includes $25 mandatory loan repayment fee and $783 licensing fee.

Illinois—Reregistration fee for nonresidents is $600. Penalty of $100 is charged if renewal is not submitted by July 31 of the year of renewal.

Kentucky—The Federation Credentials Verification Service (FCVS) is required of all physicians applying for licensure by either examination or endorsement. The applicable FCVS fee is in addition to the application fee paid to the medical board. Criminal background checks are required of those applying for an initial license; an additional fee is required.

Maryland—Reinstatement of lapsed license $600 or $700, depending on renewal year.

Ohio—The Federation Credentials Verification Service (FCVS) is required of all physicians applying for Ohio licensure by either examination or endorsement. The applicable FCVS fee is in addition to the application fee paid to the medical board. Criminal background checks are required of those applying for an initial license; an additional fee is required.

Texas—Initial applications are for licensure (not identified as examination or endorsement). The application fee is $1,002 and does not include any examination fees or criminal history check fees.

Vermont—Board will determine criteria by 8/31/12 for renewal of licenses expiring after 8/31/14.

Washington MD and DO—Note: These fees are nonrefundable.

- Impaired physician program fee on each application and for each year of the renewal period—$35 (MD), $25 (DO)
- University of Washington library fee per application or renewal—$25 (MD and DO)
- Late fee—$262.50 (MD); if license expired more than two years ago, reinstatement fee is $1,200 total; $250 (DO)
- Reissue expired license fee—$262 (MD), $250 (DO)

Wisconsin—Licensure re-registration application ($188) is required if license expired more than five years prior.

Table 20
Licensure Endorsement and Reregistration Fees, Intervals, and Requirements

	Licensure Endorsement Fee	Criminal Background Check Fee	Finger-printing Fee	Licensure Reregistration Fee	Reregistration Interval	CME Credits Required	Notes
Alabama	175	65		300	1 yr	Yes	
Alaska	300			300	2 yrs	Yes	
Arizona	500			500	2 yrs	Yes	
Arizona DO	400			636	2 yrs	Yes	Biennial fee
Arkansas	400	38.50		200	1 yr	Yes	$100 processing fee
California*	1,299			808	2 yrs	Yes	
California DO	249			400	2 yrs	Yes	Plus $25 loan repayment fee
Colorado	—			—	2 yrs	No	
Connecticut	565			565	1 yr	Yes	
Delaware	331	59		331	2 yrs	Yes	
DC	805			500	2 yrs	Yes	
Florida	500			429	2 yrs	Yes	Even-numbered years on Dec. 31 (renewal)
Florida DO	655			855	2 yrs	Yes	Other fees apply
Georgia	500			230	2 yrs	Yes	
Guam	400			250	2 yrs	Yes	
Hawaii	290			240	2 yrs	Yes	
Hawaii DO	400			190	2 yrs	No	
Idaho	500			250	1 or 2 yrs	Yes	Reregistration $250 per yr
Illinois*	300			300	3 yrs	Yes	$300 reregistration in state; $600 out of state
Indiana	250			200	2 yrs	No	
Iowa	505			450	2 yrs	Yes	Online renewal $450; paper renewal $550
Kansas	300	50		330	1 yr	Yes	
Kentucky	300			250	1 yr	Yes	
Louisiana	382		42.50	232	1 yr	Yes	
Maine	450			500	2 yrs	Yes	Added charge for FCVS
Maine DO	350			525	2 yrs	Yes	
Maryland*	790 or 890			522	2 yrs	Yes	$890 for international medical graduates
Massachusetts	600			600	2 yrs	Yes	
Michigan	150		62.75	285	3 yrs	Yes	
Michigan DO	150		62.75	285	3 yrs	Yes	
Minnesota	200			192	1 yr	Yes	
Mississippi	600			200	1 yr	Yes	$200 if renewed online
Missouri	300			135	1 yr	Yes	
Montana	325			400	2 yrs	No	
Nebraska	300		38	121	2 yrs	Yes	
Nevada	600	75		800	2 yrs	Yes	
Nevada DO	600		70	500	1 yr	Yes	FCVS fee additional
New Hampshire	300			350	2 yrs	Yes	
New Jersey	225			580	2 yrs	Yes	
New Mexico	400		36	600	3 yrs	Yes	
New Mexico DO	300			100	1 yr	Yes	
New York	735			600	2 yrs	No	
North Carolina	350			175	1 yr	Yes	$50 late fee if registration is >30 days after birthday; $9.50 for NPDB/HIPDB query (licensure endorsement)

(continued on next page)

Table 20 (continued)
Licensure Endorsement and Reregistration Fees, Intervals, and Requirements

	Licensure Endorsement Fee	Criminal Background Check Fee	Finger-printing Fee	Licensure Reregistration Fee	Reregistration Interval	CME Credits Required	Notes
North Dakota	200			200	1 yr	Yes	$400 late fee
Ohio*	335			305	2 yrs	Yes	FCVS fee additional
Oklahoma	500			200	1 yr	Yes	
Oklahoma DO	—			225	1 yr	Yes	$150 late fee
Oregon	375			253	2 yrs	Yes	$150 late fee
Pennsylvania	—			360	2 yrs	Yes	
Pennsylvania DO	45			220	2 yrs	Yes	
Puerto Rico	200			75	3 yrs	Yes	
Rhode Island	—			650	2 yrs	Yes	
South Carolina	600			180	2 yrs	Yes	
South Dakota	200	43.25		200	1 yr	No	$400 late fee ($200 reinstatement plus $200 renewal)
Tennessee	235			235	2 yrs	Yes	$280 out-of-state and international application processing fee (nonrefundable)
Tennessee DO	—			285	2 yrs	Yes	
Texas*	—			826	2 yrs	Yes	
Utah	200			183	2 yrs	Yes	$20 late fee; $50 reinstatement fee (FCVS required)
Utah DO	200			183	2 yrs	Yes	See note above for Utah MD board
Vermont*	625			500	2 yrs	Yes	$25 (+ $5/month) late fee; CME credits required for licenses expiring after 8/31/2014
Vermont DO	500			500	2 yrs	Yes	
Virgin Islands	NA			500	1 yr	Yes	
Virginia	302			337	2 yrs	Yes	
Washington*	500			675	2 yrs	Yes	
Washington DO*	625			600	1 yr	Yes	Add $25 for substance abuse monitoring prgm
West Virginia	400			400	2 yrs	Yes	Fee includes $50 for physician health program; late fee equal to 50% of renewal fee
West Virginia DO	400			400	2 yrs	Yes	
Wisconsin*	150			141	2 yrs	Yes	Initial $15 contract fee for USMLE Exam. Endorsement fee is $75, plus $75 for state law exam, for $150 total.
Wyoming	600			250	1 yr	Yes	

Abbreviations

CME—continuing medical education

CSR—Controlled Substance Registration (Rhode Island)

FCVS—Federation Credentials Verification Service

USMLE—United States Medical Licensing Examination

* Refer to introductory text to this table for more information on this state's regulations.

Note: All information should be verified with the licensing board; medical licenses are granted to those physicians meeting all state requirements—at the discretion of the board.

Continuing Medical Education for Licensure Reregistration

The majority of boards require continuing medical education (CME) for license reregistration (Table 21). Some states also mandate CME content, such as HIV/AIDS, risk management, or end of life palliative care. In addition, many states also require that a certain percentage of CME be *AMA PRA Category 1 Credit*™ or equivalent. About two thirds of states accept the AMA PRA certificate or application as equivalent for purposes of licensure reregistration. Some states also accept certificates/awards of the American Osteopathic Association, American Board of Medical Specialties, a state medical society, and a national specialty society, as well as completion of graduate medical education residency/fellowship programs.

Additional Notes for Specific Licensing Jurisdictions

California MD and DO—All general internists and family physicians who have a patient population of which more than 25% are 65 years of age or older must complete at least 20 hours of mandatory CME in geriatric medicine or the care of older patients.

All physicians and surgeons (except pathologists and radiologists) must complete mandatory CME in the subjects of pain management and the treatment of terminally ill and dying patients (one-time requirement of 12 credits). Physicians must complete this requirement by their second license renewal date or within four years, whichever comes first.

Florida MD—First time license renewal: one hour HIV/AIDS, two hours in prevention of medical errors. *Second and subsequent renewals:* forty hours, including two hours in prevention of medical errors. *Every third renewal:* forty hours, including two hours in prevention of medical errors and two hours in domestic violence CME. *Note:* End-of-life care and palliative care can no longer be completed in lieu of HIV/AIDS or domestic violence courses.

All CME must be *AMA PRA Category 1 Credit*™, except for domestic violence and prevention of medical errors. Domestic violence and prevention of medical errors courses offered by any state or federal government agency or professional association, including any provider of *AMA PRA Category 1 Credit*™, are acceptable.

Florida DO—First time license renewal: Forty hours, including one hour HIV/AIDS, professional and medical ethics, Florida laws and rules, controlled substances; two hours domestic violence and prevention of medical errors. Of the remaining required hours, at least 20 must be AOA Category 1-A. *Second and subsequent renewals:* one hour each in professional and medical ethics, Florida laws and rules, and controlled substances; two hours in prevention of medical errors. *Every third renewal:* two hours of domestic violence. *For each license renewal:* Of the remaining required hours, at least 20 must be AOA Category 1-A; all other hours (including those in the required content categories) can be either *AMA PRA Category 1 Credit*™ or AOA Category 1-A credit.

CME on professional and medical ethics, Florida laws and rules, controlled substances, and prevention of medical errors must be obtained by completing live, participatory attendance courses.

Hawaii—The information for the CME requirements for physician license renewal were obtained from the Hawaii Medical Board website at http://hawaii.gov/dcca/pvl/boards/medical/education_info rmation/pvl_medical_physician.pdf.

Iowa—Licensure renewal fee waived for physicians on active duty (full-time training or active service) in the U.S. armed forces, reserves or national guard during their renewal period.

Kansas—Requirement is 50 credits in 18 months (20 Category 1), or 100 credits in 30 months (30 Category 1), or 150 credits in 42 months (60 Category 1).

Maryland—Partial CME credit is offered for ABMS certification, select peer review, serving as an intervenor or monitor on a physician rehabilitation committee or professional committee, and serving as a preceptor for resident physicians or medical students. For first license renewal, the CME requirement is waived, but the licensee must have completed an approved orientation program.

Missouri—The CME license renewal requirement can be met by a) completing 50 hours *AMA PRA Category 1 Credits*™, AOA Category 1-A or 2-A credits, or American Academy of Family Physicians prescribed credits; b) completing 40 hours of *AMA PRA Category 1 Credit*™ or AOA Category 1-A credit if each course, seminar, or activity includes a post-test of the material covered in the 40 CME credits; c) specialty board certification or recertification; or d) participating in an ACGME- or AOA-approved internship or residency program during the reporting period if at least 60 days of the reporting period were spent in the internship or residency.

New Jersey—The six credits for cultural competence are in addition to the 100-hour requirement for physicians licensed prior to 3/24/05; these credits may be included if licensed after this date. For more information, see: *www.njconsumeraffairs.gov/bme/press/cultural.htm.*

For newly licensed physicians, the Board requires attendance at an orientation program; no CME is given for this.

Oregon—Additional one-hour pain management course specific to Oregon provided by the pain management commission of DHS. Additionally, licensees in residency training and those serving in the military (and deployed outside Oregon for 90 days or more) are exempt from the CME requirement.

Vermont—Of the 30 required credits, at least 1 hour must be on hospice, palliative care, and/or pain management services. In addition, for each licensee who has or has applied for a DEA number, at least 1hour must be on safe and effective prescribing of controlled substances.

Washington MD—The board classifies CME into five different categories. A candidate for relicensure may earn all 200 required hours every four years in Category 1; a maximum of 80 hours may be earned in any of the other four categories. See: *www.doh.wa.gov/Portals/1/Documents/3000/657-128.pdf*

Table 21
Continuing Medical Education for Licensure Reregistration

	Required Number of CME Credits per Year(s)		Average Credits per Year	AMA PRA Category 1™ or Equivalent AOA, AAFP or ACOG Credits	Certificates/Awards Accepted as Documentation								State-Mandated CME Content/ Additional Notes
					AMA PRA	AMA PRA app.	AOA	ABMS	SMS	NSS	GME	Other	
Alabama	25	1 yr	25	25			Yes	Yes					No rollover of credits
Alaska	50	2 yrs	25	50	Yes			Yes			Yes		
Arizona	40	2 yrs	20		Yes	Yes	Yes	Yes			Yes	Yes	
Arizona DO	40	2 yrs	20	12 per yr (AOA 1-A)			Yes	Yes			Yes		No more than 8 hours are obtained annually by completing CME classified by the ACCME as Category 1
Arkansas	20	1 yr	20	*	Yes		Yes				Yes		* 50 percent in Category 1 and in primary area of practice
California*	50	2 yrs	25	50		Yes		Yes	Yes		Yes		Pain management, geriatric medicine, end-of-life care (see intro)
California DO*	150	3 yrs	50	60 (AOA 1-A or B)			Yes*						Pain management, geriatric medicine, end-of-life care (see intro); AOA cert. accepted when accompanied by AOA activity registration
Colorado	none												
Connecticut	50	2 yrs	25										Infectious disease, risk management, sexual assault, domestic violence, cultural competence
Delaware	40	2 yrs	20	40		Yes							
DC	50	2 yrs	25	50		Yes	Yes				Yes		3 credits HIV/AIDS
Florida*	40	2 yrs	20	40	Yes						Yes		See intro
Florida DO*	40	2 yrs	20	20 (AOA 1-A)	Yes	Yes	Yes	Yes			Yes		See intro
Georgia	40	2 yrs	20	40			Yes	Yes			Yes		
Guam	100	2 yrs	50	25		Yes	Yes			Yes		ACEP	
Hawaii	40	2 yrs	20	40	Yes		Yes		Yes	Yes	Yes		See intro
Idaho	40	2 yrs	20	40	Yes	Yes	Yes	Yes			Yes		
Illinois	150	3 yrs	50	60	Yes				Yes	Yes	Yes		SMS, NSS if ACCME-accredited
Indiana	none												
Iowa	40	2 yrs	20	40	Yes			Yes			Yes		Required every 5 yrs: Training for identifying and reporting child and dependent adult abuse; chronic pain management, end-of-life care
Kansas*	50	18 mos	50	20	Yes	Yes	Yes	Yes	Yes		Yes		
Kentucky	60	3 yrs	20	30	Yes		Yes			Yes	Yes		One-time domestic violence course for primary care physicians; 2 credits HIV/AIDS every 10 yrs; course must be KY-approved
Louisiana	20	1 yr	20	20	Yes								One-time board orientation course
Maine	100	2 yrs	50	40	Yes	Yes		Yes	Yes		Yes		
Maine DO	100	2 yrs	50	40 (AOA 1-A or B)									Specialists may obtain other than AOA Category 1 credits
Maryland*	50	2 yrs	25	50		Yes		Yes†					† Partial credit for ABMS
Massachusetts	100	2 yrs	50	40 (AOA 1-A)	Yes	Yes		Yes	Yes				Study board reqs; risk management; 3 credits pain management for renewals; 2 credits for end-of-life care; 3 credits in Electronic Health Records for renewals after 1/1/15
Michigan	150	3 yrs	50	75			Yes	Yes	Yes	Yes			

(continued on next page)

Table 21 (continued)
Continuing Medical Education for Licensure Reregistration

	Required Number of CME Credits per Year(s)		Average Credits per Year	AMA PRA Category 1™ or Equivalent AOA, AAFP or ACOG Credits	Certificates/Awards Accepted as Documentation								State-Mandated CME Content/ Additional Notes
					AMA PRA	AMA PRA app.	AOA	ABMS	SMS	NSS	GME	Other	
Michigan DO	150	3 yrs	50	60 (AOA 1-A or B)		Yes		Yes	Yes	Yes	Yes		
Minnesota	75	3 yrs	25	75	Yes			Yes				MOCOMP	ABMS cert or MOC accepted
Mississippi	40	2 yrs	20	40 (DOs: AOA 1-A)		Yes		Yes*			Yes		Initial certification only (not renewal)
Missouri*	50	2 yrs	25	50				Yes			Yes		See intro
Montana	none												
Nebraska	50	2 yrs	25	50	Yes		Yes						
Nevada	40	2 yrs	20	40		Yes					Yes		Ethics (2 credits), 20 credits in specialty; other 18 credits can be any in Category 1; prevention of transmission of infectious agents through safe injection practices
Nevada DO	35	1 yr	35	10 (AOA 1-A)		Yes	Yes	Yes					
New Hampshire	100	2 yrs	50	40	Yes			Yes			Yes		Credits reported to NH Med Society
New Jersey*	100	2 yrs	50	40							Yes		Cultural competence
New Mexico	75	3 yrs	25	75	Yes			Yes			Yes		5 credits in pain management
New Mexico DO	75	3 yrs	25	75	Yes			Yes				USMLE	Active membership in AOA may replace 75 CME credits
New York	none												Infection control, child abuse
North Carolina	60	3 yrs	20	60			Yes	Yes					Must be practice-relevant; ongoing ABMS MOC or AOA OCC accepted in lieu of CME
North Dakota	60	3 yrs	20	60	Yes	Yes		Yes				MOCOMP	
Ohio	100	2 yrs	50	40 (DOs: AOA 1-A or B)		Yes	Yes						CME must be OSMA/OOA-certified. Physician owner/operator of pain management clinics must complete at least 20 hrs Category 1 CME in pain medicine every 2 yrs
Oklahoma	60	3 yrs	20	60	Yes			Yes			Yes†		†50 hrs for each yr of GME
Oklahoma DO	16	1 yr	16	16 (AOA 1-A or B)									1 credit on prescribing controlled substances (every 2 yrs)
Oregon*	60	2 yrs	30	60	Yes		Yes	Yes			Yes		6 credits pain management and/or treatment of the terminally ill and dying w/i first 12 mos of licensure
Pennsylvania	100	2 yrs	50	20					Yes		Yes		12 credits risk management or patient safety
Pennsylvania DO	100	2 yrs	50	20 (AOA 1-A)					Yes		Yes		12 credits risk management or patient safety
Puerto Rico	60	3 yrs	20	40	Yes								
Rhode Island	40	2 yrs	20	40	Yes	Yes	Yes	Yes	Yes	Yes	Yes		2 credits: universal precautions, bioterrorism, end of life, OSHA, ethics, pain management, infection control, modes of transmission, or palliative care
South Carolina	40	2 yrs	20	40				Yes			Yes		75% specialty education (30 credits every 2 yrs)
South Dakota	none												

(continued on next page)

Table 21 (continued)
Continuing Medical Education for Licensure Reregistration

	Required Number of CME Credits per Year(s)		Average Credits per Year	AMA PRA Category 1™ or Equivalent AOA, AAFP or ACOG Credits	Certificates/Awards Accepted as Documentation								State-Mandated CME Content/ Additional Notes
					AMA PRA	AMA PRA app.	AOA	ABMS	SMS	NSS	GME	Other	
Tennessee*	40	2 yrs	20	40	Yes								1 credit (every 2 years) in prescribing controlled substances; providers of intractable pain management must have specialized CME in pain management
Tennessee DO	40	2 yrs	20	24 (AOA 1-A or 2-A)									See note above for Tennessee MD board
Texas	48	2 yrs	24	12 (DOs: AOA 1-A)	Yes		Yes	Yes			Yes		Of 24 Category 1 credits, at least 2 in ethics and/or prof. responsibility 10 credits pain management annually for those who practice in a pain clinic
Utah	40	2 yrs	20	34							Yes		Six hours may be from Division of Occupational and Professional Lic.
Utah DO	40	2 yrs	20	34							Yes		See note above for Utah MD board
Vermont*	30	2 yrs	15	30	Yes								See intro
Vermont DO	30	2 yrs	15		Yes								At least 12 of 30 credits must be osteopathic medical education
Virgin Islands	25	1 yr	25	25									
Virginia	60	2 yrs	30	30	Yes						Yes		
Washington*	200	4 yrs	50	Not specified	Yes			Yes	Yes	Yes			
Washington DO	150	3 yrs	50	60 (AOA 1-A or B)	Yes	Yes		Yes	Yes		Yes	(See note)	Also accepted as equivalent: Current certification of CME from medical practice academies and original certification or recertification within 6 yrs by specialty board
West Virginia	50	2 yrs	25	50	Yes			Yes					30 credits related to physician's designated specialty, CME required in best practice prescribing of controlled substances and drug diversion, unless the physician does not prescribe, administer or dispense a controlled substance
West Virginia DO	32	2 yrs	16	16 (AOA 1 A or B)			Yes				Yes		2 credits (one-time requirement) in end-of-life care; 3 Credit hours required in Board-approved pain management prescribing/drug diversion CME each renewal cycle
Wisconsin	30	2 yrs	15	30	Yes								
Wyoming	60	3 yrs	20	60	Yes		Yes	Yes			Yes	Yes	

Abbreviations

ABMS—American Board of Medical Specialties

ACCME—Accreditation Council for Continuing Medical Education

AMA PRA—American Medical Association Physician's Recognition Award

AOA—American Osteopathic Association

AAFP—American Academy of Family Practice

ACEP—American College of Emergency Physicians

ACOG—American College of Obstetricians and Gynecologists

CMA—California Medical Association

CAFP—California Academy of Family Physicians

CME—continuing medical education

EM—emergency medicine

FM—family medicine

GME—graduate medical education

GP—general practice

MOCOMP—Maintenance of Competence Program, Royal College of Physicians and Surgeons of Canada

NSS—National specialty society

OOA—Ohio Osteopathic Association

OB/GYN—obstetrics-gynecology

OSHA—Occupational Safety and Health Administration

OSMA—Ohio State Medical Association

Psych—psychiatry

SMS—State medical society

USMLE—United States Medical Licensing Examination

WMD—weapons of mass destruction

* Refer to introductory text to this table for more information on this state's regulations.

Note: *All information should be verified with licensing board; medical licenses are granted to those physicians meeting all state requirements—at the discretion of the board.*

Resident/Fellow Physician Licenses

Nearly all boards issue educational licenses, permits, certificates, or registration to resident/fellow physicians in graduate medical education (GME) programs (Table 22). (The GME program director generally provides a list of residents/fellows and any other required information directly to the licensing jurisdiction.) For many of those boards, residents/fellows must obtain a new permit or license when changing residency/fellowship programs within the state.

Medical boards in less than half of states require that prospective MD residents have passed United States Medical Licensing Examination (USMLE) Step 1 to receive a permit/license. A small number of states require passage of Steps 1 and 2.

Some states also require that resident/fellow physicians obtain full licensure (not limited or training licenses) at some point in their training (usually after having completed a certain number of years of GME).

Additional Notes for Specific Licensing Jurisdictions

California—International medical graduates (IMGs) must submit an application to determine that all core requirements have been met and must be issued a Postgraduate Training Authorization Letter before they may begin training in California.

Illinois—Limited temporary licenses (valid for 6 months) are awarded to persons in non-Illinois residency programs who are accepted for a specific period of time to perform a portion of that program at a clinical residency program in Illinois due to the lack of adequate facilities in their state.

Visiting Resident Permits are issued for 180 days to persons who have been invited or appointed for a specific period of time to perform a portion of that clinical residency program under the supervision of an Illinois-licensed physician in an Illinois patient care clinic or facility affiliated with the out-of-state GME program.

Massachusetts—Limited registration is issued to physicians enrolled in accredited residency programs and physicians enrolled in fellowships at hospitals with accredited residency programs in the area of the applicant's specialty.

Mississippi—Institutional license is issued to first-year residents and IMGs providing health care in state institutions. Applicants are not required to meet all requirements for permanent unrestricted licensure.

Restricted temporary license is issued to physicians enrolled in first year of GME at the University of Mississippi School of Medicine for practice limited to that school.

Addictionology Fellowship License is issued to physicians admitted for treatment in a board-approved drug and/or alcohol addiction treatment program or to physicians enrolled in fellowship of addictionology of the Mississippi State Medical Association Impaired Professionals Program.

Oregon—Limited license granted to fellows for one year and renewed for one additional year. Limited license for graduate training granted annually until training is completed.

Pennsylvania—Interim limited license (up to 12 consecutive months) is issued to physicians providing medical service other than at the training location of the licensee's accredited GME program.

Graduate license allows for participation for up to 12 consecutive months in GME within the complex of the hospital to which the licensee is assigned and any satellite facility or other training location used in the program.

Table 22
Resident/Fellow Physician Licenses

	Licenses, Permits, Certificates, & Registration	Must Obtain New Permit/License When Changing Residency Programs Within State	Prospective Residents Applying for License Must Have Passed USMLE Step 1	Full licensure required at any point during training?	Notes
Alabama	Yes				Limited license for residency education only.
Alaska	Yes				Residency permits for up to 36 mos to physicians in accredited residency programs in the US.
Arizona	Yes, $50/yr	Yes	Yes		
Arizona DO	Yes	Yes			
Arkansas	—				License is not required while in a training program.
California*	Yes		Yes (and Step 2)	Yes; after 2 yrs (3 yrs for IMGs)	
California DO				Yes; prior to 3rd yr	No CME required.
Colorado	Yes, $10	Yes			Training license valid for duration of program; renews every 3 yrs.
Connecticut	Yes, $0	Yes			
Delaware	Yes, $55	Yes			Training license must be renewed annually.
DC	Yes, $100	Yes	Yes	Yes (entering fellows)	Physicians have 5 yrs from medical school to obtain full license.
Florida	Yes, $200	Yes		Yes	Training registration number (for residents and fellows).
Florida DO	Yes, $100	Yes			
Georgia	Yes, $150	No		Yes; after 7 yrs	Board must be notified of resident changing program within state.
Guam	Yes	Yes	Yes	Yes; after 3 yrs	
Hawaii	Yes, $75	Yes			
Hawaii DO	Yes, $75				
Idaho	Yes, $20	Yes			
Illinois*	Yes	Yes			
Indiana	Yes, $100	Yes	Yes		Resident permit good for 1 yr, may be renewed annually.
Iowa	Yes, $205	Yes			Resident physician license for GME in board-approved pgm under supervision of licensed physician. Issued for full length of pgm.
Kansas	Yes, $50	Yes			Practice restricted to the GME program, no moonlighting allowed.
Kentucky	Yes, $75	Yes	Yes		Institutional Practice Limited License or Residency Training License to physicians beyond first yr of GME while still in training.
Louisiana	Yes, $50	Yes	Yes		Intern registration for first 12 mos of GME after completing medical school.
Maine	Yes, $100	Yes	Yes		Educational permits for 1 yr in a specific training program, renewable for 7 yrs.
Maine DO	Yes, $200	Yes			Temp. educational permits for 1 yr in a specific training pgm only.
Maryland	Yes, $100	Yes			Registration of med school grads in GME programs.
Massachusetts*	Yes, $100	Yes	Yes	Yes; after 7 yrs	Limited license for residency/fellowship training.
Michigan	Yes, $170	Yes		Yes; after 6 yrs	Limited annual license for up to 6 yrs for GME, renewable each yr; includes controlled substance license.
Michigan DO	Yes, $170	Yes		Yes; after 6 yrs	Limited annual license for up to 6 yrs for GME; includes controlled substance license.

(continued on next page)

Table 22 (continued)
Resident/Fellow Physician Licenses

	Licenses, Permits, Certificates, & Registration	Must Obtain New Permit/License When Changing Residency Programs Within State	Prospective Residents Applying for License Must Have Passed USMLE Step 1	Full licensure required at any point during training?	Notes
Minnesota	Yes, $25	Yes			
Mississippi*	Yes, $50/$200		Yes (and Step 2)	Yes; after 5 yrs	
Missouri	Yes, $30	Yes			Temporary licenses issued to residents and fellows only.
Montana	Yes, $100/$50				Refer to 37-3-305, Montana Code Annotated.
Nebraska	Yes, $25	Yes			Temporary educational permits for residents.
Nevada	Yes, $425	No	No	No	Limited 1-yr license for clinical residents ($300 initial, $50 renewal, $75 criminal background investigation).
Nevada DO	Yes, $200	No	No	No	Resident license good for 1 yr, renewable on yearly basis.
New Hampshire	Yes, $50	Yes	Yes (and Step 2)		
New Jersey	Yes, $50	Yes		Yes; after 5 yrs	Residency training permit required for unlicensed residents in GY2+.
New Mexico	Yes, $10		Yes	Yes; after 8 yrs	
New Mexico DO	Yes, $25				
New York	Yes, $105				Requires limited permit for all medical school graduates except individuals in ACGME- or AOA-accredited residency programs. Requires ECFMG certificate from all IMGs for limited permit.
North Carolina	Yes, $100 (permit); $125 (registration)	Yes	Yes (and Step 2)		Limited license to resident physicians (ineligible for licensure by endorsement).
North Dakota	Yes, $200		Yes (and Step 2)		Limited license for residents in clinical program, renewable annually; initial $100 fee covers full duration of residency program.
Ohio	Yes, $75 (initial) $35 (renewal)	Yes		Yes; after 6 yrs	Training certificate or full license mandatory for residents and clinical fellows.
Oklahoma	Yes, $250	Yes	Yes (and Step 2)		
Oklahoma DO	Yes			Yes; after 1 yr	
Oregon*	Yes, $185	Yes			
Pennsylvania*	Yes, $30				Graduate license renewal fee is $15.
Pennsylvania DO	Yes, $30	Yes			Temporary license for GME valid for up to 12 mos; renewal fee $25.
Puerto Rico	Yes				Internship/residency licenses to qualified applicants enrolled in an ACGME-accredited residency program who have successfully completed the first part of the medical board examination (basic sciences) or its equivalent (NBME, FLEX, or USMLE).
Rhode Island	Yes, $40	Yes		Yes; after 5 yrs	Limited medical registration to residents or fellows. Practice limited to the designated institution and must be under the supervision of a staff physician licensed in RI.
South Carolina	Yes, $150	Yes			Limited licenses for residency programs or limited practices renewable on a yearly basis.
South Dakota	Yes, $50	Yes	Yes	No	Residents not eligible for full licensure.
Tennessee	Yes, $25	Yes			
Tennessee DO	Yes, $50				

(continued on next page)

Table 22 (continued)
Resident/Fellow Physician Licenses

	Licenses, Permits, Certificates, & Registration	Must Obtain New Permit/License When Changing Residency Programs Within State	Prospective Residents Applying for License Must Have Passed USMLE Step 1	Full licensure required at any point during training?	Notes
Texas	Yes, $212	Yes			
Utah	Yes, $200		Yes (and Step 2)		
Vermont	Yes, $70				Limited license to residents, fellows, or house officers enrolled in ACGME-accredited residency programs and working under supervision of licensed physician at a state-licensed institution or clinic.
Vermont DO	Yes, $70				
Virgin Islands	Yes				For residents, institutional license only.
Virginia	Yes, $55				Limited license for fellowship and teaching positions. Temporary licenses (renewable annually) to residents and fellows in accredited programs in Virginia.
Washington	Yes, $385				Limited license to physicians in GME and teaching/research at state institutions and city/county health departments.
Washington DO	Yes, $325				Limited licensure for GME only.
West Virginia					
West Virginia DO	Yes, $100				Educational permit valid for 1 yr; must be renewed annually.
Wisconsin	Yes, $10			Yes; after 5 yrs	Temporary educational permits for residency education after first year.
Wyoming	Yes, $25 (1st yr); $100 (2nd and 3rd yrs		Yes (and Step 2)	Yes; after 2 yrs (see note)	If eligible for full license (including successful completion of Step 3 of USMLE/COMLEX).

* Refer to introductory text to this table for more information on this state's regulations.

Abbreviations

ACGME—Accreditation Council for Graduate Medical Education

AOA—American Osteopathic Association

CME—Continuing medical education

ECFMG—Educational Commission for Foreign Medical Graduates

FLEX—Federation Licensing Examination

GME—graduate medical education

GY—graduate year

IMGs—international medical graduates

NBME—National Board of Medical Examiners

USMLE—United States Medical Licensing Examination

Note: *All information should be verified with licensing board; medical licenses are granted to those physicians meeting all state requirements—at the discretion of the board.*

Resident/Fellow Physician Licenses: Documentation and Verification

Each state has varying requirements as to the documentation sent to teaching hospitals and/or residents/fellows for those physicians who have a limited educational license for the purposes of graduate medical education. Wall certificates, wallet cards, and letters are three commonly used forms of documentation (Table 23).

In addition, most boards maintain archival records of resident/fellow licenses, for varying periods of time, and will provide these records to other state boards for licensing and credentialing purposes.

Table 23
Resident/Fellow Physician Licenses: Documentation and Verification

	Documentation that resident/fellow physicians receive with their license information	Verification of the resident/fellow license is provided to other state boards	Length of time resident/fellow license records are maintained
Alabama		Not applicable	
Alaska	Permit only	Yes	
Arizona	None	Yes	Since 1964
Arizona DO	Wall certificate	Yes	5 yrs/10 yrs
Arkansas		No	
California	Letter (IMGs only)	No	
California DO	Wall certificate; wallet card	Yes	
Colorado	License	Yes	Indefinitely
Connecticut	None	No	
Delaware	License sent to hospital	Yes	Indefinitely
DC	Letter to program; posted on Web	Yes	Indefinitely
Florida	Letter	Yes	
Florida DO	Letter	Yes	Indefinitely
Georgia	Wallet card	Yes	Since 2004
Guam	Primary verification	No	
Hawaii	Pocket ID	Yes	10 yrs
Hawaii DO	Pocket ID	Yes	10 yrs
Idaho	Permit only	Yes	Indefinitely
Illinois	Letter to program; printed license with program name	Yes	Indefinitely
Indiana	Email	Yes	Indefinitely
Iowa	Letter sent to resident and program	Yes	10 yrs
Kansas	Wall certificate, letter	Yes	Indefinitely
Kentucky	Letter	Yes	Indefinitely
Louisiana	Wall certificate, letter, orientation info, DEA info	Yes	
Maine	Permit to program, posted on Web	Yes	Indefinitely
Maine DO	Permit to program, posted on Web	Yes	5 yrs
Maryland		Yes	4 yrs
Massachusetts	Certificate	Yes	Indefinitely
Michigan	License and wallet card	Yes	Indefinitely
Michigan DO	License and wallet card	Yes	Indefinitely
Minnesota	Letter	Yes	Since 1940
Mississippi	Wallet card	Yes	Indefinitely
Missouri	Wall certificate	Yes	Indefinitely
Montana	Temporary license	Yes	2 yrs after termination status reached
Nebraska	License card and letter	Yes	Indefinitely
Nevada	Wallet card	Yes	Indefinitely
Nevada DO	Wall certificate; wallet card	Yes	5 yrs
New Hampshire	Letter	Yes	

(continued on next page)

Table 23 (continued)
Resident/Fellow Physician Licenses: Documentation and Verification

	Documentation that resident/fellow physicians receive with their license information	Verification of the resident/fellow license is provided to other state boards	Length of time resident/fellow license records are maintained
New Jersey	Training permit to program	Yes (only to confirm that a training permit was issued; no verification of "standing")	
New Mexico	License sent to program	Yes licensed in NM	3 yrs after GME; 80 yrs if permanently
New Mexico DO	Wall certificate, letter, and wallet certificate	Yes	Since 1992
New York		No	
North Carolina	Certificate	Yes	Indefinitely
North Dakota	Letter with informal certificate	Yes	Since 2001
Ohio	Letter to the program	Yes	Since 1999
Oklahoma	Wall certificate, wallet card	Yes	Indefinitely
Oklahoma DO	Wall certificate	No	
Oregon	Certificate of registration	Yes	
Pennsylvania	Wallet card, 5x7 certificate sent to program	Yes	
Pennsylvania DO	Training permit/registration to hospital	Yes	
Puerto Rico		No	
Rhode Island		Yes	25 yrs
South Carolina	Wallet card	Yes	Since 2003
South Dakota	Wall certificate, letter, wallet card	Yes	Electronic record since 2000
Tennessee	None	Yes	Indefinitely
Tennessee DO		No	
Texas	Letter to program	Yes	Records on computer since mid-1980s
Utah	Hardcopy of license, wallet card	—	
Vermont	Hardcopy of license, wallet card	Yes	
Vermont DO		No	
Virgin Islands	—	—	
Virginia	License renewal certificate	Yes	Indefinitely
Washington	Wall certificate to program only	Yes	Indefinitely
Washington DO	Letter	Yes	75 yrs
West Virginia	Resident/training license not issued	—	
West Virginia DO	Letter	Yes	
Wisconsin	Wall certificate	Yes	Indefinitely
Wyoming	Certificate	Yes	Indefinitely

Abbreviations

GME—graduate medical education

Note: All information should be verified with licensing board; medical licenses are granted to those physicians meeting all state requirements—at the discretion of the board.

Noneducational Temporary or Limited Licenses

Most boards issue noneducational temporary permits, limited and temporary licenses, or other certificates for the practice of medicine (Table 24). The terms for the issuance of such certificates vary, but in general they must be renewed once a year with a stipulated maximum number of renewals allowed (usually five years). Often, a board will issue a temporary license or permit valid until the next board meeting, at which a candidate's application will be considered.

Some states permit state institutions to hire unlicensed physicians to work under the supervision of licensed physicians. In many instances, the state departments of mental health and public health that operate these hospitals will not hire physicians who have not had at least one year of graduate medical education in an English-speaking hospital. International medical graduates are generally not considered for these positions unless they are in the United States with a permanent resident visa. An unlicensed physician employed by a state hospital is required in most states to register with the state board of medical examiners, which may issue a limited permit to practice within the institution.

Some jurisdictions issue locum tenens permits or inactive licenses (for physicians who want to maintain licensure in that state although they are currently practicing in another state). About half of jurisdictions issue retired physicians' licenses. A small number also issue camp licenses or allow for practice by physicians who hold a retired/inactive license (often restricted to charity care).

Additional Notes for Specific Licensing Jurisdictions

Florida—Temporary Certificate to Practice in Area of Critical Need ($300) is available to physicians with current valid license in another state to practice in Florida communities with a critical need for physicians and a population of less than 7,500.

Limited License ($210) is available to retired physicians who meet the same minimum education and training requirements as required for a full medical license and have been licensed to practice medicine in any jurisdiction in the US for at least 10 years. Practice restricted to public agencies or institutions or 501(c)(3) nonprofit agencies or institutions located in areas of critical medical need.

A Public Psychiatry Certificate is available for board-certified psychiatrists who are licensed to practice medicine without restriction in another state and who meet the minimum education and training requirements required for a full medical license. Practice is restricted to a public mental health facility or program funded in part or entirely by state funds.

A Public Health Certificate is available for physicians who are graduates of an accredited medical/osteopathic school and hold a master of public health degree or are board-eligible or certified in public health or preventive medicine. It is also available to physicians who (1) are licensed to practice medicine without restriction in another US jurisdiction, (2) hold a master of public health degree or are board eligible or certified in public health or preventive medicine, and (3) meet the minimum education and training requirements required for a full license.

Practice is restricted to employment duties with the Department of Health and Rehabilitative Services.

Iowa—Temporary licensure is intended for physicians to participate in any of the following board-approved activities:

- Covering for an Iowa-licensed physician who is unexpectedly unavailable to provide medical care to patients
- Demonstrating or proctoring that involves providing hands-on patient care to patients in Iowa
- Conducting a procedure on a patient in Iowa when the consultant's expertise in the procedure is greater than that of the Iowa licensed physician who requested the procedure
- Providing medical care to patients in Iowa, if the physician is enrolled in an out-of-state GME program and does not hold a resident or permanent license in the home state of the GME program
- Serving as a camp physician
- Participating as a learner in a program of further medical education that allows hands-on patient care when the physician does not currently hold a license in good standing in any US jurisdiction

Temporary licensure is not to be used as a way for a physician to practice before a permanent license is granted. It is also not intended for locum tenens.

Kansas—

- Inactive license, $150 [65-2809(g)].

- Exempt license, $150, to (1) serve as a coroner or as paid employee of a local health department, (2) practice as a charitable health care provider for an indigent health care clinic, or (3) perform administrative functions [65-2809(f)].

- Institutional license, $200 biannually, to work only in approved state institutions [65-2895].

- Limited license, $30, for providing charitable health care; must hold valid license in another state [65-28, 125].

Mississippi—Ninety-day Youth Camp Permit issued to physicians providing health care only at youth camps approved by the Mississippi State Department of Health. License available for retired physicians who wish to volunteer their services. A physician must complete an application documenting his educational training, issuance of an unrestricted license to practice medicine in MS or another state, documentation that he will devote his volunteer service to care for indigent patients or underserved areas of Mississippi, and will not receive compensation. Renewable annually, no fee.

Missouri—Limited license for retired physicians who have been licensed for at least 10 years in either MO or another state. No more than five annual CME hours required for renewal. Restricted to primary or preventative care services provided gratuitously at city, county, nonprofit, or federally funded health centers. Cannot prescribe controlled substances. Fee not to exceed $25.

Ohio—Special Activity Certificate ($125) may be issued to qualified applicants seeking to practice in conjunction with a special activity, program, or event taking place in Ohio. The certificate may not be used for locum tenens, is valid either for 30 days or the duration of the special activity (whichever is shorter), and cannot be renewed.

Pennsylvania—Temporary license allows licensee to participate in a medical procedure necessary for the well-being of a specified patient within the Commonwealth or to practice medicine and surgery at a camp or resort for no more than three months. Applicants for a temporary license must hold an unrestricted license in another state, territory, possession, or country.

Extraterritorial license granted to licensed physicians maintaining an office to practice near the boundary line of an adjoining state whose medical practice extends into Pennsylvania.

Puerto Rico—Public service licenses to qualified applicants who have completed at least one year of accredited residency education and who have passed all three parts of the medical board examination or its equivalent (NBME, FLEX, or USMLE).

Tennessee—Special licensure category for physicians practicing medicine at St. Jude Children's Research Hospital Global Collaboration.

Texas—

- Conceded Eminence
- Faculty Temporary License
- Provisional License
- Public Health
- Telemedicine
- Visiting Professor Temporary License
- Voluntary Charity Care

Table 24
Noneducational Temporary or Limited Licenses

	Temporary/ Limited License	Locum Tenens Permit	Inactive License	Retired Physicians' License	Practice with Retired/ Inactive License?	Camp License	Notes
Alabama	Yes, $175			Yes, $0			Limited license for work in penal and mental institutions. Retired physicians may obtain limited license, renewable annually, if they have been licensed in any state previously. Licensees must volunteer 100 or more hours annually of outpatient services at free clinics.
Alaska	Yes, $200 (6 months)	Yes (90 days)	Yes, $125	Yes, $50 (one-time)	No		
Arizona	Yes	Yes, $350 (180 days)					Pro bono license available for no fee. Must hold an active license from any state or territory or hold active or inactive Arizona license. Restricted to providing free care and < 60 days of practice per year.
Arizona DO	Yes	Yes, $300 (90 days)		Yes, $0	Yes (volunteer)		Limited license is undefined in law; none issued to date. Locum tenens permit may be extended once for additional 90 days ($300). Retired license holder must have active Arizona license prior to retired status; may practice as volunteer up to 10 hours a week or teach at osteopathic medical school.
Arkansas $50	Yes,	No	No	No	No	No	Temporary permits for limited time, only after application for licensure is complete and waiting to be presented to the board. Valid until the next board meeting.
California	Yes		Yes	Yes, $25	No		1) Ten-day health fair - voluntary service registration; 2) limited practice license limiting the physician's scope of practice due to a disability. Fees vary for these two types of licenses.
California DO			Yes, $300				Inactive licensee fee $300 every 2 yrs, plus $25 loan repayment program fee
Colorado	No	No	Yes	No			Pro bono license available.
Connecticut	Yes, $150 (1 yr)			No			Temporary permits, not renewable, only to those physicians who have been offered a position in a state hospital or state facility.
Delaware	No	No	No	No	No	No	
DC			Yes, $500	No			
Florida*	Yes (See note)		Yes, $121	Yes			Limited license for retired physicians wishing to volunteer to practice with government or nonprofit organization in area of critical need.
Florida DO	Yes		Yes	Yes	No		
Georgia	Yes, $150	No	Yes, $200	No	No	No	Temporary licenses for endorsement applicants between board meetings once requirements are met. Special license to practice medicine as a volunteer for public agencies or nonprofit institutions that provide indigent services.
Guam	Yes, $275		Yes, $300				Temporary permits for reciprocity/endorsement applicants between board meetings.
Hawaii	Yes	No	No	No	No	No	Temporary license to physicians working in a state or county agency in conditions of shortage or emergency, and to physicians under the supervision of a licensed MD who plan to take the USMLE exam within 18 months.
Idaho (120 days)	Yes, $100	$100	Yes,	Yes	No		Temporary license while awaiting criminal background check outcome; volunteer license to retired physicians for free care.
Illinois	Yes		Yes	No			Visiting Physician Permits for up to 180 days to persons invited to study, demonstrate or perform a specific subject or technique in a school, hospital, or other health care facility.
Indiana*	Yes, $100 (90 days)	Yes, $100 (30 days)	Yes, $100	Yes, $100	Yes (free care)	Yes, $100	
Iowa*	Yes, $155			No			

(continued on next page)

Table 24 (continued)
Noneducational Temporary or Limited Licenses

	Temporary/ Limited License	Locum Tenens Permit	Inactive License	Retired Physicians' License	Practice with Retired/ Inactive License?	Camp License	Notes
Kansas*	Yes		Yes, $150	Yes (exempt)	No		
Kentucky	Yes, $75			No			Temporary permit until board meets (for endorsement candidates).
Louisiana*	Yes, $0 (90 days)			Yes, $150			Unrestricted temporary permits only under extreme circumstances.
Maine	Yes, $300 (1 yr)	Yes		Yes, $75	Yes (free care)	Yes, $100 (1 yr)	
Maine DO	Yes	Yes, $200				Yes, $100	
Maryland			Yes, $50	No	No		
Massachusetts		Yes		No			
Michigan MD and DO				Yes, $0	Yes (free care)		For practice in underserved areas; reviewed annually.
Minnesota	Yes, $60			Yes, $50		Yes, $0	Temporary license valid until next board meeting at which application is to be considered.
Mississippi*	Yes					Yes, $25	
Missouri*				Yes, $25	Yes (free care)	Yes	Camp license not required if service is less than 2 weeks.
Montana	Yes, $325		Yes	Yes			Montana Health Corps registration available for retired physicians.
Nebraska		Yes, $100 (90 days)	Yes	No	No		Locum tenens permit for a qualified physician with current license in another state for replacement of a Nebraska physician on leave.
Nevada	Yes	Yes, $475 (90 days)	Yes, $400	No	Yes (free care)		Temporary licenses for practice in medically underserved areas. Special volunteer license, for providing free care exclusively either for indigent or uninsured people or as part of a disaster relief operation.
Nevada DO	Yes, $200	Yes (6 mos)	Yes, $200				
New Hampshire*	Yes, $50	Yes, $150 (100 days)	N/A	No	No	Yes, $75	
New Jersey	Yes (4 mos)		Yes	Yes, $125	No	No	Reduced fee license for physicians offering exclusively free care or in some limited circumstances. Temporary license for a physician of another state to take charge of NJ physician's practice during an absence from the state. Licensure exemption to work in county or state institution for limited period.
New Mexico	Yes, $100		Yes, $25	Yes	No	Yes, $50	
New Mexico DO	Yes, $0						Issued to physicians who have applied for and met licensure requirements between regular board meetings.
New York	Yes			No			Retired physicians exempt from registration fee.
North Carolina	Yes			Yes, $0	Yes		Volunteer and retired volunteer license for indigent clinics only.
North Dakota*	Yes, $200	Yes, $200 (3 mos)		Yes	No		No fee for lifetime special emeritus license status (may not practice). Temporary license between intervals of board meetings. All licensure requirements must be met and file must be processed completely before a temporary license or locum tenens permit will be issued.
Ohio*	Yes		Yes, $0 volunteer	Yes, $0 Emeritus	Yes (free care)		Special activity certificate $125.
Oklahoma MD and DO	Yes			Yes	Yes (free care)		Emeritus (may not practice); limited volunteer license for retired physicians who wish to provide free care exclusively to the needy and indigent. Physician must have previously held a medical license in any state. Volunteer license valid for 1 year, is renewable; no fee.

(continued on next page)

Table 24 (continued)
Noneducational Temporary or Limited Licenses

	Temporary/ Limited License	Locum Tenens Permit	Inactive License	Retired Physicians' License	Practice with Retired/ Inactive License?	Camp License	Notes
Oregon*	Yes, $185	Yes	Yes, $506	Yes, $0	No	Yes, $0	Limited License SPEX (LL-SPEX) valid while awaiting results of SPEX examination; maximum of 6 months. Limited license, Special valid if all requirements for full licensure met until next regular issuance of full licenses by the Board.
Pennsylvania*	Yes			Yes			
Pennsylvania DO	Yes			Yes		Yes, $45	
Puerto Rico*	Yes						
Rhode Island			Yes, $0				Emeritus status (inactive license).
South Carolina	Yes, $75		Yes, $0				Temporary license to any applicant who meets all requirements pending final board approval.
South Dakota		Yes, $50					One-time 60-day certificate; $43.25 criminal background check fee.
Tennessee	Yes	Yes					Volunteer licenses available to physicians with no previous history of discipline, if working in setting that provides free medical services.
Tennessee DO							See note above.
Texas*	Yes, $50-$1,002			Yes			Physicians with a retired or inactive license can practice in voluntary charity care settings.
Utah			Yes, $50				Inactive license must be renewed every 2 yrs; $50 to reactivate.
Vermont							
Vermont DO	Yes						
Virgin Islands	Yes						Temp licenses (2 yrs) for government employment only.
Virginia	Yes		Yes, $168			Yes $25	Exemptions authorized for CME, summer camps, and free clinics Volunteer restricted license ($25) for practice in free clinics
Washington	Yes, $50 (90 days)		Yes				Temporary permit only in conjunction with full application; applicant must have been previously licensed in an approved state.
Washington DO	Yes (180 days)		Yes				Temporary license only for applicants for full license, not renewable. Applicant must be licensed and in good standing in another state.
West Virginia	Yes, $100		Yes, $100		Yes		If eligible, temporary license (valid until subsequent board meeting) is issued, after completed application for permanent license has been filed, processed, and found in order.
West Virginia DO	Yes						Temp. license, at board discretion, for specific location and need.
Wisconsin	Yes, $10 (90 days)	Yes, $216				Yes, $150 (90 days)	90-day temporary license: Obsolete provision, subject to amendment.
Wyoming	Yes		Yes; only if living in state	Yes; only if living in state	No	Yes	All applicants are considered for temporary license; well-qualified applicants receive a temporary license pending completion of application file and final approval of the Board.

Abbreviations

FLEX—Federation Licensing Examination

GME—graduate medical education

NBME—National Board of Medical Examiners

SPEX—Special Purpose Examination

USMLE—United States Medical Licensing Examination

Note: All information should be verified with licensing board; medical licenses are granted to those physicians meeting all state requirements—at the discretion of the board.

Physician Re-entry

The AMA defines physician re-entry as "a return to clinical practice in the discipline in which one has been trained or certified following an extended period of clinical inactivity not resulting from discipline or impairment." Many states have specific rules for physicians seeking to reenter clinical practice, and some require passage of the Special Purpose Examination (SPEX), Comprehensive Osteopathic Medical Variable-Purpose Examination (COMVEX), or similar examinations to prove current competence (Table 25).

AMA recommendations on physician re-entry

In 2010, the AMA worked with a wide range of stakeholders—including leaders in licensure, board certification and medical education, as well as directors of re-entry programs—to develop the following recommendations on physician re-entry. In particular, the American Academy of Pediatrics and Federation of State Medical Boards contributed to the consensus process leading to these recommendations.

Note: For more information on this and other aspects of physician re-entry, refer to the AMA's Physician Re-entry website at www.ama-assn.org/go/reentry.

Regulatory policies

Principle: Ensure that there is a comprehensive, transparent and feasible regulatory process for physicians to return to clinical practice.

1. Develop an understanding of the expectations and needs that relevant stakeholder groups—physicians, patients, regulators and the public—have for a physician re-entry system.

2. Develop physician re-entry policy guidelines across state medical licensing jurisdictions that are consistent and evidence-based. These guidelines should clarify:

   • The length of time away from clinical practice which necessitates participating in a re-entry process

   • The definition of how much involvement in clinical care constitutes active clinical practice and the clinical practice requirements for maintaining licensure

   • The impact of loss of specialty board certification on maintenance of licensure

3. Establish mechanisms to permit reentering physicians to engage in clinical practice under supervision as they participate in a re-entry program. These include:

   • A site (medical school, graduate medical education program, teaching hospital and medical home, as well as non-traditional sites such as mental health hospitals and nursing homes) that provides reentering physicians with opportunities for supervised clinical practice in their previous clinical fields

   • Hospital credentialing committees that allow re-entry program participants to work under supervision

   • State medical licensing boards that establish a non-disciplinary licensure status option for reentering physicians during their re-entry education and training

   • Development and validation of a process for previously board certified physicians not eligible for maintenance of certification to participate in re-entry training necessary to return to their field and original scope of clinical practice

4. Work with state medical licensing boards and medical societies to develop a certificate of program completion that meets the need to document physician readiness for clinical practice.

Physician re-entry program policies

Principle: Develop policies that assure the quality of re-entry programs and the readiness to resume practice of their graduates.

5. Increase consistency among re-entry programs by establishing a mechanism by which programs can assess and demonstrate graduates' comparable preparation and readiness for independent practice within the physician's intended scope of practice.

6. Encourage the development of modular programs to meet the specific learning needs of individual reentering physicians.

7. Consider a physician re-entry program accreditation process that includes a review of program outcomes.

Research and evaluation

Principle: Create an evidence base that can be used to inform policymakers, reentering physicians and re-entry program development.

8. Study the feasibility of introducing alternate licensure tracks for reentering physicians that allow a limited scope of practice.

9. Study the relationship between time away from practice and maintenance of clinical knowledge, skills and behaviors.

10. Study new models of organizing physician re-entry programs to include the feasibility of providing physicians with an educational "home" base.

11. Continue to develop valid and reliable assessment tools for physician knowledge and skills. Assessment of reentering physicians should occur at three points: (1) entry to a physician re-entry program, (2) completion of a physician re-entry program, and (3) a standard time after which a physician has returned to active clinical practice.

12. Establish a national physician re-entry database to:

   • Provide programmatic information to reentering physicians

   • Track trends in re-entry such as number of reentering physicians, program costs and outcomes

13. Study the workforce implications of a system that supports physician re-entry.

Program funding

Principle: Develop means to ensure that a physician re-entry system is financially feasible.

14. Pursue multiple funding streams to support the development, implementation and evaluation of a national physician re-entry system.

Collaboration and communication among stakeholders

Principle: Ensure that all stakeholders participate in planning for a physician re-entry system.

15. Establish process for ongoing communication between medical regulatory bodies, physician re-entry programs, medical associations and societies, and other key stakeholders to further the development of a national re-entry system.

   • Mitigating the cost of physician re-entry programs for physicians and regulatory bodies

   • Supporting the development and maintenance of physician re-entry programs

   • Creating mechanisms for the assessment and evaluation of physician re-entry programs

16. Continue to educate medical students, residents and practicing physicians on career-planning strategies and resources should they need to take a hiatus from clinical practice.

Table 25
Physician Re-entry Regulations

	Board has policy on physician re-entry to practice*	Length of time out of practice after which re-entry program completion is required	Board developing/ planning to develop policy	Decided on Case-by-Case Basis	SPEX/ COMVEX May Be Required	CME May Be Required	Notes
Alabama	No		No	Yes	Yes		
Alaska	No	—	No				Full board interview may be required.
Arizona	Yes		—	Yes	Yes	Yes	PACE may also be required.
Arizona DO	Yes	2 yrs	—	Yes	Yes	Yes	Practice monitoring may be required, structured as non-disciplinary probation.
Arkansas	Yes	2 yrs	Yes	Yes	Yes	Yes	50 hours of specialty-specific Category 1 credit for each year. Re-entry plan as determined by the board.
California	No		No	Yes			
California DO	Yes	5 yrs	—			Yes	Under 5 yrs: completion of questionnaire and 20 CME credits required. Over 5 yrs: new application required.
Colorado	Yes	2 yrs	—				Personalized competency evaluation report prepared by Board-approved program, and completion of any education/training that is recommended by the program.
Connecticut	Yes	2 yrs	—				
Delaware	Yes	3 yrs					
DC	Yes	2 yrs	—	Yes	Yes	Yes	Physicians not actively practicing for 1 to 5 yrs must submit proof of 50 Category 1 CME credits for each inactive year. To reactivate a paid inactive license after 5 yrs, 1 yr of clinical training in an ACGME- or AOA-accredited program or 300 Category 1 CME credits is required. Physicians who have been out of practice for 2 yrs or longer are required to undergo a re-entry plan as determined by the board to demonstrate current knowledge, skill, and proficiency. Formal regulations will be promulgated.
Florida	Yes	4 yrs	—	Yes	Yes	Yes	
Florida DO	Yes	4 yrs	—	Yes	Yes	Yes	Board recommends U. of Florida CARES or CAPS program, or CPEP. Applicant required to appear before Board and establish ability to practice in safe manner. Also required: COMVEX, and an accounting for activities while not practicing.
Georgia	Yes	30 mos	—	Yes		Yes	Demonstrate current knowledge, skill, and proficiency.
Guam							
Hawaii	No		No				
Hawaii DO							
Idaho	No		No	Yes	Yes		
Illinois	Yes	2 yrs	—				See Section 1285.95 of Administrative Rules.
Indiana	No		Yes	Yes			Personal appearance before board is required.
Iowa	Yes	3 yrs	—	Yes			Competency evaluation required.
Kansas	Yes	2 yrs	—				Additional testing, training, or education may be deemed necessary.
Kentucky	Yes	2 yrs	—	Yes			
Louisiana	No		No				Must meet requirements for reinstatement or relicensure.
Maine	No		Yes	Yes			

(continued on next page)

Table 25 (continued)
Physician Re-entry Regulations

	Board has policy on physician re-entry to practice*	Length of time out of practice after which re-entry program completion is required	Board developing/ planning to develop policy	Decided on Case-by-Case Basis	SPEX/ COMVEX May Be Required	CME May Be Required	Notes
Maine DO	No		No			Yes	
Maryland	Yes	5 yrs	—	Yes	Yes		A physician with license on inactive status or who has failed to renew a license by the 2-month late renewal period and who wishes to practice medicine may apply for reinstatement.
Massachusetts	No		Yes				Must complete "re-entry to practice plan."
Michigan	No		No			Yes	Complete 150 hours of CME with a minimum of 75 hrs AMA Category 1 within immediately previous 3 yrs from date of application.
Michigan DO	No		No			Yes	(See above.)
Minnesota	Yes	3 yrs	—	Yes	Yes	Yes	Assessment or mentorship may be required.
Mississippi	Yes	3 yrs	—				Board-approved physician assessment or clinical skills assessment program.
Missouri	No		Yes				
Montana	Yes	2 yrs	—		Yes		
Nebraska	Yes	2 yrs	—	Yes			May issue a re-entry license (Neb. Rev. Stat. 38-202601).
Nevada	Yes	1 yr	—		Yes	Yes	PACE, CPEP, peer review, preceptorship, or fellowship may be required.
Nevada DO	Yes		—			Yes	Additional $500 and proof of CME for inactive yrs required to reactivate practice.
New Hampshire	No		Yes	Yes			
New Jersey	Yes	5 yrs	—	Yes	Yes	Yes	See Board regulation NJAC 13:35-3.14.
New Mexico	Yes	2 yrs	—			Yes	Mini-Sabbatical or CPEP may be required.
New Mexico DO							
New York	No		No				A licensed physician in inactive status must re-register.
North Carolina	Yes	2 yrs	—			Yes	Completion of re-entry program required. See 21 NCAC 32B.1370.
North Dakota	No		Yes	Yes			Re-entry plan developed, as appropriate.
Ohio	Yes	2 yrs	—	Yes	Yes		Exam to determine current fitness to practice or Board certification or recertification examination may be required (Sec 4731.222).
Oklahoma	No		Yes				
Oklahoma DO	No		No	Yes			
Oregon	Yes	2 yrs	—	Yes	Yes	Yes	A physician out of practice more than 24 months may be required to take a competency exam or training. Refer to OAR 847-020-0183.
Pennsylvania	Yes	4 yrs	—		Yes	Yes	Re-entry to practice plan may be required, to include completion of a clinical skills assessment program, refresher training, mentorship program, a mini-residency, passing ABMS board exams, etc.
Pennsylvania DO	No		Yes		Yes	Yes	Additional training may be required, as well as completion of application and payment of fee.
Puerto Rico							

(continued on next page)

Table 25 (continued)
Physician Re-entry Regulations

	Board has policy on physician re-entry to practice*	Length of time out of practice after which re-entry program completion is required	Board developing/ planning to develop policy	Decided on Case-by-Case Basis	SPEX/ COMVEX May Be Required	CME May Be Required	Notes
Rhode Island	No		Yes			Yes	Mentorship may be required.
South Carolina	Yes	4 yrs	—				
South Dakota	No		Yes	Yes		Yes	Re-entry to practice plan may be required, to include completion of a clinical skills assessment program, refresher training, mentorship program, a mini-residency, passing ABMS board exams, etc. It is the physicians's responsibility to demonstrate competence and fitness to practice.
Tennessee	Yes	5 yrs	—	Yes	Yes		Must display clinical competency.
Tennessee DO	Yes	Variable	—	Yes	Yes		Must display clinical competency.
Texas	No	See note					Applicants for licensure must have practiced full time for 1 of the 2 years preceding date of application. Licensees are not required to demonstrate active practice.
Utah	Yes	5 yrs	—		Yes		See R-156-67-302(d)(2).
Utah DO	Yes	5 yrs	—				
Vermont	Yes	3 yrs	—		Yes		
Vermont DO	Yes	1 yr	—		Yes		See Rule 2.3.2.
Virgin Islands							
Virginia	Yes	4 yrs	—		Yes		
Washington	Yes	2 yrs (depending on specialty)	—		Yes		After 2 yrs out of practice, an application, fee, and CME credits are required; after 4 yrs, SPEX is usually required.
Washington DO	No		Yes				
West Virginia	No	2 yrs	No	Yes			
West Virginia DO	No		Yes	Yes			
Wisconsin	No	5 yrs	Yes				Oral examination may be required. If less than 5 yrs, licensure renewal is allowed. Re-registration application is required ($141 plus $75 state law exam, for total of $216).
Wyoming	No		No	Yes	Yes	Yes	Other requirements that may be imposed include preceptorship, supervision, chart review, and evaluation (CPEP or similar prgm).

* As defined by the AMA.

Abbreviations

ACGME—Accreditation Council for Graduate Medical Education

ABMS—American Board of Medical Specialties

AOA—American Osteopathic Association

CME—continuing medical education

COMVEX—Comprehensive Osteopathic Medical Variable-Purpose Examination

CPEP—Center for Personalized Education for Physicians

PACE—Physician Assessment and Clinical Education program

SPEX—Special Purpose Examination

Note: *All information should be verified with licensing board; medical licenses are granted to those physicians meeting all state requirements—at the discretion of the board.*

Regulations on the Practice of Telemedicine and Out-of-state Consulting Physicians

For purposes of this publication, telemedicine is defined as the delivery of health care services via electronic means from a health care provider in one location to a patient in another. Applications that fall under this definition include the transfer of medical images, such as pathology slides or radiographs, interactive video consultations between patient and provider or between primary care and specialty care physicians, and mental health consultations. A number of states have adopted or have begun to develop regulations concerning the practice of telemedicine (Table 26).

The AMA has monitored the development of telemedicine over the years and has official policy on this issue (see Appendix E, AMA Policy on Medical Licensure). At its 2010 annual meeting, for example, the AMA House of Delegates adopted Council on Medical Education Report 6, which describes the use of telemedicine to increase access to health care services for patients in underserved areas and allow for physicians to share expertise. The report also notes that physicians who are interested in practicing telemedicine across state lines may be stymied by having to be licensed in multiple jurisdictions. Nonetheless, AMA has policy supporting the current state-based licensing system and the need for physicians to be licensed in the states where the patients they treat reside.

The AOA adopted a policy on telemedicine in 2012. This policy supports state-based licensure and provides a framework for states to work together to ease the licensure process while allowing states to provide adequate protections for their citizens.

Additional Notes for Specific Licensing Jurisdictions

Connecticut—In the case of electronic transmissions of radiographic images, a medical license is required of any out-of-state physician who provides, through an ongoing, regular, or contractual arrangement, official written reports of diagnostic evaluations of such images to Connecticut physicians or patients. No license is required of a physician residing out of state who consults on an irregular basis with a licensed Connecticut physician, is located in-state, or is with a state medical school for educational or medical training purposes.

Florida—A physician licensed in another state, territory, or foreign country is permitted to examine the patient, take a history and physical, review laboratory tests and radiographs, and make recommendations about diagnosis and treatment to a licensed Florida physician. The term "consultation" does not include such physician's performance of any medical procedure on or the rendering of treatment to the patient.

Kansas—License required if orders for services are issued for individuals located in Kansas. No license required for consultant licensed in another state who does not open an office or maintain a place to meet patients or receive calls in Kansas. No license required for services performed under supervision or by order of or referral from a licensed Kansas physician.

Mississippi—Full license required for physicians rendering a medical opinion concerning diagnosis or treatment via electronic or other means, unless the evaluation, treatment, and/or medical opinion to be rendered by a physician outside this state (a) is requested by a physician duly licensed to practice medicine in this state, and (b) the physician who has requested such evaluation, treatment, and/or medical opinion has already established a doctor/patient relationship with the patient to be evaluated and/or treated.

South Dakota—Any nonresident MD or DO who, while located outside South Dakota, provides diagnostic or treatment services through electronic means to a patient in this state under a contract with a health care provider, a clinic in this state that provides health services, or health care facility, is engaged in the practice of medicine or osteopathy in South Dakota. Out-of-state MDs or DOs who consult on an irregular basis with a licensed South Dakota physician are not considered to practice in South Dakota.

Table 26
Regulations on the Practice of Telemedicine and Out-of-state Consulting Physicians

	State Requires Full License for Practice of Telemedicine	State has Adopted Specific Telemedicine Regulations	State has Specific Regulations on Out-of-state Consultants	Incidental, Infrequent Consultation With Out-of-State Consultants is Allowed	Notes
Alabama		Yes			Issues a "special purpose" license.
Alaska	Yes		Yes	Yes	
Arizona	Yes	Yes	Yes	Yes	
Arizona DO	Yes	No	No	Yes	
Arkansas	Yes	Yes	No		
California MD/DO		Yes	Yes		No license required for consultations with a primary care physician licensed in California.
Colorado	Yes	Yes			Licensed Colorado physician may consult with physicians licensed in other states.
Connecticut*		Yes			See note in introduction.
Delaware	Yes	No	Yes	Yes	
DC	Yes				A telemedicine taskforce completed its work; guidelines, policies, and ultimately regulations will be deveoped.
Florida MD, DO*	Yes	Yes	Yes	Yes	See note in introduction.
Georgia	Yes	Yes			
Guam		Yes	Yes		
Hawaii		Yes	Yes	Yes	
Idaho	Yes		Yes	Yes	Has policy statement for teleradiologists and pathologists.
Illinois	Yes	Yes			
Indiana		No			
Iowa			Yes	Yes	Out-of-state consultant must be licensed in Iowa if providing medical services to Iowa patients.
Kansas*		Yes	Yes	Yes	See note in introduction.
Kentucky	Yes	Yes	Yes	Yes	
Louisiana		Yes			
Maine		Yes	Yes	Yes	Out-of-state consultant must be licensed in Maine if providing medical services directly to patients in Maine.
Maryland	Yes	Yes	Yes	Yes	
Massachusetts	Yes				
Michigan MD/DO			Yes	Yes	
Minnesota		Yes	Yes	Yes	Telemedicine registration not required for physicians providing services in response to an emergency condition.
Mississippi*	Yes		Yes	Yes	Consultation period cannot exceed 5 days.
Missouri	Yes		Yes		Licensed Missouri physician may consult with physicians licensed in another state.
Montana	Yes		Yes		License required if out-of-state consultant establishes regular, direct physician/patient relationship.
Nebraska					Refer to Neb Rev Stat 38-2024 and 38-2025.
Nevada	Yes		Yes		Special purpose license required.
Nevada DO	Yes	Yes	Yes		Licensure application required.
New Hampshire	Yes		Yes	Yes	License required if consultation not made directly with licensed New Hampshire physician or if consulting is more than incidental.

(continued on next page)

Table 26 (continued)
Regulations on the Practice of Telemedicine and Out-of-state Consulting Physicians

	State Requires Full License for Practice of Telemedicine	State has Adopted Specific Telemedicine Regulations	State has Specific Regulations on Out-of-state Consultants	Incidental, Infrequent Consultation With Out-of-State Consultants is Allowed	Notes
New Jersey					
New Mexico	Yes	Yes			
New York	Yes	No			
North Carolina	Yes	No		Yes	Board has position statement, not regulations.
North Dakota	Yes	Yes			
Ohio	Yes	Yes			Telemedicine license Sec. 4731.296 Ohio Revised Code.
Oklahoma	Yes	Yes	Yes	Yes	License required for regular, ongoing treatment.
Oregon	Yes	Yes			Full license required for telemedicine, teleradiology, or telemonitoring.
Pennsylvania	Yes	Yes			
Puerto Rico					
Rhode Island	Yes		Yes	Yes	
South Carolina	Yes				
South Dakota*	Yes		Yes	Yes	See note in intro.
Tennessee	Yes	Yes			Telemedicine license required of out-of-state physicians diagnosing or treating patients in Tennessee. Some exceptions granted.
Texas	No	Yes	Yes	Yes	Telemedicine license required for practice of medicine across state lines; visiting physician temporary license required for out-of-state physicians.
Utah	Yes	Yes	Yes	Yes	Full license required if consulting directly with Utah patients by any means.
Vermont	Yes				
Virgin Islands					
Virginia	Yes	No			Virginia license required if practice of medicine occurs in state.
Washington			Yes	Yes	Out-of-state consultant may not set up an office, appoint a place for meeting patients, or receive calls within this state.
West Virginia	Yes	Yes			License required (with exceptions).
West Virginia DO	Yes				
Wisconsin	Yes	No			Wisconsin license required.
Wyoming	Yes	No	Yes	Yes	License required if consultations exceed total of 12 days in any 52-week period; exceptions may be granted on case-by-case basis. Consultation must be in conjunction with licensed physician in Wyoming.

Note: *All information should be verified with licensing board; medical licenses are granted to those physicians meeting all state requirements—at the discretion of the board.*

Regulations Related to Violations of Ethical Standards

The following table summarizes responses from state boards as to whether the board's statutes, rules or policies specifically refer to the AMA *Code of Medical Ethics* for violations of ethical standards (Table 27).

Opinion 1.01 of the Code, "Terminology" notes that "the term 'ethical' is used in opinions of the Council on Ethical and Judicial Affairs to refer to matters involving (1) moral principles or practices and (2) matters of social policy involving issues of morality in the practice of medicine. The term 'unethical' is used to refer to professional conduct which fails to conform to these moral standards or policies.

"Many of the Council's opinions lay out specific duties and obligations for physicians. Violation of these principles and opinions represents unethical conduct and may justify disciplinary action such as censure, suspension, or expulsion from medical society membership."

For more information on the AMA *Code of Medical Ethics*, see www.ama-assn.org/go/ethics.

The American Osteopathic Association Code of Ethics is available at www.osteopathic.org/inside-aoa/about/leadership/Pages/aoa-code-of-ethics.aspx.

Table 27
Regulations Related to Violations of Ethical Standards

| | Reference to AMA Code of Ethics | | |
	Yes/No	Citation	Specific Language and/or Comments
Alabama			
Alaska	Yes	12 AAC 40.955.(a) ETHICAL STANDARDS	The Principles of Medical Ethics of the AMA on page xiv of the 2002-2003 Edition of the Council on Ethical and Judicial Affairs, *Code of Medical Ethics*, published by the AMA, are adopted by reference as the ethical standards for physicians and applies to all physicians subject to this chapter.
Arizona	No		
Arkansas	Yes		ASMB Regulation 32 in Medical Practice Act.
California			
Colorado			
Connecticut	No		
Delaware	No		The Board routinely uses the AMA Code of Ethics as the standard.
DC	No		The Board routinely uses the AMA Code of Ethics as a guide.
Florida			
Florida DO	No		
Georgia	No		
Guam			
Hawaii	Yes		
Idaho	No		
Illinois			
Indiana			
Iowa	Yes	IAC 653-13.20	"The Code of Medical Ethics prepared and approved by the American Medical Association . . . shall be utilized by the board as guiding principles in the practice of medicine and surgery . . . in this state."
Kansas			
Kentucky	Yes	KRS 311.595(9), and 311.597(1)	
Louisiana			
Maine	Yes		Board policy.
Maryland	No		
Massachusetts			
Michigan	No		An expert may rely on the AMA Code to explain the underpinnings of what he/she deems to be the controlling standard.
Minnesota	No		
Mississippi			
Missouri			
Montana			
Nebraska	Yes	172 NAC88-013 item 1	
Nevada			
Nevada DO	No		Board Regulations NAC 633.
New Hampshire	Yes		In the Board's rules.
New Jersey	No		The Board routinely refers to the AMA Code.
New Mexico	Yes		"Determination of Medical Ethics": A. The board adopts the ethical standards set forth in the latest published version of the *Code of Medical Ethics*, current opinions with annotations of the Council on Ethical and Judicial Affairs of the AMA or its successor publication.

(continued on next page)

Table 27 (continued)
Regulations Related to Violations of Ethical Standards

	Reference to AMA Code of Ethics		
	Yes/No	Citation	Specific Language and/or Comments
New York			
North Carolina	Yes	2.06 and 9.07	Position statements on capital punishment (2.06), medical testimony (9.07), and use of social media.
North Dakota			
Ohio	Yes	Section 4731.22(B)(18) Ohio Revised Code	". . . violation of any provision of a code of ethics of the American Medical Association . . ."
Oklahoma	No		
Oregon	No	ORS 677.188 (4)(a)	"Unprofessional or dishonorable conduct" includes conduct or practice "contrary to recognized standards of ethics of the medical or podiatric profession" . . . The Board uses the AMA Code to interpret "recognized standards."
Pennsylvania	No		
Puerto Rico			
Rhode Island	Yes		The board notes AMA ethical standards in relation to treating family members.
South Carolina	No	SECTION 40-47-70. Code of ethics. 40-47-110(13) Reg. 81-10(b) Reg. 81-60. Principles of Medical Ethics.	"A practitioner shall conduct himself or herself in accordance with the applicable codes of ethics adopted by the board in regulation"; "violated the code of medical ethics adopted by the board or has been found by the board to lack the ethical or professional competence to practice"; "violation of any of the principles of medical ethics as adopted by the Board."
South Dakota			
Tennessee	Yes		The board adopted the AMA code in its rules.
Texas	No		
Utah	Yes		Referred to in board rules.
Vermont	No		The board routinely uses the AMA code.
Virgin Islands			
Virginia	No		
Washington			
West Virginia	Yes	11 CSR 1A at 12.2(d).	
Wisconsin	No		The code is asserted in consensus with the profession's standards for minimal standards of care.
Wyoming	No		Considers the AMA Code when establishing the standard.

Note: *All information should be verified with licensing board; medical licenses are granted to those physicians meeting all state requirements—at the discretion of the board.*

Universal Licensure Application Form

A number of state boards are moving to the to help simplify the licensing process, especially for physicians seeking licenses in more than one state.

A small but growing number of boards are using the Uniform Application for Physician State Licensure, from the Federation of State Medical Boards (FSMB), or are in the process of adopting it (Table 28), according to the FSMB. The majority using the form offer it in electronic format.

The form was developed by the FSMB "as part of its license portability demonstration project, which is funded by a grant from the federal Office of the Advancement of Telehealth." As of April 26, 2011, more than 18,600 physicians have successfully submitted their application for licensure utilizing the form.

Table 28
Universal Licensure Application Form

	Currently Using Form?	Format	Implementation in process?	Comments
Alabama				
Alaska			Yes	
Arizona				
Arkansas				
California				
Colorado				
Connecticut			Yes	
Delaware				
DC				Adoption of Universal Licensure Application being discussed.
Florida				
Georgia				
Guam			Yes	
Hawaii				
Idaho	Yes	Electronic		
Illinois				
Indiana	Yes			
Iowa	Yes			
Kansas	Yes	Electronic or paper		
Kentucky				
Louisiana				Implementation on hold.
Maine	Yes	Electronic		
Maryland	No		No	
Massachusetts				
Michigan				
Minnesota	Yes	Electronic		
Mississippi				
Missouri				
Montana	Yes			
Nebraska				
Nevada	Yes	Electronic		
New Hampshire	Yes	Electronic		
New Jersey				
New Mexico				
New York				
North Carolina	No			Board seeking to have UA data auto-fill NCMB application.
North Dakota				
Ohio	Yes	Electronic		
Oklahoma DO	Yes			
Oregon				
Pennsylvania				

(continued on next page)

Table 28 *(continued)*
Universal Licensure Application Form

	Currently Using Form?	Format	Implementation in process?	Comments
Puerto Rico				
Rhode Island	Yes	Electronic		
South Carolina				
South Dakota	No		No	
Tennessee				
Texas	No		Yes	
Utah				
Vermont	Yes	Electronic		UA available on board website.
Virgin Islands				
Virginia				
Washington	Yes			
West Virginia	Yes	Electronic		
Wisconsin				
Wyoming	Yes	Electronic		

Chapter 2

Licensing Board Statistics

Data in this section were taken from the AMA Physician Masterfile, an electronic database that tracks physicians' entire educational and professional careers, from medical school and graduate medical education (GME) through practice. Data include *only* full and unrestricted licenses; limited educational permits or licenses for resident physicians in GME programs are *not* included. Licenses issued to doctors of osteopathic medicine (DOs) are also included. Please note the following definitions:

Initial License—When a physician without *any* previous licensure receives his/her first professional license.

New License—When a physician without previous licensure from a given state receives a license from that state.

These two figures overlap, as all initial licenses are a subset of new licenses.

In 2012, 64,822 licenses were issued to doctors of medicine (MDs) and doctors of osteopathy (DOs) by medical licensing boards (Table 29). Of these, 24,912, or 38%, were identified as initial licenses.

Table 30 shows a breakdown of total licenses awarded in 2012 by licensing jurisdiction, by US medical graduates and international medical graduates (IMGs).

Tables 31 through 33 present data on initial licensure. As previously noted, an initial license is the physician's first ever full and unrestricted license.

Table 31 shows the percentage of initial licenses awarded in a given jurisdiction. As previously noted, the national average for 2012 was 38%. In the states with higher percentages, then, the physician population is growing more rapidly than the national average.

Table 31 also breaks down the total initial licenses in each state by US medical school graduates and IMGs. Of the 24,912 physicians who received their initial licenses in 2011, 7,226 (29%) were issued to IMGs.

Table 32 provides an historical picture of the numbers of initial licenses awarded since 1955 and how the percentages have varied between US medical graduates and IMGs. In 1950, for example, only 5% of initial licensees were IMGs; in 2012, 29% were IMGs. The highest percentage of IMGs as initial licensees occurred in 1972 and 1973, with 46% and 44%, respectively (by 1979, however, the percentage had dropped back to 18%).

Table 33 provides an historical picture of the numbers of IMGs receiving initial licenses by state since 1975.

Table 29
Licenses Issued to Physicians by State Medical/Osteopathic Boards, 1990–2012

Year	Total New Licenses	Total Initial Licenses
1990	44,341	20,853
1991	45,249	20,962
1992	45,132	19,760
1993	48,834	20,182
1994	49,912	20,857
1995	51,332	22,250
1996	55,716	23,920
1997	55,886	24,151
1998	56,237	23,419
1999	54,586	22,999
2000	51,866	19,581
2001	52,305	21,078
2002	52,877	20,383
2003	52,281	20,632
2004	55,435	22,599
2005	57,184	23,180
2006	61,724	24,287
2007	60,336	23,837
2008	61,738	24,460
2009	60,687	24,597
2010	61,681	24,774
2011	62,804	24,482
2012	64,822	24,912

Table 30

Full Unrestricted Licenses (Whether Physician's Initial or Subsequent) Issued to MDs and DOs by State Medical/Osteopathic Boards, 2012

	Total	US Medical Graduates	IMGs	Percentage of Licenses Awarded to IMGs
Alabama	823	621	202	25
Alaska	278	239	39	14
Arizona	1,551	1,132	419	27
Arkansas	484	337	147	30
California	5,789	4,454	1,335	23
Colorado	1,145	985	160	14
Connecticut	1,032	670	362	35
Delaware	323	243	80	25
DC	837	624	213	25
Florida	3,323	2,118	1,205	36
Georgia	1,761	1,271	490	28
Hawaii	495	405	90	18
Idaho	384	334	50	13
Illinois	2,239	1,595	644	29
Indiana	1,585	1,082	503	32
Iowa	808	608	200	25
Kansas	682	543	139	20
Kentucky	978	709	269	28
Louisiana	823	588	235	29
Maine	433	325	108	25
Maryland	1,765	1,322	443	25
Massachusetts	1,910	1,433	477	25
Michigan	1,834	1,197	637	35
Minnesota	1,267	930	337	27
Mississippi	551	406	145	26
Missouri	1,523	1,159	364	24
Montana	399	340	59	15
Nebraska	611	508	103	17
Nevada	495	370	125	25
New Hampshire	473	347	126	27
New Jersey	1,821	1,153	668	37
New Mexico	658	479	179	27
New York	4,017	2,676	1,341	33
North Carolina	2,136	1,680	456	21
North Dakota	386	292	94	24
Ohio	2,430	1,658	772	32
Oklahoma	716	517	199	28
Oregon	798	671	127	16
Pennsylvania	2,884	1,924	960	33
Puerto Rico	99	71	28	28
Rhode Island	221	168	53	24
South Carolina	839	649	190	23
South Dakota	4	3	1	25
Tennessee	1,188	942	246	21
Texas	3,389	2,354	1,035	31
Utah	630	551	79	13
Vermont	236	204	32	14
Virginia	2,133	1,578	555	26
Virgin Islands	0	0	0	0
Washington	1,532	1,237	295	19
West Virginia	379	285	94	25
Wisconsin	1,383	977	406	29
Wyoming	342	273	69	20
Total	**64,822**	**47,237**	**17,585**	**27 (average)**

Table 31
Initial Licenses Issued to MDs and DOs by State Medical/Osteopathic Boards, 2012

	Total	US Medical Graduates	IMGs	Initial Licenses Awarded as Percentage of Full Unrestricted Licenses (Table 30)
Alabama	390	309	81	47
Alaska	22	21	1	8
Arizona	365	252	113	24
Arkansas	155	87	68	32
California	3,172	2,575	597	55
Colorado	285	253	32	25
Connecticut	390	193	197	38
Delaware	67	47	20	21
DC	232	166	66	28
Florida	980	560	420	29
Georgia	523	360	163	30
Hawaii	92	77	15	19
Idaho	46	43	3	12
Illinois	1,065	710	355	48
Indiana	546	342	204	34
Iowa	244	163	81	30
Kansas	158	118	40	23
Kentucky	264	154	110	27
Louisiana	401	281	120	49
Maine	104	61	43	24
Maryland	531	365	166	30
Massachusetts	1,095	819	276	57
Michigan	932	542	390	51
Minnesota	616	458	158	49
Mississippi	148	99	49	27
Missouri	521	395	126	34
Montana	22	16	6	6
Nebraska	258	225	33	42
Nevada	76	42	34	15
New Hampshire	87	53	34	18
New Jersey	441	196	245	24
New Mexico	148	100	48	22
New York	2,200	1,500	700	55
North Carolina	684	575	109	32
North Dakota	53	28	25	14
Ohio	1,251	863	388	51
Oklahoma	292	188	104	41
Oregon	234	185	49	29
Pennsylvania	1,416	909	507	49
Puerto Rico	83	58	25	84
Rhode Island	51	34	17	23
South Carolina	202	148	54	24
South Dakota	0	0	0	0
Tennessee	373	310	63	31
Texas	1,368	1,076	292	40
Utah	239	211	28	38
Vermont	44	31	13	19
Virginia	819	605	214	38
Virgin Islands	0	0	0	0
Washington	456	369	87	30
West Virginia	128	96	32	34
Wisconsin	620	406	214	45
Wyoming	23	12	11	7
Total	**24,912**	**17,686**	**7,226**	**38.4 (average)**

Table 32

Initial Licenses Issued to MDs and DOs by State Medical/Osteopathic Boards, 1955-2012

Year	Total	US Medical Graduates		IMGs	
1955	7,737	6,830	88%	907	12%
1956	7,463	6,611	89%	852	11%
1957	7,455	6,441	86%	1,014	14%
1958	7,809	6,643	85%	1,166	15%
1959	8,269	6,643	80%	1,626	20%
1960	8,030	6,611	82%	1,419	18%
1961	8,023	6,443	80%	1,580	20%
1962	8,005	6,648	83%	1,357	17%
1963	8,283	6,832	82%	1,451	18%
1964	7,911	6,605	83%	1,306	17%
1965	9,147	7,619	83%	1,528	17%
1966	8,851	7,217	82%	1,634	18%
1967	9,424	7,343	78%	2,081	22%
1968	9,766	7,581	78%	2,185	22%
1969	9,978	7,671	77%	2,307	23%
1970	11,032	8,016	73%	3,016	27%
1971	12,257	7,943	65%	4,314	35%
1972	14,476	7,815	54%	6,661	46%
1973	16,689	9,270	56%	7,419	44%
1974	16,706	10,093	60%	6,613	40%
1975	16,859	10,794	64%	6,065	36%
1976	17,724	11,288	64%	6,436	36%
1977	18,175	12,324	68%	5,851	32%
1978	19,393	14,815	76%	4,578	24%
1979	19,896	16,330	82%	3,566	18%
1980	18,172	14,862	82%	3,310	18%
1981	18,831	15,700	83%	3,131	17%
1982	17,605	13,409	76%	4,196	24%
1983	20,601	15,848	77%	4,753	23%
1984	18,340	14,246	78%	4,094	22%
1985	18,288	15,239	83%	3,049	17%
1986	19,528	16,592	85%	2,936	15%
1987	20,324	17,096	84%	3,228	16%
1988	21,235	18,005	85%	3,230	15%
1989	20,115	17,366	86%	2,749	14%
1990	20,853	17,254	83%	3,599	17%
1991	20,962	16,959	81%	4,003	19%
1992	19,760	16,008	81%	3,752	19%
1993	20,182	15,805	78%	4,377	22%
1994	20,857	15,961	77%	4,896	23%
1995	22,520	17,201	76%	5,319	24%
1996	23,920	17,486	73%	6,434	27%
1997	24,151	16,714	69%	7,069	31%
1998	23,419	17,786	76%	5,633	24%
1999	22,999	17,700	77%	5,299	23%
2000	19,581	14,586	74%	4,995	26%
2001	21,078	15,392	73%	5,686	27%
2002	20,383	14,888	73%	5,495	27%
2003	20,632	15,019	73%	5,613	27%
2004	22,599	16,239	72%	6,360	28%
2005	23,180	16,391	71%	6,789	29%
2006	24,287	17,506	72%	6,781	28%
2007	23,837	17,018	71%	6,819	29%
2008	24,460	17,458	71%	7,002	29%
2009	24,597	17,474	71%	7,123	29%
2010	24,774	17,583	71%	7,191	29%
2011	24,482	17,381	71%	7,101	29%
2012	24,912	17,686	71%	7,226	29%

Table 33
Initial Licenses Issued to International Medical Graduates by State Medical/Osteopathic Boards, 1975-2012

	1975	1980	1985	1990	1995	2000	2005	2010	2012
Alabama	1	0	8	11	136	28	73	130	113
Alaska	1	0	0	1	15	1	3	3	1
Arizona	20	16	17	14	8	28	80	86	113
Arkansas	8	5	9	13	31	27	48	65	68
California	212	276	243	355	435	392	701	663	597
Colorado	6	6	18	29	6	15	22	23	32
Connecticut	13	54	71	23	11	146	169	197	197
Delaware	9	3	4	9	4	16	25	23	20
DC	426	59	45	19	13	49	44	50	66
Florida	325	114	114	156	155	204	333	406	420
Georgia	74	165	113	38	67	62	106	154	163
Hawaii	14	9	6	15	14	9	26	19	15
Idaho	0	1	0	0	0	1	2	0	3
Illinois	481	94	75	369	631	360	393	361	355
Indiana	46	58	85	50	2	412	228	243	204
Iowa	71	36	132	49	107	73	71	95	81
Kansas	25	23	12	31	122	25	53	38	40
Kentucky	30	30	2	20	38	53	69	86	110
Louisiana	11	21	26	3	35	70	97	160	120
Maine	197	172	3	14	21	11	27	27	43
Maryland	258	244	125	239	213	0	127	152	166
Massachusetts	199	170	42	151	202	208	247	297	276
Michigan	565	146	195	31	431	323	474	414	390
Minnesota	39	16	49	38	50	84	80	167	158
Mississippi	9	5	0	5	0	15	32	27	49
Missouri	124	30	20	16	63	61	77	119	126
Montana	0	4	1	0	3	0	2	3	6
Nebraska	20	30	22	35	5	16	16	26	33
Nevada	5	4	0	1	5	17	34	28	34
New Hampshire	22	4	5	4	38	6	25	32	34
New Jersey	139	262	324	318	321	199	262	232	245
New Mexico	14	11	11	26	7	27	55	75	48
New York	805	594	352	975	640	683	724	636	700
North Carolina	66	19	35	18	57	56	90	101	109
North Dakota	45	20	6	0	6	8	9	18	25
Ohio	183	70	71	43	63	444	309	317	388
Oklahoma	30	72	39	20	25	42	73	104	104
Oregon	14	13	3	6	10	39	24	28	49
Pennsylvania	490	137	253	107	390	342	399	482	507
Puerto Rico	157	4	46	25	97	—	301	54	25
Rhode Island	7	11	20	11	17	30	29	22	17
South Carolina	2	13	1	2	160	20	25	50	54
South Dakota	3	12	5	0	6	3	7	12	0
Tennessee	18	23	20	25	57	48	66	65	63
Texas	201	100	49	54	18	54	190	255	292
Utah	4	1	12	36	237	16	26	44	28
Vermont	46	0	1	3	3	5	6	7	13
Virginia	327	49	43	49	79	113	235	216	214
Washington	22	23	263	30	89	53	83	98	87
West Virginia	119	38	14	35	23	13	35	42	32
Wisconsin	18	33	33	75	136	86	150	223	214
Wyoming	5	10	6	2	1	2	7	16	11
Total	**5,926**	**3,310**	**3,049**	**3,599**	**5,303**	**4,995**	**6,789**	**7,191**	**7,226**

Chapter 3

Medical Licensing Examinations and Organizations

The United States Medical Licensing Examination® (USMLE®)

National Board of Medical Examiners
Philadelphia, Pennsylvania

Federation of State Medical Boards
Dallas, Texas

The United States Medical Licensing Examination®
(USMLE®) is a three-step examination for medical licensure in the United States. It is designed to assess a physician's ability to apply knowledge, concepts, and principles, and to demonstrate fundamental patient-centered skills, that are important in health and disease and that constitute the basis of safe and effective patient care. The USMLE is a single examination with three Steps. Each Step is complementary to the others; no Step can stand alone in the assessment of readiness for medical licensure. The USMLE is sponsored by the Federation of State Medical Boards (FSMB) and the National Board of Medical Examiners® (NBME®).

A Composite Committee, appointed by the FSMB and NBME, governs the USMLE. The Composite Committee establishes rules for the USMLE program. Membership includes representatives from the FSMB, NBME, the Educational Commission for Foreign Medical Graduates (ECFMG®), and the American public.

In the United States and its territories, the individual medical and osteopathic licensing authorities ("state medical boards") of the various jurisdictions grant a license to practice medicine. Each medical licensing authority sets its own rules and regulations and requires passing an examination that demonstrates qualification for licensure. Results of the USMLE are reported to these authorities for use in granting the initial license to practice medicine. The USMLE provides them with a common evaluation system for applicants for medical licensure. Because individual medical licensing authorities make their own decisions regarding use of USMLE results, licensure applicants should obtain complete information from the licensing authority. Also, the FSMB can provide general information on medical licensure.

Note: Portions of this chapter reprinted with permission from the *USMLE 2013 Bulletin of Information*, copyright © 2012 by the Federation of State Medical Boards of the United States, Inc, and the National Board of Medical Examiners®; and also from the *2011 NBME Annual Report*, copyright © 2012 by the National Board of Medical Examiners®.

The Three Steps of the USMLE: Step 1, Step 2, and Step 3

Step 1 assesses whether medical school students or graduates can understand and apply important concepts of the sciences basic to the practice of medicine, with special emphasis on principles and mechanisms underlying health, disease, and modes of therapy. Step 1 ensures mastery of not only the sciences that provide a foundation for the safe and competent practice of medicine in the present, but also the scientific principles required for maintenance of competence through lifelong learning.

Step 2 has two separately administered components, the Clinical Knowledge component (Step 2 CK) and the Clinical Skills component (Step 2 CS). Step 2 assesses whether medical school students or graduates can understand and apply the knowledge, skills, and understanding of clinical science considered essential for the provision of patient care under supervision and includes emphasis on health promotion and disease prevention. The inclusion of Step 2 in the USMLE sequence is intended to ensure that due attention is devoted to principles of clinical sciences and basic patient-centered skills that provide the foundation for safe and competent medical practice.

Step 3 assesses whether physicians can apply the medical knowledge and understanding of biomedical and clinical science considered essential for the unsupervised practice of medicine, with emphasis on patient management in ambulatory settings. The inclusion of Step 3 in the USMLE sequence ensures that attention is devoted to the importance of assessing the knowledge of physicians who are assuming independent responsibility for delivering general medical care to patients.

USMLE Eligibility Requirements and Examination Policies

To be eligible to sit for USMLE Step 1, Step 2 CK, and Step 2 CS, an applicant must be in one of the following categories at the time of application and on the examination day:

- A medical student officially enrolled in, or a graduate of, a US or Canadian medical school program leading to the MD degree that is accredited by the Liaison Committee on Medical Education (LCME)

- A medical student officially enrolled in, or a graduate of, a US medical school program leading to the DO degree that is accredited by the American Osteopathic Association (AOA)

- A medical student officially enrolled in, or a graduate of, a medical school outside the United States and Canada and eligible for examination by the ECFMG for its certificate

To be eligible to sit for USMLE Step 3, an applicant must meet all of the following requirements:

- Obtain the MD degree (or its equivalent) or the DO degree

- Obtain a passing performance on Steps 1, 2 CK and 2 CS

- If a graduate of a medical school outside the United States and Canada, obtain certification by the ECFMG or successfully complete a Fifth Pathway program (see page 34 for more information) (*Note:* The USMLE program will cease acceptance of Fifth Pathway certificates for the purpose of meeting Step 3 eligibility requirements, effective January 1, 2017.)

- Meet the requirements for taking Step 3 set by the medical licensing authority to which the applicant is applying

The USMLE program recommends that, for Step 3 eligibility, licensing authorities require the completion, or near completion, of at least one training year in a GME program accredited by the Accreditation Council for Graduate Medical Education (ACGME) or the AOA. Applicants should contact the FSMB or the individual licensing authority for complete information on Step 3 eligibility requirements in the state where they plan to be licensed.

Medical students or graduates planning to take USMLE must obtain the most recent information from the appropriate registration entity (see page 109) before applying for the examination. See the USMLE website at www.usmle.org for updated information.

Computer-based Testing

Through computer-based testing (CBT), continuous test administration of the USMLE Step 1, Step 2 CK, and Step 3 is available to all examinees. Prometric® provides scheduling and test centers for the USMLE. The Step 1 and Step 2 CK examinations are administered worldwide; the Step 3 examination is administered only in the United States.

Step 2 CS Testing

USMLE Step 2 CS is administered at five regional Clinical Skills Evaluation Centers in the United States:

- Atlanta, Georgia
- Chicago, Illinois
- Houston, Texas
- Philadelphia, Pennsylvania
- Los Angeles, California

Step 2 CS is offered regularly throughout the year at these five sites.

Description of the Examinations

Step 1, Step 2 CK, and Step 3 are administered in sessions of eight or nine hours, broken up into sections, or "blocks." The computer keeps track of overall session time, including breaks and time allocated for each block of the test. Step 2 CS consists of 12 patient cases. Examinees have 15 minutes for each patient encounter and 10 minutes to record the patient note. The testing session is approximately 8 hours. Further information on examination content and sample test materials for all three steps of the USMLE are available at the USMLE website (www.usmle.org).

Step 1

Step 1 has approximately 325 multiple-choice test questions, divided into seven 60-minute blocks, administered in one eight-hour testing session. It includes test questions in anatomy, behavioral sciences, biochemistry, microbiology, pathology, pharmacology, and physiology, as well as interdisciplinary topics such as nutrition, genetics, and aging. Step 1 is a broadly based, integrated examination.

Test questions commonly require examinees to interpret graphic and tabular material, to identify gross and microscopic pathologic and normal specimens, and to apply basic science knowledge to clinical problems. Step 1 is constructed according to an integrated content outline that organizes basic science material along two dimensions: system and process.

Step 2 CK

Step 2 CK has approximately 350 multiple-choice test questions, divided into eight 60-minute blocks, administered in one 9-hour testing session. It includes test questions in internal medicine, obstetrics and gynecology, pediatrics, preventive medicine, psychiatry, surgery, and other areas relevant to provision of care under supervision. The majority of the test questions describe clinical situations and require that examinees provide a diagnosis, prognosis, indication of underlying mechanisms of disease, or the next step in medical care, including preventive measures. Step 2 CK is a broadly based, integrated examination. Interpretation of tables and laboratory data, imaging studies, photographs of gross and microscopic pathologic specimens, and results of other diagnostic studies is frequently required. Step 2 CK is constructed according to an integrated content outline that organizes clinical science material along two dimensions: physician task and disease category

Step 2 CS

Step 2 CS has 12 patient cases, administered in a testing session of approximately eight hours. Examinees have 15 minutes for each patient encounter and 10 minutes to record each patient note.

Step 2 CS uses standardized patients, ie, people trained to portray real patients. Examinees are expected to establish rapport with the standardized patients, elicit pertinent historical information from them, perform focused physical examinations, answer questions, and provide counseling when appropriate. After each interaction with a standardized patient, examinees record pertinent history and physical examination findings, list diagnostic impressions, and outline plans for further evaluation, if necessary. The cases cover common and important situations that a physician is likely to encounter in clinics, doctors' offices, emergency departments, and hospital settings in the United States. The sample of cases selected for each examination reflects a balance of cases that is fair and equitable across all examinations. On any examination day, the set of cases will differ from the combination presented the day before or the following day, but each set of cases has a comparable degree of difficulty. The criteria used to create individual examinations focus primarily on presenting complaints and conditions. Presentation categories include, but are not limited to, cardiovascular, constitutional, gastrointestinal, genitourinary, musculoskeletal, neurological, psychiatric, respiratory, and women's health.

Three subcomponents of Step 2 CS are assessed: (1) Integrated Clinical Encounter, which includes data gathering skills, including history taking and physical examination, and a patient note; (2) Communication and Interpersonal Skills, which includes questioning skills, information-sharing skills, and professional manner and rapport; and (3) Spoken English Proficiency. Examinees are assessed on their data gathering, physical examination, and communication skills (including spoken English) by the standardized patient, and on their ability to complete the patient note by physician raters.

Examinees must pass all three components in a single administration to obtain the overall designation of passing Step 2 CS. Step 2 CS results are reported as pass or fail, with no numerical scores.

Step 3

Step 3 has approximately 470 multiple-choice test questions, divided into blocks of 35 to 50 items, with 45 to 60 minutes to complete each block. In addition, Step 3 has between nine and 12 computer-based case simulations, with 10 or 20 minutes of maximum real time. Step 3 is administered in two 8-hour testing sessions.

Step 3 is organized along three principal dimensions: clinical encounter frame, physician task, and normal conditions and diseases. Step 3 content reflects a data-based model of generalist medical practice in the United States. Encounter frames capture the essential features of circumstances surrounding physicians' clinical activity with patients. They range from encounters with patients seen for the first time for nonemergency problems, to encounters with regular patients seen in the context of continued care, to patient encounters in life-threatening emergency situations. Encounters occur in clinics, offices, skilled nursing care facilities, hospitals and emergency departments, and on the telephone.

Step 3 includes Primum® computer-based case simulations (CCS), a test format developed by the NBME that allows the physician taking the test to provide care for a simulated patient. The test-taker decides which diagnostic information to obtain and how to treat and monitor the patient's progress. The computer records each step taken in caring for the patient and scores overall performance. This format permits assessment of clinical decision-making skills in a more realistic and integrated manner than multiple-choice formats.

In the CCS cases, the test-taker may request information from the history and physical examination; order laboratory studies, procedures, and consultations; and start medications and other therapies. Any of the thousands of possible entries that are typed on the "order sheet" are processed and verified by the "clerk." When the test taker has confirmed that there is nothing further to do, he or she decides when to reevaluate the patient by advancing simulated time. As time passes, the patient's condition changes based on the underlying problem and interventions taken; results of tests are reported and results of interventions must be monitored. The test taker can suspend the movement of simulated time to consider next steps. While one cannot go back in time, orders can be changed to reflect an updated management plan.

The patient's chart contains the reports resulting from orders, in addition to the order sheet. By selecting the appropriate chart tabs, the test-taker can review vital signs, progress notes, patient updates, and test results. He or she may care for and move the patient among the office, home, emergency department, intensive care unit, and hospital ward.

Preparation for the Examinations

There are no test preparation courses affiliated with or sanctioned by the USMLE program. Information on such courses is not available from the ECFMG, FSMB, NBME, USMLE Secretariat, or medical licensing authorities.

USMLE Steps are broad in scope and are designed to measure the prospective physician's ability to apply knowledge. The best preparation for the USMLE is a general, thorough review of the content reflected in the descriptions for each Step (available at the USMLE website).

USMLE Minimum Passing Scores

The USMLE program recommends a minimum passing score for each Step of the USMLE. Minimum passing scores are based on achievement of specified levels of proficiency established prior to administration of examinations. Statistical procedures are employed to ensure that for each Step, the level of proficiency required to pass remains uniform across forms of the examination. As noted in the USMLE *Bulletin of Information* at www.usmle.org, the score required to meet the recommended level of proficiency is reviewed periodically and may be adjusted without prior notice. Notice of adjustments is posted at the USMLE website.

In reviewing standards for USMLE examinations, the USMLE Step Committees use information gathered from many sources, including standard-setting surveys. These surveys, which seek opinions on the appropriateness of current USMLE pass/fail standards for each Step, are sent to random samples of examinees, directors of basic and clinical science courses and clinical clerkships, associate deans for academic and student affairs, directors and chief residents from residency programs, members of USMLE test material development committees, executive directors and presidents of all state medical boards, and members of the NBME Executive Board and FSMB Board of Directors.

In addition to surveys, USMLE Step Committees consider the results of content review by standard setting panels. These panels typically consist of physicians who are not otherwise involved in the USMLE program. These panels review the content of the Step examinations and, through a series of exercises, provide data that reflect their opinions on minimally acceptable levels of performance.

Step 1

The USMLE website provides details on the performance of examinees taking Step 1 in 2011 and 2012. Data for 2012 are based upon examinees whose results were reported through February 6, 2013. Approximately 18,312 and 18,723 first-time takers from US and Canadian medical schools that grant the MD degree were tested in 2011 and 2012, respectively. First-time takers from non-US/Canadian medical schools numbered 14,855 and 14,201 for the same years. The pass rates for first-time takers from MD-granting US and Canadian medical schools were 94% in 2011 and 96% in 2012. Because

failing examinees generally retake Step 1, the ultimate passing rate across test administrations is expected to increase to approximately 99% for this same group.

Step 2 CK

The USMLE website provides details on the performance of examinees taking Step 2 CK in the 2010-2011 and 2011-2012 academic years. First-time takers from US and Canadian medical schools granting the MD degree numbered approximately 18,225 and 18,454 for 2010-2011 and 2011-2012, respectively. First-time takers from non-US/Canadian medical schools numbered 11,594 and 11,908, respectively. The pass rates for first-time takers from MD-granting US and Canadian medical schools were 97% for 2010-2011 and 98% for 2011-2012. As noted with Step 1, given the opportunity for this same group to repeat the examination, the ultimate Step 2 CK passing rate across test administrations is expected to increase to approximately 99% for this same group.

Step 2 CS

The USMLE website provides details on the performance of examinees taking Step 2 CS in the 2010-2011 and 2011-2012 academic years. First-time takers from US and Canadian medical schools granting the MD degree numbered 17,852 for 2010-2011 and 16,662 for 2011- 2012, with passing rates of 98% and 97% respectively. First-time takers from non-US/Canadian medical schools numbered 11,889 and 11,515 during these two periods. The respective passing rates for this group were 79% and 80%.

Step 3

The USMLE website provides details on the performance of examinees taking Step 3 in 2011 and 2012. Data for 2012 are based upon examinees whose results were reported through February 6, 2013. First-time takers who were graduates of MD-granting schools in the US and Canada numbered 17,486 in 2011 and 18,172 in 2012. First-time takers who were graduates of non-US/Canadian medical schools numbered 8,830 and 8,500, respectively, for the same years. The pass rate for first-time takers who were graduates of MD-granting US and Canadian medical schools was 97% in 2011 and 96% in 2012. As with Step 1 and Step 2 CK, the ultimate Step 3 passing rate, accounting for repeat attempts, is expected to increase to approximately 99% for this same group.

The Comprehensive Review of USMLE

In 1995, the membership of the NBME and the FSMB House of Delegates approved a strategic plan for the enhancement of the USMLE. This strategic plan called for two major enhancements: the move to a computer-based administration of the exam and the implementation of a clinical skills assessment into the USMLE. The objectives of this strategic plan were achieved with the shift to computer-based testing in 1999 and the addition of the Step 2 CS in 2004.

In 2005, the next generation of strategic planning began for the USMLE. Called the "comprehensive review of the USMLE" or CRU, the recommendations arising from this strategic review were approved by NBME governance and the FSMB governance in spring 2009. The major recommendations from this phase were: the USMLE should be explicitly oriented to support the licensing decisions made by state medical boards for the supervised and unsupervised practice of medicine; a general competencies schema should be adopted for the USMLE; the assessment of foundational medical sciences should be integrated throughout the USMLE sequence; the USMLE program should continue its emphasis on the assessment of clinical skills (including enhancements to the Step 2 Clinical Skills examination), and developing new testing formats to assess an individual's ability to locate, interpret and apply medicine appropriately in a clinical context.

New USMLE Item Formats: Focus on New Competencies

USMLE continues to develop new assessment formats to broaden the range of competencies that can be tested in computer-based components of USMLE by investigating simulated challenges to skills in patient care, professionalism, communication, systems-based practice, and other important, difficult-to-measure competencies. The tool set being considered is deliberately broad, including multiple new response formats that can be used in various combinations to flexibly assess key skills and hard-to-measure competencies. Where they improve the assessment of the skills to be measured, short video clips may be used to provide richer, more authentic depictions of clinical situations.

Enhancements to Existing USMLE Item Formats

Step 2 CS: Enhancements to the Step 2 CS examination extend both the nature and degree of challenges faced by examinees. Research activities underway for the past several years resulted in implementation of several changes to the Step 2 CS examination in mid-June 2012. The Communications and Interpersonal Skills (CIS) subcomponent of Step 2 CS was redesigned to assess a fuller range of competencies. Research into the assessment of more advanced communications skills continues through 2013.

Restructuring of Step 3: Changes to the Step 3 examination will occur in 2014. The current Step 3 examination is administered in two 8-hour test sessions, which must be taken on consecutive days. The restructured examination will also consist of two test days:

Step 3 Foundations of Independent Practice (FIP): this test day will focus on assessment of knowledge of foundational medicine and science essential for effective health care. Content areas covered will include applying foundational sciences; biostatistics, epidemiology/population health, and interpretation of the medical literature; and social sciences, including communication and interpersonal skills, medical ethics, and systems-based practice/patient safety. The test day will also include some content assessing knowledge of diagnosis and management. This test day will include some of the newer item formats, such as those based on scientific abstracts and pharmaceutical advertisements.

Step 3 Advanced Clinical Medicine (ACM): this test day will focus on assessment of applying comprehensive knowledge of health and disease in the context of patient management. Content areas covered will include assessment of knowledge of history and physical examination, diagnosis and use of diagnostic studies, prognosis/outcome, health maintenance/screening, therapeutics, and medical decision-making. This test day will include multiple-choice questions and computer-based case simulations.

Examinees will be able to schedule the two test days on non-consecutive days. A single score (with graphical performance profile information) and a single pass/fail outcome will be reported following completion of both examination days. The restructured Step 3 examination will be administered beginning November 2014. During an approximately one-month period (October 2014), it is likely that no Step 3 examinations will be administered. Practice materials for the restructured examinations will be posted to the USMLE website in mid-2014. There will be a score delay following the introduction of the restructured examinations. Additional information will be posted as soon as it is available.

Table 34
Contact Information for USMLE

Examination	Type of Applicant	Registration Entity to Contact
Step 1 or Step 2 (CK or CS)	Students and graduates of medical school programs in the US and Canada accredited by the Liaison Committee on Medical Education or students and graduates of medical schools in the US and Canada accredited by the American Osteopathic Association	**NBME** Examinee Support Services 3750 Market St Philadelphia, PA 19104-3190 (215) 590-9700 (215) 590-9457 Fax Email: webmail@nbme.org www.nbme.org
Step 1 or Step 2 (CK or CS)	Students and graduates of medical schools outside the US and Canada	**ECFMG** 3624 Market St Philadelphia, PA 19104-2685 (215) 386-5900 (215) 386-9196 Fax Email: info@ecfmg.org www.ecfmg.org
Step 3	All medical school graduates who have passed Step 1 and Step 2	**FSMB** Department of Examination Services 400 Fuller Wiser Rd, Suite 300 Dallas, TX 76039 (817) 868-4041 (817) 868-4098 Fax Email: usmle@fsmb.org www.fsmb.org – or – **Medical licensing authority**

Communicating About USMLE

Complete information on USMLE is available on the USMLE website. Table 34 provides contact information specific to the various Steps. General inquiries regarding the USMLE or inquires for the USMLE Secretariat may be directed to:

USMLE Secretariat
3750 Market St
Philadelphia, PA 19104-3190
(215) 590-9700
www.usmle.org

Comprehensive Osteopathic Medical Licensure Examination of the United States (COMLEX-USA)

The three-level Comprehensive Osteopathic Medical Licensure Examination of the United States (COMLEX-USA), administered by the National Board of Osteopathic Medical Examiners (NBOME), is the primary pathway to licensure for osteopathic physicians seeking to practice osteopathic medicine and surgery. A passing score on these examinations indicates that the candidate's medical knowledge and clinical skills have met a national standard. The COMLEX-USA examination sequence is accepted for licensure in all 50 states and a number of international jurisdictions.

The COMLEX-USA examination series is designed to assess the osteopathic medical knowledge and clinical skills considered essential for osteopathic generalist physicians to practice medicine without supervision. The COMLEX-USA sequence uses a primary care approach to patient care, with the distinctiveness of osteopathic medicine fully integrated throughout the examination.

COMLEX-USA is constructed in the context of medical problem-solving, which involves clinical presentations and physician tasks. Candidates are expected to utilize the philosophy and principles of osteopathic medicine to solve medical problems. The Clinical Presentation Dimension identifies high-frequency and/or high-impact health issues that osteopathic generalist physicians commonly encounter in practice. The Physician Task Dimension specifies the major steps osteopathic physicians generally undertake in solving medical problems.

Although all three Levels of COMLEX-USA have the same two-dimensional content structure, the depth and emphasis of each Level parallel the educational experiences of the candidates. This progressive nature of the COMLEX-USA series ensures the consistency and continuity of the measurement objectives of osteopathic medical licensing examinations.

COMLEX-USA Level 1

COMLEX-USA Level 1 emphasizes the medical concepts and principles necessary for understanding the mechanisms of medical problems and disease processes.

COMLEX-USA Level 1 is a one-day, computer-based multiple-choice examination covering the basic medical sciences of anatomy, behavioral science, biochemistry, microbiology, osteopathic principles, pathology, pharmacology, physiology, and other relevant areas.

Passing COMLEX-USA Level 1 certifies that candidates have demonstrated competence in the foundational medical sciences and osteopathic principles as required to solve clinical problems in the supervised practice setting and to prepare for lifelong learning.

COMLEX-USA Level 2-Cognitive Evaluation (CE)

COMLEX-USA Level 2-CE candidates are expected to demonstrate clinical concepts and principles involved in all steps of medical problem-solving. COMLEX Level 2-CE emphasizes the medical concepts and principles necessary for making appropriate medical diagnoses through patient history and physical examination findings.

COMLEX-USA Level 2-CE is a one-day, computer-based multiple-choice examination covering the clinical disciplines of community medicine/medical humanities, emergency medicine, internal medicine, obstetrics/gynecology, osteopathic principles, pediatrics, psychiatry, surgery, and other areas necessary to solve medical problems.

Passing COMLEX-USA Level 2-CE certifies that candidates have demonstrated competence in the clinical sciences and osteopathic principles as required to solve clinical problems in the supervised practice setting, enter graduate medical education, and prepare for lifelong learning.

COMLEX-USA Level 2-Performance Evaluation (PE)

The COMLEX-USA Level 2-PE is a one-day examination of clinical skills where each candidate will encounter 12 standardized patients over the course of a seven-hour examination day.

Consistent with NBOME's mission to protect the public, COMLEX-USA Level 2-PE fulfills the public and licensing authority mandate for enhanced patient safety through the evaluation of the clinical skills proficiency of graduates from osteopathic medical schools. The COMLEX-USA Level 2-PE augments the written (computer-based) COMLEX-USA Level 2-Cognitive Evaluation (CE) of osteopathic medical knowledge by providing an assessment of fundamental clinical skills. These clinical skills are:

- Doctor-patient communication
- Interpersonal skills and professionalism
- Medical history-taking and physical examination skills
- Osteopathic principles and osteopathic manipulative treatment
- Documentation skills (including synthesis of clinical findings, integrated differential diagnosis and formulation of a diagnostic and treatment plan)

These patient-centered skills are evaluated in the context of clinical encounters with standardized patients and are required to be personally performed as appropriate in a timely, efficient, safe and effective manner. The ability to communicate in the English language is required in each clinical encounter.

Passing COMLEX-USA Level 2-PE certifies that candidates have demonstrated competence in the clinical skills and osteopathic principles required for entry into graduate medical education and to prepare for lifelong learning.

COMLEX-USA Level 3

COMLEX-USA Level 3 candidates are expected to demonstrate clinical concepts and principles necessary for solving medical problems as independently practicing osteopathic generalist physicians. COMLEX-USA Level 3 emphasizes the medical concepts and principles required to make appropriate patient management decisions.

COMLEX-USA Level 3 is a one-day, computer-based multiple-choice examination covering the clinical disciplines of emergency medicine, internal medicine, obstetrics/gynecology, osteopathic principles, pediatrics, psychiatry, surgery, and other areas necessary to solve medical problems.

Passing COMLEX-USA Level 3 certifies that candidates have demonstrated competence in the clinical sciences and osteopathic principles as required to solve clinical problems and manage patient presentations in the unsupervised practice setting and to prepare for lifelong learning.

COMLEX-USA Level 1, Level 2-CE, and Level 3 Examination Scoring

The number of items answered correctly (the raw score) is converted to a three-digit standard score as well as a two-digit standard score for the purposes of making pass/fail decisions and reporting the results. The conversion for standard scores involves information about the performance of examinees who have taken these examinations previously.

The three-digit standard scores of COMLEX-USA Level 1, Level 2-CE, and Level 3 have a mean of 500. A three-digit standard score of 400 or a two-digit standard score of 75 on COMLEX-USA Level 1 or COMLEX-USA Level 2-CE is required to pass the examination. A three-digit standard score of 350 or a two-digit standard score of 75 on COMLEX-USA Level 3 is required to pass the examination.

Items included in the examination solely for research purposes are not reflected in the candidate's score.

The percentage of examinees that pass or fail the examination is not predetermined. The passing score for all COMLEX-USA examinations is based solely on a candidate's performance on the total examination, not on performance on individual content areas. The COMLEX-USA score reports include graphical performance profiles summarizing strengths and weaknesses for areas designated on the blueprint.

COMLEX-USA Level 2-PE Examination Scoring

Scores for COMLEX-USA Level 2-PE are reported as Pass or Fail as one overall score. In order to receive a passing score, candidates must perform adequately in two separate domains. These are the Humanistic Domain (doctor-patient communication, interpersonal skills and professionalism), and the Biomedical/Biomechanical Domain (medical history-taking, physical examination, osteopathic principles and osteopathic manipulative treatment, and written SOAP Notes, which assess synthesizing information garnered in the clinical encounter, clinical problem-solving and integrated differential diagnosis).

NBOME Contact Information

NBOME Client Services
(866) 479-6828 Toll-free
7 a.m. – 7 p.m. (Eastern), Monday – Friday

NBOME Corporate Offices and Conference Center
National Board of Osteopathic Medical Examiners, Inc
8765 West Higgins Road, Suite 200
Chicago, IL 60631-4174
(773) 714-0622 or (877) 714-0622 (toll-free)
(773) 714-0631 Fax

NBOME Executive Offices and National Center for Clinical Skills Testing (NCCST)
101 West Elm Street,
NCCST, Suite 150
Executive Offices, Suite 230
Conshohocken, PA 19428

NCCST Hours: 8 a.m. – 4:30 p.m. (Eastern),
Monday – Friday
(866) NBOME 97 (866 626-6397) (toll-free)
NCCST Emergency Line with recorded Level 2
Performance Evaluation status message:
(610) 825-4240
www.nbome.org

The Federation of State Medical Boards (FSMB) of the United States, Inc

The Federation of State Medical Boards of the United States, Inc (FSMB) is a nonprofit organization composed of the 70 state medical boards of the US and its territories. The FSMB leads by promoting excellence in medical practice, licensure, and regulation as the national resource and voice on behalf of state medical boards in their protection of the public.

The primary responsibility of each medical licensing board is to protect the public through the regulation of physicians and other health care providers. Within the United States, the organization and activities of each board are determined by state statute, usually referred to as a medical practice act. In general, each state medical board has the authority to license physicians, regulate the practice of medicine, and discipline those who violate the medical practice act.

Physician Data Center

The Federation Physician Data Center is a central repository for physician licensure data from state medical boards and formal actions taken against physicians by state medical boards, the Department of Defense, the US Department of Health and Human Services, and a growing number of international regulatory organizations. The Data Center offers two services used in performing credentialing functions or pre-employment background checks: the *Board Action Data Search* and the *Disciplinary Alert Service*. Both of these services are considered primary source-equivalent by National Committee for Quality Assurance and The Joint Commission. This information is available to licensing and disciplinary boards, the military, governmental and private agencies, and organizations involved in the employment and/or credentialing of physicians. The public can access a national consolidated database of state medical board disciplinary data at www.docinfo.org for a nominal search fee.

Licensure and Assessment Services

In the United States and its territories, a license to practice medicine is a privilege granted only by the individual medical licensing authority of a state or jurisdiction. Each authority sets its own rules and regulations, and each requires successful completion of an examination or certification demonstrating qualification for licensure.

The FSMB, in collaboration with the National Board of Medical Examiners (see page 116), offers two service packages used by medical licensing authorities for making licensure decisions: The United States Medical Licensing Examination® (USMLE®) and the Post-Licensure Assessment System (PLAS).

The USMLE is a 3-step examination taken by individuals preparing for initial medical licensure in the United States. With steps designed to be taken at different times during medical education and training, the USMLE provides a common pathway for evaluating an individual's ability to apply medical knowledge, concepts, and principles to patient care and to demonstrate fundamental patient centered skills that are important in health and disease and that constitute the basis of safe and effective patient care. (See page 101 for more information on USMLE.)

The Post-Licensure Assessment System (PLAS), established in 1998, is a joint program of the FSMB and the National Board of Medical Examiners (NBME). The PLAS provides comprehensive services to medical licensing authorities for use in assessing the ongoing clinical competence of licensed physicians. (More information on PLAS is provided on page 115.)

Federation Credentials Verification Service (FCVS)

The Federation Credentials Verification Service (FCVS) was launched in 1996 to provide a centralized, uniform process for state medical boards to obtain a verified, primary-source record of physicians' and physician assistants' medical credentials. This service is designed to lighten the workload of credentialing staff and reduce unnecessary effort by gathering, verifying, and permanently storing the physician's credentials in a central repository at the FSMB's offices. FCVS obtains primary source verification of medical education, postgraduate training, examination history, board action history, board specialty certification, and identity. This repository of information allows a physician to establish a confidential, lifetime professional portfolio with FCVS which can be forwarded, at the physician's request, to any state medical board that has established an agreement with FCVS as well as other health care entities. To date, more than 167,000 physicians have used FCVS.

FCVS's Student Records program provides a central repository for medical training information, housing and verifying resident training records from closed training programs. This repository of information allows physicians to continue obtaining verification of training for state licensure and hospital and managed care privileging.

To request an FCVS application, receive more detailed information about the credentialing process, or request a roster of the state medical boards that accept FCVS documents, call toll-free (888) ASK-FCVS (888 275-3287), access the FSMB website at www.fsmb.org, or send an e-mail to fcvs@fsmb.org. For more information about FCVS's Student Records program, call (817) 868-5162, or email modonnell@fsmb.org.

Government Relations and Policy

Based in Washington, D.C., the FSMB Advocacy Office houses both federal and state policy staff and serves as a leading legislative and regulatory resource to state medical boards, the U.S. Congress, U.S. Executive Branch, state legislatures, and key health care stakeholders. The FSMB's Advocacy Office monitors federal and state legislation and policies affecting the regulation of the practice of medicine.

On behalf of state medical boards, the FSMB Advocacy Office prepares letters of support or opposition to federal and state legislation as well as research materials, model policy language and written testimony. The FSMB has played a key role in state and national debates on many prominent issues, including medical license portability, maintenance of licensure, emergency preparedness,

telemedicine, Internet prescribing, physician licensure and disciplinary data, appropriate pain management, and the regulation of office-based surgery.

Publications

The FSMB leverages print and electronic publications to inform its membership, the health care community, and the public about medical licensing, regulation, discipline, and medical trends. Model guidelines and recommendations for handling key issues are set forth in published policy documents available online or in print.

On a quarterly basis, the FSMB publishes the *Journal of Medical Regulation*, which is distributed to FSMB membership, libraries, medical schools, and subscribers around the world. Member boards and their staffs are served by the quarterly newsletter *Newsline* and the twice-weekly email publication *FSMB eNews*.

The FSMB also publishes all of its policy documents, organizational updates, and the United States Medical Licensing Examination applications, all of which are available online at www.fsmb.org.

Education

The FSMB offers a variety of educational forums designed to assist state medical and osteopathic boards in carrying out their mission of public protection. The FSMB Annual Meeting is an intensive three-day program that brings together national experts in the field of medical licensure and discipline to discuss a wide range of subjects relevant to medical regulators. To meet the changing needs of its member boards, the FSMB also offers Web-based educational programs to discuss current issues in medical regulation. Recent webinars have addressed issues in physician workforce trends, conflicts of interest between physicians and industry, balancing transparency and confidentiality in physician impairment cases, changes in the current continuing medical education (CME) credit systems, and pain management and the prescribing of controlled substances. Other educational offerings include workshops for medical board attorneys and a comprehensive overview of FSMB programs and services for executives new to medical boards. CME and CLE credits are available through various program offerings.

Post-Licensure Assessment System (PLAS)

The Post-Licensure Assessment System (PLAS) is a joint program of the FSMB and the National Board of Medical Examiners (NBME®). The PLAS provides a comprehensive inventory of assessment tools that are useful in evaluating the clinical competence of licensed or previously licensed physicians.

Assessing Medical Knowledge: The Special Purpose Examination (SPEX)

The Special Purpose Examination (SPEX) is an examination of current knowledge requisite for the general undifferentiated practice of medicine and is intended for physicians who hold or have held a valid, unrestricted license to practice medicine in a US or Canadian jurisdiction. Licensing boards may require SPEX for licensure by endorsement applicants who are some years beyond passage of an initial licensing examination or to evaluate the cognitive knowledge of physicians seeking licensure reinstatement or reactivation after some period of professional inactivity. Physicians who hold a current, unrestricted license to practice in a US or Canadian jurisdiction can take SPEX independent of any request or approval from a medical licensing board.

The SPEX focuses on a core of clinical knowledge and relevant underlying scientific principles deemed necessary to form a reasonable foundation for the safe and effective practice of medicine. It is intended to reflect the knowledge and cognitive abilities of all practicing physicians, regardless of specialty practiced. The content is organized along two primary dimensions: disease categories and physician tasks. Scores are reported directly to the licensing boards for which SPEX is taken, if applicable, and to the examinee. At the request of an examinee, the FSMB will provide certified transcripts of SPEX scores to additional licensing boards.

For more information about the SPEX, call the FSMB Examination Hotline at (817) 868-4041 or consult the FSMB website at www.fsmb.org.

Clinical Competence Assessment Resources

The PLAS also provides diverse, state-of-the-art assessment modalities that, when administered together, generate comprehensive and pertinent data regarding a physician's medical knowledge, clinical judgment, and patient management skills in the current or intended area of practice. Assessment resources currently available through PLAS include Primum® Computer-based Case Simulations; standardized, practice-relevant, multiple-choice exams; and multiple-choice topic module exams. These tools are utilized by physician evaluation and remediation programs around the country to complement local, performance-based methods of assessment, such as medical record reviews, peer (preceptor) assessment and feedback, patient evaluations, and case-based evaluations of physician care.

A comprehensive assessment will help determine the strengths and weaknesses a physician has in areas such as practice-relevant medical knowledge, clinical judgment and reasoning, and patient management and communication. The information provided through the assessment will be useful to licensing boards, hospitals, group practices, managed care organizations, and other health care organizations in making physician licensure and privileging decisions; to identify educational activities needed to enhance a physician's practice patterns; or to assist in career transitions. Assessments may also be beneficial as part of a review of the clinical capabilities of physicians with personal health concerns, such as recovery from disabling illness or injury, neurocognitive concerns, substance abuse, or other issues that may affect practice. Individual physicians may also find assessment services useful in evaluating their clinical competence, particularly if they are at a point of transition in their career or are returning to clinical practice after an extended absence.

Additional information about the PLAS, its services, and the physician evaluation and remediation programs that utilize PLAS assessment resources can be obtained by calling (817) 868-4041 or by visiting the FSMB website at www.fsmb.org.

Contact Information

Federation of State Medical Boards of the United States, Inc
400 Fuller Wiser Road, Suite 300
Euless, TX 76039
(817) 868-4000
(817) 868-4099 Fax
www.fsmb.org

National Board of Medical Examiners® (NBME®)

The National Board of Medical Examiners (NBME) is an independent, not-for-profit organization that provides high-quality examinations for the health professions. Its mission is protection of the public's health through state-of-the-art assessment of health professionals, along with a major commitment to research and development in evaluation and measurement. The NBME was founded in 1915 because of the need for a voluntary, nationwide examination that medical licensing authorities could accept as the standard by which to judge candidates for medical licensure. Since that time, it has continued without interruption to provide high-quality examinations for this purpose and has become a model and a resource of international stature in testing methodologies and evaluation in medicine.

Although the NBME's mission is centered on assessment of physicians, it encompasses the spectrum of health professionals along the continuum of education, training, and practice and includes research in evaluation as well as development of assessment instruments.

United States Medical Licensing Examination® (USMLE®)

The USMLE, co-sponsored and co-owned by the NBME and the Federation of State Medical Boards (FSMB), is a three-step examination for medical licensure in the United States. Results of the USMLE are reported to medical licensing authorities in the United States for their use in granting the initial license to practice medicine. The USMLE is the largest NBME examination program. (Information on the USMLE appears on page 101.)

Services for Medical Schools and Health Professional Organizations

Through a liaison program with medical schools, the NBME fosters communication between the NBME and medical schools, and it provides subject tests in the basic and clinical sciences for assessing the educational achievement of individuals in specific subject areas. In 2012, the number of subject examinations administered by medical schools was approximately 219,000. The NBME has augmented its subject examination program by implementing a system that allows assembly of customized subject examinations. Customized assessment services were introduced in July 2007. In 2012, 63 medical schools administered 355 Web-based assessments to about 32,000 students.

The NBME also provides testing, educational, consultative, and research services to a number of medical specialty boards, societies, and health sciences organizations. Services include developing, administering, and analyzing examinations for certification, recertification, in-training, self-assessment, or evaluation of special competence. In 2012, the NBME provided services to 22 organizations, including examinations administered to approximately 68,000 examinees.

In 2003, the NBME introduced a Web-based self-assessment program for basic and clinical science content for US and international medical students and graduates. In 2005, the program added a comprehensive clinical medicine self-assessment. For information on these services, visit the NBME website at www.nbme.org.

Services for the International Community

In 2005, the NBME established an International Programs unit. Its goals include to better protect the health of the US and international public, enhance the quality of health care education throughout the world, contribute to the development of state-of-the-art assessment of health professionals internationally, and have an expanded venue for assessment and research activities.

The International Foundations of Medicine (IFOM®) examinations are a core component of NBME International Programs. The Clinical Science Examination (CSE) covers the core of clinical knowledge in medicine, surgery, pediatrics, obstetrics and gynecology, and psychiatry expected of students in the final year of undergraduate medical education. The Basic Science Examination (BSE) incorporates the common core of knowledge expected of students who have completed the preclinical curriculum and are about to begin study of clinical medicine.

More than 13,200 medical students or graduates have taken the CSE since its inception in 2007. In 2012, 3,400 candidates received performance profiles outlining their areas of strength and weakness in the disciplines covered in the examination. The IFOM CSE continues to serve as an international benchmark for individuals and medical schools and is being used for residency selection in several countries in the Middle East and Latin America.

The IFOM BSE completed a pilot phase in late 2011 with participants from North America, Europe, the Middle East, and Asia. More than 300 candidates participated in the pilot from eight medical schools. The IFOM BSE is now available in International English.

NBME International Programs offers a portfolio of consultative, faculty and institutional development, and assessment programs. Consultative services often include an on-site evaluation of the overall assessment capability for medical schools. NBME teams have consulted with schools in Lebanon, Saudi Arabia, Brazil, Italy, and the Gulf region. Faculty and institutional development activities vary according to need. NBME International Programs work with faculty and institutional staff to develop and improve assessment tools, from building an examination blueprint to aiding in the interpretation of scores.

Services for Practicing Physicians

The Post-Licensure Assessment System (PLAS) is a joint activity of the NBME and FSMB developed to assist medical licensing authorities and other health care organizations in assessing physicians who have already been licensed. The PLAS includes the Special Purpose Examination (SPEX®) and the Assessment Center Program (ACP). The SPEX is a computerized, multiple-choice examination of current knowledge requisite for the general, undifferentiated practice of medicine. It can be used for reasons such as endorsement of licensure and licensure reactivation after an extended absence from practice. In 2012, the SPEX tested more than 200 physicians. The ACP provides resources for the comprehensive objective and personalized assessments of physicians for whom there is a question regarding clinical competence.

Innovation

The NBME continually supports intramural research in the fields of clinical skills assessment, advanced methods of testing, and ongoing studies of the validity and reliability of NBME examination programs. In addition, the Edward J. Stemmler Medical Education Research Fund of the NBME supports medical school research relevant to the mission of the NBME.

The Center for Innovation, with its mission to advance and facilitate the NBME strategic vision through the development of new products and services, implements time-limited pilot projects by researching and applying a range of novel assessment approaches to the full range of medical education and health care needs.

NBME Certification and Endorsements

The NBME developed and administered its own three-part examination as part of the National Board Certification Program until it was discontinued with the implementation of the USMLE. Certification was awarded to physicians who achieved the following:

- Received the MD degree from an LCME-accredited medical school

- Passed at least one NBME Part or Step examination prior to December 31, 1994 and successfully completed all three Parts/Steps

- Completed, with a satisfactory record, 1 full year (12 months) in a GME program accredited by the Accreditation Council for Graduate Medical Education (accredited internships in Canada were also recognized as meeting this requirement)

Certification by the NBME continues to be used for licensure in the United States for those physicians certified as diplomates prior to implementation of the USMLE and for examinees certified as diplomates who completed a combination of NBME and/or USMLE examinations and passed at least one Part or Step prior to December 31, 1994. The last regular administration of Part I occurred in 1991, Part

II in April 1992, and Part III in May 1994. Because some medical students and physicians completed some part of the NBME examination sequence before the implementation of the USMLE, certain combinations of examinations may be considered by medical licensing authorities as comparable to existing examinations. Physicians who passed a combination of examinations should obtain information regarding the acceptability of the combination directly from the medical licensing authority in the jurisdiction where the physician plans to seek licensure.

For further information on NBME certification, contact:

NBME
Applicant Services
3750 Market St
Philadelphia, PA 19104
(215) 590-9700

NBME Website

Further information on the NBME and its programs and services is available at www.nbme.org.

National Board of Osteopathic Medical Examiners (NBOME)

Established in 1934, the National Board of Osteopathic Medical Examiners (NBOME) is a nonprofit organization dedicated to serving the public as well as state licensing agencies, and to its mission of protecting the public by providing the means to assess competencies for osteopathic medicine and related health care professions.

The NBOME's Comprehensive Osteopathic Medical Licensure Examination of the United States (COMLEX-USA) series is the primary pathway to licensure for osteopathic physicians seeking to practice osteopathic medicine and surgery. A passing score on these examinations indicates that the candidate's medical knowledge and clinical skills have met a national standard. The COMLEX-USA examination sequence is accepted for licensure in all 50 states and a number of international jurisdictions.

The COMLEX-USA examination series uses a primary care approach to patient care with the distinctiveness of osteopathic medicine fully integrated throughout the examination.

To maintain the validity and broad acceptance of its examinations, the NBOME continually engages in research to ensure the examinations include currently accepted principles, concepts and practices of osteopathic medicine. Testing methodology and procedures are studied to confirm the examination scores continue to accurately reflect the knowledge and skills of those who seek to practice osteopathic medicine.

The NBOME also creates and administers a number of other assessment tools, including student self-assessment examinations, subject examinations for the colleges of osteopathic medicine, in-service and certification examinations for specialty boards, and a variable purpose examination for osteopathic physicians who need to demonstrate current osteopathic medical knowledge (see COMVEX information below).

With the impending requirements for maintenance of licensure and osteopathic continuous certification, the NBOME is working closely with the Federation of State Medical Boards, the state medical and osteopathic medical licensing boards, and the specialty boards and specialty colleges to develop assessment tools to meet these important needs.

The organization was established in July 1934 as the National Board of Examiners for Osteopathic Physicians and Surgeons, Inc. The first examinations were given in February 1935; in 1987, the name of the organization was changed to the National Board of Osteopathic Medical Examiners, Inc.

Comprehensive Osteopathic Medical Variable-Purpose Examination (COMVEX)

The NBOME offers a post-licensure examination for osteopathic physicians who require reevaluation after initial licensure. The circumstances in which the Comprehensive Osteopathic Medical Variable-Purpose Examination (COMVEX) may be used include, but are not limited to, the following:

1. An osteopathic physician originally licensed through an examination devoid of osteopathic content is now applying for a license in a state that requires an osteopathic physician to take an osteopathic examination.

2. An osteopathic physician is applying for licensure in a state that imposes a time limit (e.g., completing examination within a 10-year period) and the candidate has not been tested by a licensing board or a certifying board within that time frame.

3. An osteopathic physician is requesting a reinstatement of a license following a career interruption.

4. A tenured osteopathic physician needs to demonstrate basic osteopathic medical competence.

COMVEX is a computer-delivered examination administered at professional testing centers nationwide, with at least one testing location in each of the 50 states. The examination uses the same basic design features of the COMLEX-USA examinations and employs the same "Dimensions" to assess the candidate. The examination contains 400 test items using objective type questions such as multiple choice, single best answer and matching test items.

COMVEX has been developed by the NBOME and is available to candidates through the individual state licensing boards. COMVEX provides the state medical licensing boards with a clear evaluation of a candidate's knowledge of current osteopathic medical practice.

Eligibility for the examination is solely determined by the licensing jurisdiction, and scores are ordinarily returned to the licensing authority within two to three weeks of the examination date. Licensing boards interested in utilizing this examination may contact the NBOME.

Contact Information

NBOME Client Services

(866) 479-6828 Toll-free
7 am – 7 pm (Eastern), Monday – Friday

NBOME Corporate Offices and Conference Center

National Board of Osteopathic Medical Examiners, Inc
8765 West Higgins Road, Suite 200
Chicago, IL 60631-4174
(773) 714-0622 or (877) 714-0622 (toll-free)
(773) 714-0631 Fax
www.nbome.org

NBOME Executive Offices and National Center for Clinical Skills Testing (NCCST)

101 West Elm Street
NCCST, Suite 150
Executive Offices, Suite 230
Conshohocken, PA 19428

NCCST Hours: 8 am – 4:30 pm (Eastern),
Monday – Friday
(866) NBOME 97 (866 626-6397) (toll-free)
NCCST Emergency Line with recorded COMLEX-USA
Level 2-Performance Evaluation status message:
(610) 825-4240

Chapter 4

Information for International Medical Graduates

Educational Commission for Foreign Medical Graduates (ECFMG®)

William C. Kelly, MS
Acting Vice President for Operations
Educational Commission for Foreign Medical Graduates
Philadelphia, Pennsylvania

The Educational Commission for Foreign Medical Graduates (ECFMG®), through its program of certification, assesses whether international medical graduates (IMGs) are ready to enter residency or fellowship programs in the United States that are accredited by the Accreditation Council for Graduate Medical Education (ACGME). ECFMG Certification is a requirement for IMGs who wish to enter such programs.

ECFMG Certification assures directors of ACGME-accredited residency and fellowship programs, and the people of the United States, that IMGs have met minimum standards of eligibility to enter such programs. ECFMG Certification does not, however, guarantee that these graduates will be accepted into programs; the number of applicants each year exceeds the number of available positions.

ECFMG Certification is also one of the eligibility requirements for IMGs to take Step 3 of the three-step United States Medical Licensing Examination® (USMLE®). Medical licensing authorities in the United States require that IMGs be certified by ECFMG, among other requirements, to obtain an unrestricted license to practice medicine.

The ECFMG and its organizational members define an IMG as a physician who received his/her basic medical degree or qualification from a medical school located outside the United States and Canada. Citizens of the United States who have completed their medical education in schools outside the United States and Canada are considered IMGs; non-US citizens who have graduated from medical schools in the United States and Canada are not considered IMGs.

To be eligible for ECFMG Certification, the physician's medical school and graduation year must be listed in the *International Medical Education Directory* (*IMED*) of the Foundation for Advancement of International Medical Education and Research (FAIMER®). *IMED* contains information supplied by countries about their medical schools. FAIMER is not an accrediting agency. *IMED* is available on the FAIMER website at www.faimer.org.

Important Note: FAIMER's *IMED* will merge with the *Avicenna Directory* of the World Federation for Medical Education (WFME). This merger will result in a new, combined directory called the *World Directory of Medical Schools.* The *World Directory* is expected to become available in 2014. During the transition to the *World Directory*, *IMED* and the *Avicenna Directory* will remain open to ensure continuity of service. *IMED* and the *Avicenna Directory* will close when the *World Directory* is fully operational. International medical students and graduates should monitor the ECFMG website for detailed information.

Application for ECFMG Certification

IMGs must submit an application for ECFMG Certification before they can apply to ECFMG for examination. The application for ECFMG Certification consists of questions that require applicants to confirm their identity, contact information, and graduation from or enrollment in a medical school that is listed in *IMED*. As part of the application, IMGs must also confirm their understanding of the purpose of ECFMG Certification and release certain legal claims.

ECFMG Examination Requirements

The examination requirements for ECFMG Certification include passing Step 1 and Step 2 of the USMLE. The Step 2 exam has two separately administered components, the Clinical Knowledge (CK) component and the Clinical Skills (CS) component.

---

*This policy applies only to ECFMG Certification. Use of the former FLEX Components or the former NBME Parts to fulfill eligibility requirements for Step 3 is no longer accepted. Applicants taking the Steps for the purpose of licensure should refer to *Formerly Administered Examinations* in the USMLE *Bulletin of Information*. Applicants should also contact the Federation of State Medical Boards (FSMB) for general information and the medical licensing authority of the jurisdiction where they plan to apply for licensure for definitive information on licensure requirements. Additionally, although the ECFMG Examination and FLEX, if taken prior to June 1985, satisfy the medical science examination requirement for ECFMG Certification, they have not been recognized by the US Secretary of Health and Human Services as meeting the medical science examination requirement to obtain a visa to enter the United States (see *Visas and Immigration*, page 127).

To meet the examination requirements for ECFMG Certification, applicants must:

1. Satisfy the Medical Science Examination Requirement. Step 1 and Step 2 CK of the USMLE are the exams currently administered that satisfy this requirement. There are time limits for completing these examinations for ECFMG Certification. See *Time Limit for Completing Examination Requirements,* below.

Former Examinations Accepted for ECFMG Certification: The ECFMG also accepts a passing performance on the following *former* examinations to satisfy the medical science examination requirement for ECFMG Certification: ECFMG Examination, Visa Qualifying Examination (VQE), Foreign Medical Graduate Examination in the Medical Sciences (FMGEMS), and Part I and Part II Examinations of the National Board of Medical Examiners® (NBME®). Additionally, the ECFMG accepts a score of 75 or higher on each of the 3 days of a single administration of the former Federation Licensing Examination (FLEX), if taken prior to June 1985, to satisfy this requirement.

Combinations of examinations are also acceptable. Specifically, applicants who have passed only part of the former VQE, FMGEMS, or the NBME Part I or Part II may combine a passing performance on the basic medical science component of one of these examinations or USMLE Step 1 with a passing performance on the clinical science component of one of the other examinations or USMLE Step 2 CK, provided that the components are passed within the period specified for the examination program.*

2. Satisfy the Clinical Skills Requirement. Step 2 CS of the USMLE is the exam currently administered that satisfies the clinical skills requirement for ECFMG Certification. There are time limits for completing this examination for ECFMG Certification. See *Time Limit for Completing Examination Requirements,* below.

Former Examinations Accepted for ECFMG Certification: Applicants who have *both* passed the former ECFMG Clinical Skills Assessment (CSA®) *and* achieved a score acceptable to ECFMG on an English language proficiency test (such as the Test of English as a Foreign Language™ [TOEFL®] or the former ECFMG English Test) can use these passing performances to satisfy this requirement.

Time Limit for Completing Examination Requirements*

ECFMG policy requires that applicants pass those USMLE Steps and Step Components required for ECFMG Certification within a seven-year period. This means that once an applicant passes a USMLE Step or Step Component, the applicant will have seven years to pass the other USMLE Step(s) or Step Component(s) required for ECFMG Certification. This seven-year period begins on the exam date for the first Step or Step Component passed and ends *exactly seven years from that exam date.* If an applicant does not pass all required USMLE Steps and Step Components within a maximum of seven years, the applicant's earliest USMLE passing performance will no longer be valid for ECFMG Certification.

There are exceptions to this policy:

- This seven-year limit does not apply to the former ECFMG CSA because the CSA was not a USMLE Step or Step Component. Applicants who satisfied the clinical skills requirement for ECFMG Certification by passing the CSA are required to pass only Step 1 and Step 2 CK within a seven-year period for ECFMG Certification. For these individuals, the seven-year period begins on the exam date for the first USMLE Step or Step Component passed, regardless of when the CSA was passed.

- If an applicant's earliest USMLE passing performance that is valid for ECFMG Certification took place before June 14, 2004, the applicant is required to pass only Step 1 and Step 2 CK within a seven-year period for ECFMG Certification; if required for ECFMG Certification, Step 2 CS can be passed outside the seven-year period.

If an applicant has passed a Step or Step Component but this passing performance is no longer valid for ECFMG Certification, the applicant may request an exception to retake the previously passed exam that is no longer valid.

* These policies apply only to ECFMG Certification. The USMLE program recommends to state medical licensing authorities that they require applicants to pass the full USMLE sequence (including Step 3, which is not required for ECFMG Certification) within a seven-year period. Refer to *Number of Attempts Allowed to Complete All Steps and Time Limits* and *Retakes* in the USMLE *Bulletin of Information.* Applicants should also contact the FSMB for general information and the medical licensing authority of the jurisdiction where they plan to apply for licensure for definitive information, since licensure requirements vary among jurisdictions.

Medical Education Credential Requirements

The physician's medical school and graduation year must be listed in the *International Medical Education Directory* (*IMED*), available from the ECFMG website.

IMGs must have been awarded credit for at least four credit years (academic years for which credit has been given toward completion of the medical curriculum) by a medical school listed in *IMED*. There are restrictions on credits transferred to the medical school that awards an applicant's medical degree that can be used to meet this requirement.

Important Note: See page 122.

IMGs must document the completion of all requirements for, and receipt of, the final medical diploma. ECFMG verifies every applicant's final medical diploma with the appropriate officials of the medical school that issued the diploma and requests the medical school to provide the applicant's final medical school transcript. Verification by ECFMG with the issuing school may also be required for transcripts that are submitted to document transferred credits. An applicant's credentials are not considered complete until ECFMG receives and accepts verification of the medical diploma, final medical school transcript, and, if required, transfer credit transcript(s) directly from the issuing school(s).

Standard ECFMG Certificate

IMGs who wish to enter accredited GME programs in the United States must be certified by ECFMG.

The ECFMG issues the Standard ECFMG Certificate to applicants who meet all certification requirements. Applicants must also pay any outstanding charges on their ECFMG financial accounts before certificates are issued. Standard ECFMG Certificates are sent approximately two weeks after all these requirements have been met.

The Standard ECFMG Certificate includes:

- The name of the applicant
- The applicant's USMLE/ECFMG Identification Number
- The dates that examination requirements were met
- The date that the certificate was issued

Important Note: Prior to June 14, 2004, passing performances on an English language proficiency test and the ECFMG Clinical Skills Assessment (CSA) were requirements for ECFMG Certification. Passing performances on these exams were subject to expiration for the purpose of entering US GME programs; Standard ECFMG Certificates based on these exams may list "valid through" dates, the dates through which the passing performances are valid for this purpose. Effective June 14, 2004, some of these examinations are no longer subject to expiration, regardless of whether a "valid through" date is listed on the Standard ECFMG Certificate. See *Validity of Examinations for Entry into GME*, below.

Validity of Examinations for Entry into GME

Clinical Skills Examinations

For applicants who satisfy the clinical skills requirement by passing Step 2 CS, this passing performance is not subject to expiration for the purpose of entering US GME programs.

For applicants who satisfied the clinical skills requirement for ECFMG Certification by passing the former ECFMG CSA and an English language proficiency test, passing performance on the CSA may be subject to expiration for the purpose of entering GME programs, as described below.

- Passing performances on **CSA administrations that took place on or after June 14, 2001**, are not subject to expiration for the purpose of entering GME programs. Applicants who are certified by ECFMG and whose Standard ECFMG Certificate lists a "valid through" date for an administration of the CSA that took place on or after June 14, 2001, may request a permanent validation sticker to be affixed to the certificate. Applicants can request the sticker online by accessing the On-line Applicant Status and Information System (OASIS) on the ECFMG website.

- Passing performances on **CSA administrations that took place before June 14, 2001**, are valid for 3 years from the date passed for the purpose of entering GME programs. The date through which passing performance on the CSA remains valid for entry into GME (the CSA "valid through" date) will be listed on the applicant's Standard ECFMG Certificate. If the applicant entered a

program before expiration of the "valid through" date, the applicant may request permanent validation. This means that the CSA date is no longer subject to expiration. To request permanent validation, the applicant and an authorized official of the training institution must complete a *Request for Permanent Validation* (Form 246), available on the ECFMG website. On receipt of this form, ECFMG will provide a permanent validation sticker to be affixed to the certificate. If an applicant who passed CSA before June 14, 2001, did not enter a GME program within 3 years of the CSA pass date, the applicant's CSA passing performance has expired for the purpose of entering GME. Before entering a program, these applicants must pass Step 2 CS. Passing performance on Step 2 CS does not expire for the purpose of entry into GME.

English Examinations

Passing performances on the English language proficiency test formerly required by ECFMG (such as the TOEFL exam or the former ECFMG English Test) are not subject to expiration for the purpose of entering GME programs, regardless of the date passed. Applicants who are certified by ECFMG and whose Standard ECFMG Certificate lists a "valid through" date for an English language proficiency test may request a permanent validation sticker to be affixed to the certificate. Applicants can request the sticker online by accessing OASIS on the ECFMG website.

Important Note: The preceding discussion of validity and expiration of examinations, and the "valid through" and "valid indefinitely" designations on the Standard ECFMG Certificate (if applicable), are relevant *only* for the purpose of entry into US GME programs. They do *not* pertain to eligibility for USMLE Step 3 or to any time limits imposed by medical licensing authorities or other entities for the completion of all USMLE Steps.

Step 1 and Step 2 of the USMLE

The USMLE is a three-step examination for medical licensure in the United States that provides a common system to evaluate applicants for medical licensure. The USMLE is sponsored by the FSMB and the NBME. The USMLE is governed by a committee consisting of representatives of the FSMB, NBME, ECFMG, and the American public. The USMLE Steps 1, 2, and 3 replaced FLEX and the NBME Parts I, II, and III.

Table 35

Examinee Performance for International Medical Graduates/Students Taking
USMLE Step 1 and Step 2 (CK and CS) Examinations

	USMLE Step 1 January 1, 2012 - December 31, 2012			USMLE Step 2 CK July 1, 2011 - June 30, 2012			USMLE Step 2 CS July 1, 2011 - May 19, 2012		
	Number of Administrations	Number Passing	Percent Passing	Number of Administrations	Number Passing	Percent Passing	Number of Administrations	Number Passing	Percent Passing
Total	**18,430**	**12,448**	**68**	**14,103**	**11,269**	**80**	**13,787**	**10,668**	**77**
First Takers	14,167	10,741	76	11,912	10,088	85	11,518	9,184	80
Repeaters	4,263	1,707	40	2,191	1,181	54	2,269	1,484	65
US Citizens	**5,659**	**3,654**	**65**	**4,005**	**3,100**	**77**	**3,831**	**3,189**	**83**
First Takers	3,983	3,059	77	3,151	2,641	84	3,343	2,864	86
Repeaters	1,676	595	36	854	459	54	488	325	67
Foreign Citizens	**12,771**	**8,794**	**69**	**10,098**	**8,169**	**81**	**9,956**	**7,479**	**75**
First Takers	10,184	7,682	75	8,761	7,447	85	8,175	6,320	77
Repeaters	2,587	1,112	43	1,337	722	54	1,781	1,159	65

Notes: Step 1 first takers are those examinees with no prior Step 1 and no prior NBME Part I examinations.

Step 2 CK first takers are those examinees with no prior Step 2 CK and no prior NBME Part II examinations.

Step 2 CS first takers are those examinees with no prior Step 2 CS and no prior ECFMG CSA examinations.

Administrations include those with results of Pass, Fail, Incomplete, Indeterminate, and Withheld.

The data for repeaters represent examinations given, not number of examinees.

Citizenship is as of the time of entrance into medical school.

Source: ECFMG database. Data current as of February 7, 2013, and include administrations for which results were available as of February 6, 2013.

The ECFMG verifies whether international medical students/graduates are eligible to take USMLE Step 1 and Step 2 and registers eligible applicants to take these exams. The NBME performs these functions for students/graduates of US and Canadian medical schools/programs that are accredited by the Liaison Committee on Medical Education or the American Osteopathic Association.

USMLE Step 1 and Step 2 CK are multiple-choice examinations that are administered by computer. Prometric™ provides scheduling and test centers for Step 1 and Step 2 CK. These exams are delivered throughout the year at Prometric test centers worldwide.

Step 2 CS uses standardized patients in simulated clinical encounters to evaluate clinical and communication skills. Step 2 CS is administered throughout the year at test centers in Atlanta, Chicago, Houston, Los Angeles, and Philadelphia.

Table 35 shows the performance of IMGs for recent administrations of Step 1 and Step 2 (CK and CS).

Standard ECFMG Certificates Issued in 2012

During 2012, ECFMG issued 9,642 Standard ECFMG Certificates. Table 36 shows the distribution of recipients of Standard ECFMG Certificates by country of medical school and by country of citizenship. In 2012, medical schools in India and Grenada had the largest number of recipients: 1,438 (14.9%) and 855 (8.9%), respectively.

Based upon country of citizenship, citizens of the United States formed the largest group of recipients. Of the certificates issued in 2012, 2,826 (29.3%) were to US citizens. Citizens of India were the second largest group with 1,528 (15.8%) recipients.

Table 36

Standard ECFMG Certificates Issued in 2012: Distribution of Recipients by Country of Medical School and Citizenship

Country	Country of Medical School		Country of Citizenship	
	Number	%	Number	%
Antigua and Barbuda	298	3.1	4	<0.1
Australia	77	0.8	47	0.5
Bangladesh	53	0.5	57	0.6
Brazil	62	0.6	60	0.6
Canada	0	0.0	669	6.9
Cayman Islands	185	1.9	0	0.0
China	245	2.5	235	2.4
Colombia	85	0.9	85	0.9
Cuba	65	0.7	46	0.5
Dominica	785	8.1	2	<0.1
Dominican Republic	134	1.4	59	0.6
Egypt	209	2.2	191	2.0
Germany	102	1.1	88	0.9
Grenada	855	8.9	7	0.1
India	1,438	14.9	1,528	15.8
Iran	184	1.9	195	2.0
Iraq	143	1.5	160	1.7
Ireland	144	1.5	63	0.7
Israel	209	2.2	115	1.2
Japan	59	0.6	58	0.6
Jordan	153	1.6	132	1.4
Lebanon	120	1.2	116	1.2
Mexico	201	2.1	79	0.8
Myanmar	74	0.8	78	0.8
Nepal	66	0.7	69	0.7
Nigeria	180	1.9	223	2.3
Pakistan	544	5.6	504	5.2
Peru	62	0.6	62	0.6
Philippines	149	1.5	121	1.3
Poland	137	1.4	15	0.2
Russia	82	0.9	46	0.5
Saba	166	1.7	0	0.0

Citizenship is as of the time of entrance into medical school.
Percentages may not equal 100% due to rounding.
Data current as of January 10, 2013.

Country	Country of Medical School		Country of Citizenship	
	Number	%	Number	%
Saint Kitts and Nevis	209	2.2	2	<0.1
Saudi Arabia	148	1.5	142	1.5
Sint Eustatius	85	0.9	0	0.0
Sint Maarten	252	2.6	0	0.0
South Korea	84	0.9	91	0.9
Sudan	59	0.6	59	0.6
Syria	110	1.1	121	1.3
United Kingdom	91	0.9	97	1.0
United States	0	0.0	2,826	29.3
Venezuela	71	0.7	71	0.7
Countries with fewer than 50 recipients	1,267	13.1	1,119	11.6
Total	9,642	100.0	9,642	99.9

Electronic Residency Application Service (ERAS®)

The Association of American Medical Colleges (AAMC) developed the Electronic Residency Application Service (ERAS®) to allow Web-based applications to US residency programs. ECFMG serves as the designated Dean's office for all IMGs who use ERAS. In this role, ECFMG assists these individuals with the ERAS application process for first- and second-year residency positions. This includes providing applicant support as well as processing and transmitting applicants' supporting documents, reports of ECFMG certification status, and, if requested by the applicant, USMLE transcripts to the ERAS PostOffice, where they are available for downloading by residency programs to which applicants have applied.

Most US GME programs participate in ERAS. Participating programs require applicants to apply for positions using ERAS.

For a list of specialties and programs participating in ERAS for residency programs that begin in 2014, visit http://services.aamc.org/eras/erasstats/par/.

Additional specialties may use ERAS for residency programs that begin in 2015. Applicants should contact residency program directors for specific requirements and deadlines.

More than 21,000 IMGs used ERAS for the academic year commencing in 2013. For these applicants, ERAS Support Services at ECFMG uploaded more than 180,000 documents to the ERAS PostOffice.

For information, visit the ECFMG website at www.ecfmg.org/eras. Applicants may also contact:

ERAS Support Services at
ECFMG
3624 Market St
Philadelphia, PA 19104-2685
Email: eras-support@ecfmg.org
(215) 966-3520

Visas and Immigration

In addition to the specific credential requirements for IMGs who seek to train or practice medicine in the United States, the US government has stipulated certain visa and immigration requirements for those who are foreign national physicians.

Visa and immigration information for foreign national physicians can be found on the following websites:

* ECFMG Exchange Visitor Sponsorship Program
  www.ecfmg.org/evsp

* US Embassies or Consulates of the US Department of State (DOS)
  www.usembassy.gov

* Immigration Bureaus of the US Department of Homeland Security (DHS)
  www.dhs.gov

Exchange Visitor Sponsorship Program

The ECFMG is designated by the United States Department of State (DOS) to serve as the visa sponsor for all foreign national physicians who participate in graduate medical education (GME) or training as J-1 Exchange Visitor physicians. The objectives of this program are to enhance international exchange in the field of medicine and to promote mutual understanding between the people of the United States and other countries through the interchange of persons, knowledge, and skills.

The ECFMG administers its J-1 program in accordance with the Federal Regulations 22 CFR Part 62 and a Memorandum of Understanding between the ECFMG and the DOS. The ECFMG is responsible for ensuring that all J-1 Exchange Visitor physicians and host institutions meet the federal requirements for participation.

IMGs seeking ECFMG J-1 visa sponsorship to enroll in GME programs must meet the following basic requirements:

* Have passed USMLE Step 1, Step 2 CK, and Step 2 CS (Other formerly administered NBME/ECFMG exams may be recognized in some cases.).

* Hold a Standard ECFMG Certificate. (Foreign national physicians who are graduates of US or Canadian Liaison Committee on Medical Education [LCME]-accredited medical school programs or US American Osteopathic Association [AOA]-accredited medical schools are not required to be ECFMG-certified.).

* Hold a contract or an official letter of offer for a position in an approved GME or training program.

* Provide a statement of need from the Ministry of Health of the country of nationality or most recent legal permanent residence. This statement must provide written assurance that the country needs specialists in the area in which the Exchange Visitor will receive training. It also serves to confirm the physician's commitment to return to that country upon completion of training in the United States.

The duration of stay for a J-1 Exchange Visitor physician is limited to the time typically required to complete the advanced medical education program. This refers to the specialty and subspecialty certification requirements published by the American Board of Medical Specialties (ABMS). Participation is further limited to seven years and is reserved for those progressing in approved training programs.

Foreign national physicians who seek participation in nonclinical programs primarily involved with observation, consultation, teaching, or research may, in limited cases, be eligible for ECFMG sponsorship as J-1 *research scholars*. ECFMG Certification is not required for physicians spon-

Table 37

Exchange Visitor Sponsorship Program for Physicians: Number of J-1 Physicians in Graduate Medical Education or Training Programs in the United States, 2011-2012 Academic Year

Specialty	Count
Allergy and Immunology	7
Anesthesiology	129
Colon and Rectal Surgery	11
Dermatology	17
Emergency Medicine	74
Family Medicine	643
General Preventive Medicine, Occupational Medicine, Aerospace Medicine, and Public Health	8
Hospice and Palliative Medicine	14
Internal Medicine	3,853
Internal Medicine/Emergency Medicine	1
Internal Medicine/Pediatrics	47
Internal Medicine/Preventive Medicine	4
Internal Medicine/Psychiatry	13
Medical Genetics	16
Medical Genetics and Pathology	5
Neurological Surgery	83
Neurology	375
Nuclear Medicine	10
Obstetrics and Gynecology	150
Ophthalmology	42
Orthopaedic Surgery	95
Otolaryngology	37
Pain Medicine	6
Pathology-Anatomic and Clinical	170
Pediatrics	913
Pediatrics/Emergency Medicine	1
Pediatrics/Medical Genetics	3
Pediatrics/Psychiatry/Child and Adolescent Psychiatry	2
Physical Medicine and Rehabilitation	30
Plastic Surgery (including integrated)	33
Psychiatry	428
Psychiatry/Family Medicine	1
Radiation Oncology	8
Radiology-Diagnostic	116
Sleep Medicine	16
Surgery-General	564
Thoracic Surgery	60
Transitional Year	20
Urology	45
Vascular Surgery-Integrated	2
Total:	**8,052**

sored as J-1 research scholars. The host institution is responsible for providing ECFMG with a detailed description of the non-clinical activities and official confirmation of *no patient or incidental patient contact*. The maximum duration of stay for approved activity as a J-1 research scholar is five years.

Once a foreign national physician is approved for J-1 sponsorship, the ECFMG creates an electronic record for the physician in the Student and Exchange Visitor Information System (SEVIS) and issues Form DS-2019, "Certificate of Eligibility for Exchange Visitor (J-1) Status." Through an interagency partnership between the DOS and the DHS, SEVIS tracks and monitors the activities of all J, F, and M visa holders (22 CFR §62.70(a)(6)). The foreign national physician with an active SEVIS record and an ECFMG-issued Form DS-2019 may apply for J-1 visa and/or visa status from agencies of the US government.

Table 37 shows that the ECFMG sponsored 8,052 J-1 Exchange Visitor physicians in US GME or training programs for the 2011-2012 academic year. The ECFMG sponsored 5,493 J-1 physicians in clinical residency (specialty) programs and 2,519 in clinical fellowships (subspecialty training) in 2011-2012. A total of 40 physicians were sponsored for non-clinical activities as J-1 research scholars. Foreign nationals from India, Canada, and Pakistan represented approximately 45% of ECFMG sponsored J-1 physicians for this period.

For application materials and specific information on ECFMG sponsorship, applicants should visit the ECFMG website at www.ecfmg.org/evsp. Applicants may also contact:

ECFMG
Exchange Visitor Sponsorship Program
3624 Market St
Philadelphia, PA 19104-2685
(215) 823-2121
(215) 386-9766 Fax

Certification Verification Service (CVS)

The ECFMG's Certification Verification Service provides primary-source confirmation of the ECFMG certification status of IMGs. The Joint Commission, the organization that evaluates and accredits US health care organizations and programs, has determined that direct verification with

ECFMG of a physician's certification status satisfies The Joint Commission's requirement for primary-source verification of medical school completion for IMGs.

The ECFMG will confirm an applicant's certification status when a request is received from a US medical licensing authority, residency program director, hospital, or other organization that, in the judgment of ECFMG, has a legitimate interest in such information. For status reports sent to medical licensing authorities, the request can also be made by the applicant. Requesting organizations must normally secure and retain the applicant's signed authorization to obtain certification information. Please note that there may be a fee for this service.

Requests for confirmation must contain the applicant's name, date of birth, and USMLE/ECFMG Identification Number, as well as the name and address of the organization to which the confirmation should be sent. Confirmations are sent to the requesting organization within approximately two weeks. Confirmations are not sent to applicants directly.

For individuals who apply to residency programs through ERAS, the ECFMG automatically sends an electronic ECFMG status report to the ERAS PostOffice, where it can be accessed by the residency programs to which the individual applies.

If an applicant's ECFMG certification status changes during the ERAS application season, the ECFMG will automatically send an updated status report to the ERAS PostOffice.

To obtain information, request form(s), or make an online request, refer to the ECFMG website at www.ecfmg.org/cvs or contact:

ECFMG
CVS Department
PO Box 13679
Philadelphia PA 19101-3679
(215) 386-5900

ECFMG Certificate Holders Office (ECHO)

The ECFMG Certificate Holders Office (ECHO) provides support and service to physicians who are certified by ECFMG, or are about to be certified, as they plan their careers. Each month, ECHO provides free resources that connect these physicians with the expertise of ECFMG and others on a variety of topics. ECHO also strives to create a dialogue with ECFMG-certified physicians by attending meetings, conducting surveys, and soliciting feedback. *ECHO News,* the program's free monthly e-newsletter, highlights ECHO's latest offerings and includes important news and opportunities from ECFMG and other organizations.

For more information or to access ECHO's resources, visit the ECHO section of the ECFMG website at www.ecfmg.org/echo. Physicians may also contact:

ECFMG/ECHO
3624 Market St
Philadelphia, PA 19104-2685
(215) 386-5900
Email: echo@ecfmg.org

Contact Information

Interested individuals can access the ECFMG *Information Booklet* and apply online for USMLE Step 1 and Step 2 by visiting the ECFMG website at www.ecfmg.org.

The ECFMG website also provides access to important updates, ECFMG's online services, and more than 50 ECFMG publications and forms.

Individuals who do not have access to the Internet may contact the ECFMG for assistance.

ECFMG
3624 Market St
Philadelphia, PA 19104-2685
(215) 386-5900
(215) 386-9196 Fax
Email: info@ecfmg.org
www.ecfmg.org

Immigration Overview for International Medical Graduates

Robert D. Aronson, Managing Attorney
Aronson & Associates, PA, Minneapolis, Minnesota

This article outlines current immigration laws and policies that affect the physician community. This particular legal area has become increasingly important owing to the emerging shortage of physicians in the workforce and the maldistribution patterns largely affecting rural and inner city communities. In addition, current health care reforms promise to impose additional demands as well as mandates calling for expanded health care coverage that will add pressure to an already overstretched physician workforce. With insufficient numbers of domestic physicians to satisfy these emerging needs, several new initiatives are under way of particular relevance to the immigration of international medical graduates (IMGs).

This article deals with three broad areas of relevance to the immigration of IMGs:

1. Temporary, nonimmigrant visa options for foreign physicians
2. The J-1 waiver process for physicians
3. Options in order to qualify for permanent residence

Immigration Law Overview

All non-citizens enter the United States in one of two broad immigration categories—either under a temporary, nonimmigrant visa or as a permanent resident. There are comparative advantages to each of these categories. For temporary, nonimmigrant visa classifications, it is usually possible to gain this type of immigration coverage in a relatively short time. The two most commonly used temporary, nonimmigrant classifications by IMGs are the J-1 Exchange Visitor program (covering medical training activities) and the H-1B Temporary Worker classification (which could cover either medical training or employment positions). Both these classifications, however, limit a physician's duration of residence in the United States and impose strict limitations on the range of employment authorization. In contrast, permanent residence provides a foreign national with both an unlimited duration of residence and full, unrestricted employment authorization, although the processing time is much greater.

Temporary, Nonimmigrant Classifications

Most IMGs in graduate medical education (GME) programs arrive under the J-1 Exchange Visitor program, although the H-1B Temporary Worker category is a possible alternative.

The J-1 program is administered by the Educational Commission for Foreign Medical Graduates (ECFMG), working under the authorization of the US Department of State. J-1 training programs are intended to provide a broad range of foreign nationals with educational, employment, and training opportunities in the United States. For the past 30 years, the J-1 Exchange Visitor Program has been the preferred visa classification for IMGs doing their medical training in the United States.

To become eligible to enroll in GME, an IMG needs to establish that his/her medical competency is equivalent to that of a US physician. This professional equivalency is established through the issuance of ECFMG certification. To gain an ECFMG Certificate, an IMG needs to fulfill the following requirements:

1. Pass stipulated examinations—currently, the US Medical Licensing Examination (USMLE), Steps 1 and 2 Clinical Knowledge and Clinical Skills—to establish medical competence
2. Pass the ECFMG English language examination to establish English language competence
3. Possess an MD degree from a foreign medical school listed in the *International Medical Education Directory* of the Foundation for Advancement of International Medical Education and Research (FAIMER®)

All J-1 trainees must receive ECFMG certification, except for graduates of Canadian medical schools, who are exempt from this requirement because Canadian medical education and training are accredited under US standards (or considered equivalent to US education/training).

Upon entry into the United States, an IMG is authorized to pursue a clinical GME program for up to seven years to achieve stipulated training objectives. In some instances, it is possible to obtain extensions beyond this seven-year limit, but only upon a showing of extenuating circumstances in which the additional training will serve the vital needs of the home country. Each year, the GME program, in conjunction with the IMG, needs to file an extension application with the ECFMG.

Without exception, all J-1 physicians engaged in clinical training activities are subject to a mandatory two-year home residence obligation, regardless of country of citizenship or last permanent residence. *This two-year home residence requirement applies to every physician who enters the United States under an ECFMG-sponsored J-1 clinical training program. To ultimately qualify for permanent residence and/or an H-1B visa, an IMG must either return to his/her home country for a two-year period or obtain a waiver of this two-year obligation.*

J-1 Waiver Strategies

As noted above, all ECFMG-sponsored J-1 physicians—regardless of country of citizenship—are subject to an obligation to return to their home country for a mandatory two-year period. Unless and until this two-year home residence is either fulfilled (i.e., by returning specifically to the home country) or waived (i.e., eliminated), a physician under law is barred from obtaining an H-1B visa and/or permanent resident status. Therefore, it is critically important for long-term immigration prospects for a J-1 physician to obtain a waiver of the two-year home residence requirement. US laws do contain various provisions enabling J-1 physicians to obtain such waivers.

A waiver of this obligation is available only on the basis of at least one the following three grounds:

- If the J-1 physician will suffer from persecution in his/her home country or country of last permanent residence

- If fulfillment of the obligation will subject a US citizen spouse or child to exceptional hardship

- Based upon a recommendation issued by a government agency interested in the physician's continued residence/employment in the United States

Without question, the vast majority of J-1 physicians who receive waivers do so through recommendations issued by government agencies. Generally speaking, such waivers fall within the following three basic patterns:

- Employment by a federal agency, such as the Department of Veterans Affairs

- Recognition of outstanding academic and research achievements, as determined by the Department of Health and Human Services

- Service to medically underserved patient populations, so as to allow either a state department of health or a federal agency to recommend a waiver as a matter of public interest

Statistically, the vast majority of J-1 physicians obtain waivers through a program known as the Conrad State 30 program, which essentially empowers each state to recommend waivers for up to 30 physicians per fiscal year. These waivers specifically require the physician to practice medicine (either primary care or specialty) in a designated medically underserved location.

Most states now recommend waivers for medical specialists as well as primary care practitioners. Each state is limited to 30 waivers/year, although states now have the option of using up to 10 waivers/year to facilitate placements in non-medically underserved areas. The remaining balance can only be used for placements in designated medically underserved areas—i.e., Health Professional Shortage Areas (HPSAs) or Medically Underserved Areas/Populations (MUA/Ps). In any case, the key point is to show that the physician will be serving the needs of the indigent and medically underserved—i.e., patient populations that disproportionately face barriers in their access to physicians. A physician receiving a J-1 waiver needs to practice medicine in the community for at least three years, working specifically in H-1B status. Any premature departure from the community could result in a loss of the waiver as well as immigration status.

In addition, various federal agencies also maintain J-1 waiver programs, including the Department of Health and Human Services, Delta Regional Agency, and Appalachian Regional Commission. Most federal agencies, however, limit their waiver programs to primary care physicians, even though the law was liberalized in December 2004 to cover medical specialists. The federal agencies do not, though, have any quota limitation on the number of waivers that they can recommend.

H1-B Temporary Worker

Instead of taking part in the J-1 Exchange Visitor program with its home residence obligation, some foreign physicians are able to enter the United States for GME purposes under the H-1B Temporary Worker provisions. This visa classification enables a foreign national to enter the United States for professional-level employment for up to six years. In most instances, H-1B coverage can be obtained within approximately 60-90 days, although there are provisions for expediting the processing of an immigration case. The H-1B quota of 65,000 is normally exhausted early on in the federal fiscal year, but physicians working within universities and most university-affiliated institutions as well as J-1 physicians holding waivers are exempted from the H-1B quota.

To qualify for H-1B benefits, an IMG must meet the following four criteria:

- Possession of a full, unrestricted state medical license or the "appropriate authorization" for the position

- An MD degree or a full, unrestricted foreign license

- English language competence as established either through graduation from an accredited medical school or by holding an ECFMG Certificate

- Passage of the Federation Licensing Examination (FLEX) or its equivalents—the National Board of Medical Examiners (NBME), Parts I, II, and III, or the USMLE, Steps 1, 2, and 3

As a result of the FLEX equivalency issue, many Canadian physicians do not qualify for H-1B benefits. The standard Canadian medical credential—the Licentiate of the Medical Council of Canada (LMCC)—is widely accepted among the states for medical licensure purposes. Therefore, most Canadian physicians have traditionally not had any reason to sit for the FLEX or its equivalents. Over the course of recent years, a significant number of Canadian physicians have begun sitting for the USMLE precisely to gain H-1B eligibility as a clinical physician in the United States.

Permanent Residence Strategies

A foreign national can qualify for permanent residence in various ways, ranging from familial relationships with US citizens or permanent residents to fear of persecution that would merit refugee entitlement. In most instances, though, an IMG will need to qualify for permanent residence based upon an employment position. There are three basic pathways to permanent residence based upon employment as a physician.

Pathway One

The "normal" route to permanent residence involves a three-step process. The first and arguably most complex stage is the Labor Certification Application process. This is a procedure conducted under the auspices of the US Department of Labor to establish that the employment of a foreign national will in no manner harm the US labor market, particularly by taking a job away from a fully qualified US worker. Therefore, acting under a complex recruitment/advertisement procedure, the employer needs to show that the IMG is not simply the best-qualified applicant for the position but is the only fully qualified candidate for the specific position.

After completing the Labor Certification Application process, the employer needs to submit an Immigrant Visa Petition to the US Citizenship and Immigration Services (CIS, formerly the Immigration and Naturalization Service), establishing the complete suitability of the IMG for the position. Upon approval of this petition, the IMG is then able to actually apply for permanent residence.

Note: An IMG must possess an ECFMG Certificate. Also, an IMG cannot finalize the application for permanent residence status if he/she has an unfulfilled or unwaived J-1 two-year home residence obligation.

Pathway Two

A second pathway to employment-related permanent residence is based upon National Interest Waiver criteria. In this instance, an IMG has a streamlined, expedited pathway to permanent residence if it can be shown that the IMG will work for a five-year period in a designated medically underserved area. Under recent revisions to the law, both primary and specialty care physicians working in designated medically underserved areas can qualify for permanent residence pursuant to a National Interest Waiver. One major advantage of this filing strategy is that the IMG can basically self-sponor himself/herself rather than relying upon the employer to serve as the sponsor for immigration purposes.

Pathway Three

A third option to permanent residence is available to physicians of extraordinarily high professional capabilities, working either in clinical practice or in academic medicine. Such individuals may qualify for permanent residence under an expedited procedure established for Aliens of Extraordinary Ability and Outstanding Professors or Researchers.

Final Word

In conclusion, our immigration laws for physicians are complex, but with advance planning, it is often quite possible to attain desired immigration objectives in a time-efficient manner. Slowly but surely, our immigration laws and policies are creating some new opportunities that enable IMGs to attain immigration status based on practice in the profession, particularly if working in designated medically underserved areas. When all is said and done, we as a nation have complex and ever-expanding needs for physicians, particularly those willing to serve in isolated areas and those willing to treat minorities, ethnic populations, and the indigent. Over the years, foreign physicians have been one of the most effective physician population groups for addressing medically underserved populations, and our immigration laws have developed several meaningful and effective initiatives intended to facilitate the relocation of foreign physicians into positions of maximum benefit to various US population groups.

Robert D. Aronson is the Managing Attorney for Aronson & Associates, PA, a law firm that practices exclusively in the area of immigration and nationality law. The major area of his practice deals with immigration matters for foreign physicians and US medical institutions nationwide. He received his law degree from Indiana University and was a Fulbright Fellow at Harvard Law School and Moscow State University (Russia). Mr. Aronson has held various leadership positions on immigration matters for international physicians within the medical, legal, academic, and governmental communities. Further information is available at www.aronsonimmigration.com.

Chapter 5

Federal and National Programs and Activities

Licensure in the US Armed Forces

Department of the Air Force

Dale R. Agner, Col, USAF, MC
Chief, Clinical Quality Management Division

Kathy A. Smith, CPHQ, CPCS, CPMSM
Chief, Professional Staff Management
Air Force Medical Operations Agency/SGHQ
Office of the Surgeon General
San Antonio, Texas

The Clinical Quality Management Division of the Air Force Medical Operations Agency is responsible for oversight of clinical issues pertaining to quality improvement, licensure, credentialing and privileging, patient safety, and risk management for the Air Force Surgeon General.

Air Force licensure policy is consistent with that of the Department of Defense (DoD). Air Force Medical Service physicians (military, civil service, contract personnel, and volunteers) must possess a current, valid, and unrestricted license from an official agency of a state; the District of Columbia; or a commonwealth, territory, or possession of the United States to provide health care independently within the scope of the license. Physicians must have a medical license that meets all clinical, professional, and administrative requirements of the issuing state and be no different than that of civilian counterparts.

Personnel accessed from professional training or who complete other training and require a license must obtain such license within 1 year of the date when all required didactic and clinical requirements are met, or within 1 year of completion of graduate year one. Physicians who do not yet meet licensure requirements may practice only under a written plan of supervision by a licensed, fully qualified, independently practicing, privileged provider of same or similar specialty. The Air Force requires physicians who choose to be licensed in a state that requires more than 1 year of graduate training to first obtain a license from a state that requires only 1 year of graduate training.

Department of the Army

Howard M. Kimes, Colonel, US Army
Director, Quality Management Directorate

Janet L. Wilson, Lieutenant Colonel, US Army
Chief, Regulatory Compliance
US Army Medical Command
Fort Sam Houston, Texas

The US Army Medical Command's Quality Management Directorate is responsible for developing policy and overseeing all facets of the Army Surgeon General's Quality Assurance Program, including quality improvement, credentials review and privileging, licensure, and risk management. The Directorate serves as the conduit for issues concerning clinical standards and accreditation by The Joint Commission for US Army Medicine Worldwide.

Department of Defense physicians (military and civilian, contractors and partners) must possess a current valid, unrestricted license from an official agency of the District of Columbia or a state, commonwealth, territory, or possession of the United States to provide health care independently within the scope of their licenses. Physicians in graduate medical education (GME) programs must possess a license within 1 year from the completion of their first year of GME training. An exception exists for individuals who complete their first year of GME in a state requiring 2 or more years of GME for licensure and who are assigned with that same state. These individuals must possess a license within 1 year of completion of their second year of GME training.

Health care providers awaiting a required license may work only under the supervision of a licensed provider.

Federal regulations require physicians and other health care practitioners within the military health services system to possess a current, valid, unrestricted professional license or certification. All DON physicians (military, civilian, civilian contract, and partnership), with the exception of interns, must possess a license from a recognized, official agency of a state; the District of Columbia; or a commonwealth, territory, or possession of the United States to provide health care services independently within the scope of their license. Licenses issued by authorities allowing reduced or no fees for military personnel must meet the same licensure criteria. Health care practitioners lacking required license or certification may work only under a plan of supervision of a licensed independent practitioner of the same or a similar professional discipline. This policy supports the US Navy's goal to ensure all practitioners are available for worldwide assignment and rapid deployment.

Department of the Navy

Stazy Godlewski
Risk and Quality Management
Bureau of Medicine and Surgery
Department of the Navy
Falls Church, VA

Becky Boyrie, CPMSM
Centralized Credentials & Privileging Directorate
Jacksonville, Florida

The Clinical Operations Division within the Bureau of Medicine and Surgery, Department of the Navy (DON), is responsible for developing policy and directing the development and implementation of US Navy-wide quality management and Medical Staff Services programs to improve the quality of patient care; reduce risks to our customers, guests, and staff; advance good stewardship; and maintain accreditation by The Joint Commission of all US Navy fixed medical treatment facilities.

Federal Controlled Substances Registration

Office of Diversion Control
Drug Enforcement Administration
Washington, DC

The Controlled Substances Act of 1970 mandates that controlled substances be maintained in a "closed system of distribution" that tracks all phases of manufacturing, distribution, and dispensing. The Department of Justice, through the Drug Enforcement Administration (DEA), has the responsibility to ensure the availability of controlled substances for legitimate need while preventing their diversion into illicit markets.

The Controlled Substances Act and its implementing regulations require that any person desiring to legally manufacture, distribute, or dispense controlled substances must register with the DEA. After approval, each applicant is assigned a registration number, which must be used in every transaction involving controlled substances. Use of the DEA registration number, together with required records of transactions, allows tracking of controlled substances from the point of manufacture to the point at which they are dispensed to the patient.

As of April 20, 2009, there were 1,328,064 active DEA registrants. Practitioners account for 1,032,151of those registrants.

A physician who seeks to become registered with the DEA must submit an Application for Registration (DEA Form-224). There are several means of submitting an application.

A. Online Application Form

Application forms are available on the DEA Diversion Control Program website at www.DEAdiversion.usdoj.gov. Both the new application (DEA Form-224) and the renewal form (DEA Form-224a) may be completed online in one of the following ways:

1. Applications may be completed and submitted via DEA's "Office of Diversion Control Web Interactive Forms (ODWIF)." Physicians will need a browser that supports 128-bit encryption, and they must have their Tax ID and/or Social Security Number; State Controlled Substance Registration Information; State Medical License Information; and a credit card (American Express, Discover, Visa, or MasterCard) to complete

the transaction. This transaction takes approximately five minutes and is transmitted to DEA HQ in a secure and encrypted manner.

2. Applications may be also completed in a partially interactive form in Adobe Acrobat PDF format online, where the registrant fills in the information then prints, signs, and mails the form to the below address.

3. Blank applications may be printed from the DEA's website and then filled out manually by the registrant, signed, and mailed to the below address.

B. Paper Application Form

The form can be obtained from DEA by calling the Registration Unit at (800) 882-9539 or contacting a DEA field office with a registration assistant. The completed paper application (DEA Form-224) and the required fee must be mailed to:

Drug Enforcement Administration
Central Station
PO Box 530295
Atlanta, GA 30348-0295

Following initial processing by the Registration Unit, the application is referred to the appropriate DEA field office for completion after verification of controlled substances authority with the state. The application is approved and a certificate bearing the practitioner's DEA registration number is issued. This process normally takes from four to six weeks to complete. (Renewal applications generally are processed within four weeks.) Through the new online application, it takes approximately five days for a registration certification to be mailed. If there are no changes from the previous registration, online renewals are mailed the following day. The DEA certificate must be maintained at the registered location and must be kept available for official inspection.

The DEA also registers practitioners who have been granted limited authority by the appropriate state licensing agency to handle controlled substances. These individuals are registered as mid-level practitioners (MLPs). As of April 20, 2009, 161,833 mid-level practitioners, including nurse practitioners, certified nurse-midwives, physician assistants, and optometrists, were registered with DEA.

The fee for both new and renewal applications for all practitioners is currently $551 for a 3-year period. An exemption from payment of the application fee is provided to federal, state, or local government registrants. On August 29, 2006, the DEA published a Final Rule in the *Federal Register* (Volume 71, Number 167, pages 51105-51115) that increased the fee to $551 for a 3-year period. The fee schedule is effective for all new and renewal applications postmarked on or after November 1, 2006.

A renewal application, DEA Form 224a, is mailed to each registrant approximately 60 days prior to the expiration date. Registrants who do not receive the form within 45 days prior to the expiration of their registration should contact a DEA office with a registration assistant to request a renewal application. DEA registrations are issued for controlled substances activities at specific locations. If a physician has more than one office where controlled substances will be stored, a separate registration must be obtained for each location. If the activities at a secondary location are limited to prescribing within the same state, then separate registration is not required.

The following registration information is provided:

1. When submitting a new or renewal application, or requesting a modification of a registration, allow 4 weeks for processing; DEA receives more than 35,000 requests per month.

2. One of the primary criteria for issuing a DEA registration is that the applicant be authorized by the state in which he or she will practice. Make sure that all applications for state licensing have been completed before submitting your application for DEA registration. The same applies for registrants relocating from one state to another.

3. Keep track of the expiration date of your DEA registration. Renewal notices are mailed to registrants approximately 60 days prior to expiration. If you do not receive a renewal application within 45 days prior to the expiration of your registration, call (800) 882-9539. If a registration expires, the registrant is no longer authorized to handle controlled substances. Until the registration is renewed and a new certificate of registration is issued, use of the registration is a violation of the law.

4. As noted earlier, DEA registrations are issued for controlled substances activities at a specific location. Federal regulations require that DEA be notified in advance of any change of address. Additionally, the registration address cannot be a post office box. It must be the physical location where the controlled substance activities occur.

5. The Registration Unit can be contacted toll-free at (800) 882-9539. Whenever contacting the DEA regarding an existing registration, provide the DEA registration number.

The DEA's registration program plays an integral role in efforts to prevent the diversion of legitimately produced controlled substances to the illicit market. The program has grown in complexity with the addition of new controlled substances as well as with new automated initiatives. The continued success of the program is the result of the combined efforts and understanding of health care professionals, industry, and the DEA.

The answers to many registration questions and the locations of DEA field offices and registration assistants are listed on the Diversion Control Program website, available at www.DEAdiversion.usdoj.gov.

National Practitioner Data Bank

The National Practitioner Data Bank (NPDB), also called the Data Bank, is a flagging system that facilitates a comprehensive review of actions affecting health care practitioners' clinical privileges; medical malpractice payments made for the benefit of health care practitioners; federal and state licensure and certification actions taken against practitioners, providers, entities, and suppliers; exclusions from participating in federal and state health care programs; criminal convictions and civil judgments related to health care; adverse actions taken by peer review organizations or private accreditation entities, and other adjudicated actions and decisions. It was created by Congress originally to restrict the ability of incompetent physicians and dentists to move from state to state without the disclosure or discovery of previous damaging or incompetent performance. Since its earliest days, the NPDB's scope has expanded so that it now collects and releases information on a broad range of actions taken against health care practitioners and entities by a large number of health care actors.

The idea behind the NPDB is straightforward: By law, certain health care entities are *required* to report to the Data Bank specified actions they take against health care practitioners, providers, suppliers, and other entities; other health care entities are *permitted* to report similar actions taken against other health care actors. Then, when making decisions on issues such as employment, licensure and certification, clinical privileges, and contractual arrangements, health care entities query the NPDB to obtain from the Data Bank information they are entitled by law to receive about the other party. (Hospitals are the only entities that are *required* to query the Data Bank.) Data Bank information is not released to the general public and is released to health care entities only under well-defined circumstances. Practitioners, entities, providers, and suppliers are authorized to query on themselves for information reported to the Data Bank.

Information in the NPDB is meant to be used in combination with information from other sources when making determinations on employment, affiliation, clinical privileges, certification, licensure, or other decisions. NPDB information should not be used as the sole source to verify professional credentials. The information should serve only

to alert eligible entities that there may be a problem with the performance of a particular practitioner, entity, provider, or supplier.

The most recent expansion of the NPDB was mandated by the Patient Protection and Affordable Care Act (ACA). On May 6, 2013, NPDB operations were consolidated with those of the former Healthcare Integrity and Protection Data Bank (HIPDB), as required by the ACA. Although the older version of the NPDB and the HIPDB, for the most part, collected and provided information on different subjects and types of health care entities and practitioners, some overlap existed between the two databases. In section 6403 of the ACA, Congress decided to eliminate duplicative data reporting and access requirements by requiring the Secretary of Health and Human Services to transfer all data in the HIPDB to the NPDB and, once completed, cease HIPDB operations. Information previously collected and disclosed through the HIPDB is now collected and disclosed through the NPDB.

As a result of this consolidation, the scope of materials reported to and released by the NPDB is broader than ever. Yet the three primary statutes that controlled the former NPDB and the HIPDB still govern the new version of the NPDB. These statutes are: Title IV of the Health Care Quality Improvement Act of 1986, Public Law 99-660 ("Title IV"); section 5 of the Medicare and Medicaid Patient and Program Protection Act of 1987, Public Law 100-93, codified as section 1921 of the Social Security Act ("Section 1921"); and section 221(a) of the Health Insurance Portability and Accountability Act of 1996, Public Law 104-191, codified as section 1128E of the Social Security Act ("Section 1128E"). Regulations governing the NPDB are found at 45 CFR Part 60.

Table 38 outlines Data Bank reporting and querying requirements. In addition to medical malpractice payments made for the benefit of individual practitioners, adverse licensure actions, and adverse clinical privileges actions, the NPDB collects and releases information on the following activities:

- Negative actions or findings by state licensing authorities, peer review organizations, or private accreditation organizations;

Table 38
Who Can Report to and Query the NPDB?

	Query	Report
Title IV Requirements		
Medical malpractice payers	Prohibited	Required
Hospitals*	Required	Required
Health care entities that provide health care services and follow a formal peer review process for the purpose of furthering quality health care	Optional	Required
Professional societies that follow a formal peer review process for the purpose of furthering quality health care	Optional	Required
Boards of medical examiners	Optional	Required
Other state licensing boards	Optional	No Requirement
Drug Enforcement Administration	Prohibited	Required
Department of Health and Human Services Office of Inspector General	Prohibited	Required
Section 1921 and Section 1128E Requirements		
Hospitals	Optional†	No Requirement
Health care entities that provide health care services and follow a formal peer review process for the purpose of furthering quality health care	Optional†	No Requirement
Health plans	Optional	Required (§ 1128E)
Professional societies that follow a formal peer review process for the purpose of furthering quality health care	Optional†	No Requirement
Quality improvement organizations	Optional†	No Requirement
State licensing and certification authorities	Optional	Required (§ 1921)
Peer review organizations	Prohibited	Required (§ 1921)
Private accreditation organizations	Prohibited	Required (§ 1921)
State law enforcement agencies‡	Optional	Required (§ 1921)
State Medicaid fraud control units‡	Optional	Required (§ 1921)
State agencies administering or supervising the administration of state health care programs‡	Optional	Required (§ 1921)
Agencies administering federal health care programs, including private entities administering such programs under contract	Optional	Required (§ 1128E)
Federal licensing and certification agencies	Optional	Required (§ 1128E)
Federal law enforcement officials and agencies	Optional	Required (§ 1128E)

* Under Title IV, hospitals are required to query the NPDB.

† With a few limited exceptions, these entities have access to all of the information reported under Section 1921 and Section 1128E.

‡ NPDB regulations define "state law or fraud enforcement agency" as including but not limited to these entities.

- Employment and affiliation decisions by hospitals, managed care organizations, professional societies, and other health care entities;
- Adverse professional society membership actions;
- Registration actions taken by the Drug Enforcement Administration;
- Exclusions from participation in Medicare, Medicaid, and other federal and state health care programs;
- Criminal convictions and civil judgments related to health care; and
- Other adjudicated actions and decisions.

Data Availability and Confidentiality

Information reported to the NPDB is confidential. Access to information about practitioners or entities is restricted to legally authorized entities that are registered with the Data Bank.

Health care practitioners, entities, providers, and suppliers are allowed to query their own reports in the NPDB at any time; the Data Bank charges an $8 fee for self-queries. Subjects of a report receive, with their self-query responses, a list of all parties to whom the report has been disclosed. To self query, report subjects can visit www.npdb.hrsa.gov/pract/hasAReportBeenFiledOnYou.jsp.

The NPDB produces a Public Use Data File that contains aggregated data that does not include any information identifying individual practitioners or reporting entities. The file is designed to provide data for statistical analysis only. The NPDB also has a Data Analysis Tool that allows website visitors to generate data sets for Adverse Action Reports and Medical Malpractice Payment Reports for the years through 2012.

Reporting, Querying, Statements, and Disputing Reports

NPDB reporting and querying are done electronically through a secure Internet site, at www.npdb.hrsa.gov. A fee of $4.75 is assessed for each One-Time Query. Entities also can enroll their practitioners in the Data Bank's

Continuous Query service under which, for an annual fee of $3.25 for each practitioner enrolled, the entity receives an initial One-Time Query response and, within one day of the NPDB receiving a report on an enrolled practitioner, updates from the NPDB on the practitioner.

After processing a report from a reporting entity, the NPDB sends a notice to the entity and to the individual or organization (the subject) mentioned in the report. If there are errors, subjects must ask the reporting entity to correct the information. The NPDB is prohibited from modifying information submitted in reports except through a formal dispute resolution process established to resolve disputed reports not addressed by reporting entities.

The subjects of a Data Bank report may (1) add a statement to the report, (2) dispute either the factual accuracy of the information in a report or whether the report was submitted in accordance with NPDB reporting requirements, or (3) do both. If the reporting entity does not make a correction satisfactory to the subject of a report, the subject may request formal dispute resolution. A Disputes Resolution Manager will review whether the report was legally filed and is accurate.

Responsibilities of State Licensing Authorities

Under the NPDB statutes, state licensing authorities must submit to the Data Bank, within 30 days of an action, adverse licensing and certification actions and other negative actions and findings taken against health care entities, providers, suppliers, and practitioners. These reportable actions or findings include both final actions and actions taken as a result of formal proceedings.

These actions include revocations, suspensions, censures, reprimands, probations, surrenders, dismissals, limitations on the scope of practice, injunctions, forfeitures, or any other negative actions or findings that are publicly available information. An action must be reported to the Data Bank based on whether it satisfies NPDB reporting requirements and not based on the name affixed to the action. State licensing authorities also must report any changes or revisions to adverse licensure actions and negative actions or findings.

State licensing boards have the opportunity to opt in to the Data Bank's Electronic Report Forwarding service. Most entities that report to the NPDB are required to forward copies of those reports to appropriate state boards. If both the reporting entity and the appropriate state board choose to participate in the Electronic Report Forwarding service, the Data Bank will forward a copy of the entity's report to the state board automatically, saving both the reporting entity and the board processing time and associated costs. More information about the Electronic Report Forwarding service can be found at http://www.npdb.hrsa.gov/resources/brochures/ReportForwardingTutorial.pdf

Available Materials

The NPDB operates under the direct supervision of the Division of Practitioner Data Banks, Bureau of Health Professions, Health Resources and Services Administration, Department of Health and Human Services. The NPDB began collecting and disseminating information in 1990. The HIPDB began collecting information in 1999 and disseminating it in 2000.

Materials available from the Data Bank include guidebooks for the NPDB and the HIPDB, the Public Use Data File, the Data Analysis Tool, fact sheets on various topics, and self-query materials. A revised *NPDB Guidebook* should be available early in 2014. All materials are available on the Internet at www.npdb.hrsa.gov.

National Practitioner Data Bank
PO Box 10832
Chantilly, VA 20153-0832
(800) 767-6732
www.npdb.hrsa.gov

Chapter 6

Other Organizations and Programs

American Board of Medical Specialties (ABMS)

Established in 1933, the American Board of Medical Specialties (ABMS®) is a national, not-for-profit organization committed to delivering quality health care to all patients by means of evaluation programs that assess and certify a physician's competence to practice medicine in a medical specialty.

ABMS is made up of 24 certifying boards, known as the ABMS Member Boards, which represent distinct medical specialty areas. Each Member Board establishes and maintains high standards for the certification and continuing education of physicians in a specialty or related subspecialty. The ABMS Member Boards are approved by ABMS and the AMA Council on Medical Education (AMA CME) through the Liaison Committee for Specialty Boards (LCSB).

The Member Boards of ABMS

Certification is available from ABMS Member Boards in the fields listed below. Each Member Board's website provides complete details about eligibility for Board Certification in a specialty or subspecialty, examination dates and requirements for maintaining certification.

American Board of:

Allergy and Immunology	www.abai.org
Anesthesiology	www.theaba.org
Colon and Rectal Surgery	www.abcrs.org
Dermatology	www.abderm.org
Emergency Medicine	www.abem.org
Family Medicine	www.theabfm.org
Internal Medicine	www.abim.org
Medical Genetics	www.abmg.org
Neurological Surgery	www.abns.org
Nuclear Medicine	www.abnm.org
Obstetrics and Gynecology	www.abog.org
Ophthalmology	www.abop.org
Orthopaedic Surgery	www.abos.org
Otolaryngology	www.aboto.org
Pathology	www.abpath.org
Pediatrics	www.abp.org
Physical Medicine and Rehabilitation	www.abpmr.org
Plastic Surgery	www.abplsurg.org
Preventive Medicine	www.theabpm.org
Psychiatry and Neurology	www.abpn.com
Radiology	www.theabr.org
Surgery	www.absurgery.org
Thoracic Surgery	www.abts.org
Urology	www.abu.org

Associate Members of ABMS

ABMS collaborates with other professional medical organizations and agencies to improve the quality of graduate medical education, the standards of medical practice and the physician certification process. These include the following Associate Members of ABMS:

Accreditation Council for Continuing Medical Education (ACCME)
www.accme.org

Accreditation Council for Graduate Medical Education (ACGME)
www.acgme.org

American Hospital Association (AHA)
www.aha.org

American Medical Association (AMA)
www.ama-assn.org

Association of American Medical Colleges (AAMC)
www.aamc.org

Council of Medical Specialty Societies (CMSS)
www.cmss.org

Educational Commission for Foreign Medical Graduates (ECFMG)
www.ecfmg.org

Federation of State Medical Boards (FSMB)
www.fsmb.org

National Board of Medical Examiners (NBME)
www.nbme.org

Board Certification and Continuing Certification

Board Certification is a lifelong process that begins with initial certification and continues with ABMS Maintenance of Certification® (ABMS MOC®).

The Member Boards offer certification to physicians who meet certain requirements, including:

- Finishing four years of premedical education in a college or university;
- Earning a medical degree (MD, DO or other approved credential) from a qualified medical school;
- Completing three to five years of full-time experience in a residency training program accredited by the ACGME;
- Obtaining and maintaining an unrestricted medical license to practice medicine in the United States or Canada;
- Undergoing an evaluation by a peer of experts; and
- Passing a comprehensive examination created and administered by the Member Board which assesses the physician's medical knowledge, clinical judgment and diagnostic skills.

Candidates who meet this set of requirements are considered Board Certified as a specialist and a diplomate of the Member Board in their specialty. Physicians also can become certified in a subspecialty, which requires additional training and examination.

The ABMS MOC program for continuing certification serves as way for Board Certified physicians to maintain currency and demonstrate competency advancement in their specialty area. This involves ongoing measurement of six core competencies defined by ABMS and the ACGME in 1999:

Professionalism—carrying out responsibilities safely and ethically

Patient Care and Procedural Skills—providing compassionate, appropriate and effective patient care

Medical Knowledge—demonstrating medical knowledge and its application to patient care

Practice-based Learning and Improvement—continuously improving patient care through constant self-evaluation and lifelong learning

Interpersonal and Communication Skills—facilitating effective information exchange and collaboration with patients, their families and health professionals

Systems-based Practice—ability to call on other system resources to provide optimal health care

Each Member Board developed MOC program activities for their specialty which are built upon evidence-based guidelines, national clinical and quality standards and specialty best practices. By 2006 all boards had their MOC programs approved. The activities help physicians continue to progress in the core competencies through four broad developmental areas, including:

Professional Standing—holding and maintaining a valid, unrestricted medical license in at least one state or jurisdiction in the US, its territories or Canada.

Lifelong Learning and Self-Assessment—regular participation in educational and self-assessment activities that meet specialty-specific standards set by their Board.

Cognitive Expertise—demonstration, through formal examination, that they have up-to-date knowledge for providing quality care in their specialty.

Practice Performance Assessment—periodic evaluation of clinical practice to assess the quality of care they provide to that of their peers as well as national benchmarks, then applying best evidence or consensus recommendations to improve care.

The ABMS Member Boards have evolved a number of educational and self-assessment tools linked to the ABMS MOC program. These include clinical databases and registries, peer evaluations and practice audits that gauge the doctor, system and patient relationship. The ABMS MOC program continues to evolve by defining practice standards for physicians through:

- creating an environment for continuous learning;
- encouraging critical thinking about practice fundamentals;
- establishing a culture of professional excellence for patient safety, communication and ethics;
- measuring performance and offering methods for improvement; and
- evaluating patient outcomes.

Verification of Certification

The public may check a physician's certification through these services:

- Online through www.CertificationMatters.org
- Toll-free by calling the ABMS Physician Verification Service at 1-866-ASK-ABMS (1-866-275-2267)
- From the library by referencing the Official ABMS *Directory of Certified Medical Specialists*®

Credentialing organizations or other commercial entities can receive primary-source confirmation of a physician's Board Certification status directly from ABMS. The Joint Commission, the organization that evaluates and accredits US health care organizations and programs, has determined that direct verification of a physician's certification status with ABMS, or an ABMS-designated agent, satisfies The Joint Commission's requirement for primary-source verification of a physician's Board Certification.

For more information about ABMS, the certification of physician specialists and verifying physician certification, contact:

American Board of Medical Specialties
222 North LaSalle Street, Suite 1500
Chicago, IL 60601
(312) 436-2600
(312) 436-2700 Fax
Email: info@abms.org
www.CertificationMatters.org
www.abms.org

American Osteopathic Association

The American Osteopathic Association (AOA) was founded in 1897 by a group of students at the American School of Osteopathy in Kirksville, Mo., with the goal of uniting the efforts of individual physicians and colleges to advance the osteopathic medical profession. Today, the AOA serves as the professional family for more than 104,000 osteopathic physicians (DOs) and osteopathic medical students. The AOA promotes public health and encourages scientific research. In addition to serving as the primary certifying body for DOs, the AOA is the accrediting agency for all osteopathic medical schools and has federal authority to accredit hospitals and other health care facilities.

Continually striving to advance the distinctive philosophy and practice of osteopathic medicine, the AOA stands for the following universal principles:

- Enhancing the value of AOA membership
- Protecting and promoting the rights of all osteopathic physicians
- Accentuating the distinctiveness of osteopathic principles and the diversity of the profession
- Supporting DOs' efforts to provide quality, cost-effective care to all Americans
- Collaborating with others to advance the practice of osteopathic medicine

Bureau of Osteopathic Specialists (BOS)

The Bureau of Osteopathic Specialists (BOS) was organized in 1939 as the Advisory Board for Osteopathic Specialists to meet the needs resulting from the growth of specialization in the osteopathic profession and a desire for standardization of postdoctoral education and certification regulations in the various specialties or fields of practice. Therefore, the AOA Board of Trustees, through its agency, the Bureau of Osteopathic Specialists, became the certifying body. The body's name was changed from the Advisory Board to the Bureau in 1993.

AOA Specialty Certifying Boards

Certification is available from AOA-approved specialty boards in the following fields:

- Anesthesiology
- Dermatology
- Emergency Medicine
- Family Physicians
- Internal Medicine
- Neurology & Psychiatry
- Neuromusculoskeletal Medicine
- Nuclear Medicine
- Obstetrics and Gynecology
- Ophthalmology and Otolaryngology
- Orthopedic Surgery
- Pathology
- Pediatrics (AOBP)
- Physical Medicine & Rehabilitation
- Preventive Medicine
- Proctology
- Radiology
- Surgery

Available Certification

Osteopathic physicians may obtain these types of certification from AOA-approved specialty boards:

Primary Certification—conferred on diplomates who meet the requirements in a specified field of medical practice under the jurisdiction of a certifying board. Primary certification represents a distinct and well-defined field of osteopathic medical practice.

Certificate of Special Qualifications (CSQ)—is conferred by a certifying board in a subspecialty area of the field to which that board certifies. It requires prior attainment of general certification. The CSQ indicates possession of knowledge, skill, training and successful examination in a subspecialty field beyond that required for primary certification. The CSQ designates additional abilities in limited areas of the primary specialty field represented by that board. For example, cardiology is a limited area within the field of internal medicine for which physicians may earn special qualifications.

Certification of Added Qualifications (CAQ)—is a modification of a primary certificate or certificate of special qualifications to reflect additional training of at least one year in length and satisfactory completion of a certifying examination in that field. The training required for added qualifications must incorporate a specific and identifiable body of knowledge within the broader practice of the primary specialty. For example, a physician can hold general certification in Family Practice, with added qualifications in geriatric medicine.

When the identifiable body of knowledge for certification of added qualifications overlaps more than one specialty or subspecialty area, a conjoint examination program may be developed by the corresponding certifying boards. The CAQ requires maintenance of valid primary or special qualifications certification from which the added qualification was modified. Recertification in areas of added qualifications requires maintenance of valid primary or special qualifications certification from which the added qualification was modified.

Osteopathic Continuous Certification (OCC)—Rather than being a single event, certification should be a continuous, lifelong process. OCC ensures that board-certified DOs maintain currency and demonstrate competency in their specialty area. The only change to the current osteopathic recertification process is the addition of a Practice Performance Assessment.

There are five components of OCC:

- COMPONENT 1 - Unrestricted Licensure
- COMPONENT 2 - Lifelong Learning/Continuing Medical Education
- COMPONENT 3 - Cognitive Assessment
- COMPONENT 4 - Practice Performance Assessment and Improvement
- COMPONENT 5 - Continuous AOA Membership

All Specialty Certifying Boards operating under the jurisdiction of the AOA have been qualified by the Centers for Medicare and Medicaid Services (CMS) for the 2013 PQRS MOC Program Incentive. This allows qualifying diplomates to apply for an additional 0.5% incentive payment for 2013 submitted Medicare/Medicaid claims. The MOC incentive program requires physicians "to perform activities more frequent than is required" for OCC.

Healthcare Facilities Accreditation Program

Healthcare Facilities Accreditation Program (HFAP) is authorized by CMS to survey all hospitals for compliance with the Medicare Conditions of Participation and Coverage. HFAP is a nationally recognized healthcare facility accreditation organization, with deeming authority from CMS. HFAP meets or exceeds CMS standards to provide accreditation to all hospitals, ambulatory care/surgical facilities, mental health facilities, physical rehabilitation facilities, clinical laboratories, and critical access. HFAP also provides certification to primary stroke centers.

Healthcare Facilities Accreditation Program
142 E. Ontario Street, Chicago, IL 60611
(312) 202-8258

Other AOA programs and activities

The **Council on Continuing Medical Education** (CCME) directs the AOA's continuing medical education program. It coordinates the activities for continuing educational programs, recommends CME policy to the Bureau of Osteopathic Education, establishes guidelines for the evaluation of CME programs, and approves Category 1 CME Sponsors.

The **Commission on Osteopathic College Accreditation** (COCA) serves as the accrediting agency for colleges of osteopathic medicine. In this capacity, the COCA reviews, evaluates, and takes final action on college accreditation status, and communicates such action to appropriate state and federal education regulatory bodies. In addition, the COCA approves the standards, policies and procedures for college accreditation.

The **Osteopathic Graduate Medical Education (OGME) Development Initiative** assists non-teaching hospitals interested in establishing osteopathic residency programs, hospitals with allopathic (MD) training that want to add osteopathic programs, and osteopathic training programs in need of assistance. Contact OGME at (202) 414-0155 or OGMEDevelopment@osteopathic.org.

Under a data licensing agreement with the AOA, the American Osteopathic Information Association (AOIA) provides comprehensive, up-to-date, primary source verification of DO credentials to state medical licensing boards, hospital medical staff administrators and health plans through the **Osteopathic Physician Profile Service.** See DOprofiles.org or email credentials@osteopathic.org.

Accreditation Council for Graduate Medical Education (ACGME)

The Accreditation Council for Graduate Medical Education (ACGME) is a private, nonprofit accrediting organization. Its board of directors comprises individuals elected from slates nominated by five national associations interested in graduate medical education (GME): the American Board of Medical Specialties (ABMS), American Hospital Association (AHA), American Medical Association (AMA), Association of American Medical Colleges (AAMC), and Council of Medical Specialty Societies (CMSS).

The ACGME elects three public directors, and the Board may also elect up to three directors at large. The chair of the Council of Review Committee Chairs also serves on the board, along with two voting resident physicians: a resident director nominated by the Resident and Fellow Section of the AMA, with the advice of other national organizations that represent residents, and the chair of the Council of Review Committee Residents. A federal government representative serves as a nonvoting member of the board, as does a representative of the Department of Veterans Affairs. Numerous other organizations are invited as observers to the public sessions of the ACGME Board and a number of its Board committees.

Each of the 26 Residency Review Committees (RRCs) sponsored by the ACGME consists of representatives appointed by the AMA, the ABMS specialty board, and, in most cases, the medical specialty society. The Transitional Year Review and Institutional Review Committees are composed of members appointed by the Board of Directors. The term *review committee* is used to denote a Residency Review Committee, Transitional Year Review Committee, or Institutional Review Committee.

GME programs are accredited by the appropriate review committee through authority delegated by the ACGME. Accreditation of a residency program indicates that it is judged to be in substantial compliance with the program requirements for residency education in the particular specialty.

A list of programs accredited by the ACGME, including detailed information about each program, is published annually by the AMA in the *Graduate Medical Education Directory.* An online listing can be found on the ACGME website at www.acgme.org.

ACGME General Competencies

In 1999, the ACGME endorsed six General Competencies. ACGME Program Requirements state that GME programs must define the specific knowledge, skills, and attitudes required and provide educational experiences as needed in order for their residents/fellows to demonstrate these competencies to the level expected of a practitioner entering the unsupervised practice of medicine in their chosen discipline. The ACGME, in concert with colleagues from the certifying boards and others in each specialty, have developed the Milestones, which are behavioral descriptors of the trajectory of learning in each specialty, framed by the six General Competencies. These Milestones will be used in the evaluation of the professional development of each resident and fellow in ACGME-accredited programs.

Patient Care that is compassionate, appropriate, and effective for the treatment of health problems and the promotion of health

Medical Knowledge about established and evolving biomedical, clinical, and cognate (e.g., epidemiological and social-behavioral) sciences and the application of this knowledge to patient care

Practice-Based Learning and Improvement that involves investigation and evaluation of their own patient care, appraisal and assimilation of scientific evidence, and improvements in patient care

Interpersonal and Communication Skills that result in effective information exchange and teaming with patients, their families, and other health professionals

Professionalism, as manifested through a commitment to carrying out professional responsibilities, adherence to ethical principles, and sensitivity to a diverse patient population

Systems-Based Practice, as manifested by actions that demonstrate an awareness of and responsiveness to the larger context and system of health care and the ability to effectively call on system resources to provide care of optimal value.

Contact Information

Accreditation Council for Graduate Medical Education
515 N State St, Suite 2000
Chicago, IL 60654
(312) 755-5000
www.acgme.org

Accreditation Council for Continuing Medical Education (ACCME)

The mission of the Accreditation Council for Continuing Medical Education (ACCME®) is to identify, develop and promote rigorous national standards for quality continuing medical education (CME) that improves physician performance and medical care for patients and their communities.

The ACCME fulfills its mission through a voluntary self-regulated system for accrediting CME providers and a peer-review process responsive to changes in medical education and the health care delivery system.

The primary responsibilities of the ACCME are to:

- Serve as the body accrediting institutions and organizations offering CME

- Serve as the body recognizing institutions and organizations offering CME accreditation

- Develop criteria for evaluation of both educational programs and their activities by which ACCME and state accrediting bodies will accredit institutions and organizations and be responsible for assuring compliance with these standards

- Develop, or foster the development of, methods for measuring the effectiveness of CME and its accreditation, particularly in its relationship to supporting quality patient care and the continuum of medical education

- Recommend and initiate studies for improving the organization and processes of CME and its accreditation

- Review and assess developments in CME's support of quality health

- Review periodically its role in continuing medical education to ensure it remains responsive to public and professional needs.

The 2006 *Accreditation Criteria*, which incorporate the *Standards for Commercial Support^{SM}: Standards to Ensure Independence in CME Activities*, were designed to position the CME enterprise as a strategic asset to US health care quality improvement imperatives and to align with emerging continuing professional development systems such as the American Board of Medical Specialties Maintenance of Certification® (MOC) and the Federation of State Medical Boards Maintenance of Licensure (MOL) initiatives. The ACCME accreditation requirements state that CME activities must be independent, based on valid content and free of commercial influence. CME activities should be designed to address professional practice gaps and to change physicians' competence, by teaching them strategies for translating new knowledge into action, or physicians' performance (what they actually do in practice), or patient outcomes.

The ACCME system includes approximately 700 organizations that are directly accredited by ACCME and more than 1,300 organizations accredited within the ACCME's state-based system. The state-based CME system is made up of 43 state and territory medical societies that are "Recognized" by the ACCME as accreditors of state-based CME providers. State and territory medical societies that are designated as ACCME Recognized CME Accreditors must meet the ACCME's recognition requirements, the Markers of Equivalency. The recognition requirements are designed to maintain a uniform, national system of CME accreditation. All accreditation decisions made within the ACCME system are based on the 2006 *Accreditation Criteria*.

Contact Information

Accreditation Council for Continuing Medical Education
515 N State St, Suite 1801
Chicago, IL 60654
(312) 527-9200
www.accme.org

American Medical Association Survey and Data Resources

The AMA Division of Survey and Data Resources is dedicated to effectively and accurately collecting, analyzing, and managing physician data within the Physician Masterfile. The AMA Physician Masterfile is a data source both for AMA internal use as well as use by other professional medical organizations, universities and medical schools, research institutions, governmental agencies, and other related groups. The use of Physician Masterfile data by agencies and organizations concerned with verifying physicians' credentials and health manpower planning is fundamental to the AMA's mission to strengthen the medical profession and ensure quality health care for the American public.

The Physician Masterfile is a database comprising current and historical data for more than 1.4 million residents/fellows and physicians and 93,000 medical students in the United States, both AMA members and nonmembers. This figure includes approximately 411,000 graduates of foreign medical schools who reside in the United States and who have met the educational and credentialing requirements necessary for recognition and approximately 78,000 doctors of osteopathy. Physicians' records are subject to change and are updated continuously through the extensive data collection activities described below.

Additional data (state licensure, board certification, geographical location and address, type of practice, present employment, and practice specialty) are added from primary data sources or from surveying the physicians directly as their training and careers develop.

Masterfile records are never removed even in the case of a physician's death. The AMA maintains information on more than 205,000 deceased physicians. These data are shared with other organizations and agencies who credential physicians and are used to identify individuals who attempt to fraudulently assume the credentials of deceased physicians.

Survey and Data Resources is composed of the following units:

- Department of Data Integration and Quality Analysis
- Department of Data Survey and Verification Services
- eCommunications and Data Release Services

These units are essential in maintaining the Masterfile as one of the most comprehensive and accurate sources of physician data.

Department of Data Integration and Quality Analysis

The responsibility of the Department of Data Integration and Quality Analysis is to ensure that the AMA's Physician Masterfile contains timely and high-quality data on physicians, residents, medical students, medical education institutions, and other healthcare organizations. A core function performed within this department is to establish new AMA Physician Masterfile records, assigning a unique identifier that will remain the same throughout a physician's medical career.

In addition, the department processes resident information collected via the National Graduate Medical Education (GME) Census, an annual survey conducted jointly with the Association of American Medical Colleges (AAMC). Each year, approximately 9,200 ACGME-accredited GME programs are surveyed. The reported residency information is internally validated and incorporated into a physician's record. The survey also includes questions on GME program characteristics, such as clinical and research facilities and the learning environment, which are used to update FREIDA Online® (www.ama-assn.org/go/freida).

This department is also responsible for processing over 55 million updates received annually from state regulatory and federal agencies, medical specialty groups and organizations, educational and training institutions, and membership and subscription services. Of utmost importance to the division is ensuring timely data load cycles to the Masterfile. On average, 97 percent of the matched records are loaded to the Masterfile within five business days of receipt. Timely processing of incoming data is key to ensuring accurate and comprehensive reporting to credentialing groups and health care organizations.

Department of Data Survey and Verification Services

The responsibility of the Department of Data Survey and Verification Services is to verify physician biographical, educational and professional information and track physicians throughout their professional careers by collecting, updating and maintaining current practice and communications data. The department targets an average of 540,000 physicians with mail, phone and Web-based surveys annually, applies approximately 200,000 communications (phone, fax, email) changes, and updates approximately 400,000 physician mailing and office addresses per year.

Once physicians complete residency and/or fellowship training, the department tracks them throughout their professional careers. The annual Census of Physicians mail survey, for example, reaches approximately 250,000 physicians per year and collects information on a physician's professional medical activities, preferred mailing address, primary office location, and practice specialties. In addition to the mail survey, this group also reaches out to 250,000 to 300,000 physicians each year through telephone and Web-based surveys and uses over 20 additional sources to supplement data collected via surveys. The information that is captured is used to conduct AMA membership campaigns, communicate with physicians, segment physician markets, draw samples for health-related research, perform workforce analysis, and track professional trends.

This department is also responsible for the investigation and verification of physician biographic, education and professional information with primary sources in compliance with recognized accreditation standards. Staff investigate an average of 9,000 physician and customer reported discrepancies related to this data on the Masterfile each year. These data verification efforts ensure the accuracy and reliability of Masterfile data in support of many membership, credentialing and other business activities.

Department of eCommunication and Data Release Services

This business unit within the Division of Survey and Data Resources educates others about, facilitates access to, and evaluates the quality of the AMA Physician Masterfile.

The unit educates data users about the Physician Masterfile by managing and responding to telephone, email, and written inquiries regarding Physician Masterfile data, as well as fulfilling specific data requests when appropriate. This effort supports the communications, marketing and planning efforts of other AMA units.

In addition, this unit is responsible for coordinating the distribution of most of the AMA's electronic communications, including flagship newsletters like *AMA Wire*, as well as many other communications regarding the AMA's advocacy initiatives, news for physicians, and AMA products and services.

One of the primary roles of the unit is production of the book *Physician Characteristics and Distribution in the US*, an annual publication with comprehensive statistical data on the physician supply in the United States. In addition, Data Release Services supports the AMA's Partnership for Growth Data Reciprocity Project, which promotes data sharing with state medical associations and national medical specialty organizations.

Other activities performed within the division include:

- Managing the AMA's corporate mailing list application, which includes more than 100 different list directories and supports key Association activities involving the AMA board, councils, committees, advisory groups, and House of Delegates

- Providing a mechanism and data resources for use by medical schools, universities, research institutions, governmental agencies, and other organizations interested in the study of heath care policy issues

- Coordinating the distribution of Masterfile-related reports, physician profiles, and data to state, county, and national specialty medical societies

- Developing, measuring, and monitoring key performance indicators

Contact Information

Division of Survey and Data Resources
Monica Quiroz, Director
monica.quiroz@ama-assn.org

Department of Data Integration and Quality Analysis
Mark Long, Director
mark.long@ama-assn.org

Department of Data Survey and Verification Services
Susan Montrimas, Director
susan.montrimas@ama-assn.org

Department of eCommunications and Data Release
 Services
Derek Smart, Manager
derek.smart@ama-assn.org

American Medical Association Continuing Medical Education

Advances in biomedical science and changes in the other facets of the US health care delivery environment engage physicians in a continuous process of professional development. To ensure that they provide patients with the most current and appropriate treatment, services, and information, physicians continue learning through participation in a wide array of structured educational activities, as well as through independent study. The American Medical Association (AMA) supports these physician efforts by:

- Administering the only non-specialty-specific credit system that recognizes physician completion of continuing medical education (CME) activities—the AMA PRA credit system

- Establishing learning modalities (e.g., performance improvement CME [PI CME] and Internet point of care [PoC]) to enhance physician professional development and improve patient care

- Establishing agreements to enable US physicians to obtain *AMA PRA Category 1 Credit*™ for participation in international meetings

- Offering certified CME activities (live, journal-based CME, manuscript review, enduring materials, and performance improvement CME)

The AMA Physician's Recognition Award

In 1968, the AMA House of Delegates established the AMA Physician's Recognition Award (PRA) to recognize the achievements of those physicians who demonstrate commitment to lifelong learning and improving patient care by participating in CME. Activities that meet education standards established by the AMA can be certified for *AMA PRA Category 1 Credit*™ by organizations accredited by either the Accreditation Council for Continuing Medical Education (ACCME) or an ACCME-recognized state medical society. These accredited CME providers typically include state medical societies, medical specialty societies, medical schools, and hospitals. Physicians may also be awarded *AMA PRA Category 1 Credit*™ directly by the AMA for learning that occurs in completing certain activities that do not occur under the auspices of an accredited CME provider. Other activities, usually independent or physician-directed learning, may be reported for *AMA PRA*

Category 2 Credit™ if the physician individually determines that the activities meet the requirements as found in the PRA booklet.

The AMA offers one-, two-, and three-year AMA PRAs, with the following requirements:

One-year award:

- Twenty *AMA PRA Category 1 Credits*™ and 30 *AMA PRA Category 1 Credits*™ or *AMA PRA Category 2 Credits*™ (50 credits total), or

- One year of ACGME-accredited residency/fellowship training

Two-year award:

- Forty *AMA PRA Category 1 Credits*™ and 60 *AMA PRA Category 1 Credits*™ or *AMA PRA Category 2 Credits*™ (100 credits total), or

- Two years of ACGME-accredited residency/fellowship training

Three-year award:

- Sixty *AMA PRA Category 1 Credits*™ and 90 *AMA PRA Category 1 Credits*™ or *AMA PRA Category 2 Credits*™ (150 credits total), or

- Three years of ACGME-accredited residency/fellowship training, or

- ABMS board certification or Maintenance of Certification

Note: At least half of the credits submitted for this award must be within the physician's specialty or area of practice.

The AMA also offers the AMA PRA with Commendation, an award that recognizes physicians who regularly demonstrate a high level of commitment to their continuing education and requires obtaining more *AMA PRA Category 1 Credits*™ than for the standard PRA. More information about the credit system and the AMA PRA is available at www.ama-assn.org/go/pra.

The AMA has agreements with specialty societies, state medical societies, medical staff groups, and other organizations whereby an AMA PRA can be issued to any US licensed physician as established by the agreement.

Many state and territory licensing jurisdictions will accept the AMA PRA or approved application as evidence that physicians have met the CME requirements for licensure. A list of these states can be found in Table 21, Continuing Medical Education for Licensure Reregistration.

The AMA PRA application form and the AMA PRA Information Booklet, respectively, are available online at:

www.ama-assn.org/go/pra
www.ama-assn.org/go/prabooklet

For questions on applying for the PRA, contact pra@ama-assn.org. For questions about the AMA PRA credit system, contact cme@ama-assn.org.

AMA-certified CME Activities

Conferences and Live Events

As an ACCME-accredited provider, the AMA certifies multiple conferences and live events for *AMA PRA Category 1 Credit*™. Physicians may participate in education on topics of interest to all disciplines and specialties. Recent AMA-provided live events have addressed ethics, health care disparities, health care reform, and practice management.

Enduring Materials

The AMA offers a number of enduring CME activities for physicians. These modules offer quality CME in a convenient format that permits learners to work at their own pace and at a time that fits a busy schedule, and are available in print and online formats. A current list of available activities can be accessed at www.ama-assn.org/go/cme.

Journal CME

CME is available through many of the AMA journals. Physicians can earn *AMA PRA Category 1 Credit*™ by reading the designated articles and achieving a minimum performance level on post-tests. AMA members can take advantage of all journal-based CME at no extra charge.

Individual journal subscribers have access to CME as part of their paid subscription. A current list of participating journals is available online at jamanetwork.com.

Other Activities

The AMA also provides opportunities for physicians to earn *AMA PRA Category 1 Credit*™ through participation in select PI CME activities and manuscript review for *JAMA* and the *Archives* journals.

More information about AMA CME activities can be found at www.ama-assn.org/go/cme.

International CME

Physicians may earn *AMA PRA Category 1 Credit*™ for participation in select international educational activities.

Agreement with the European Union of Medical Specialties (UEMS)

The AMA will convert CME credit issued to physicians for participation in live and e-learning activities certified by the European Accreditation Council for Continuing Medical Education (EACCME), the accrediting arm of the UEMS, to *AMA PRA Category 1 Credit*™ .

Agreement with the Royal College of Physicians and Surgeons of Canada

The AMA will convert RCPSC MOC credits, issued to physicians for participation in select activities approved by national specialty societies and simulation programs accredited by the RCPSC, to *AMA PRA Category 1 Credit*™.

International Conference Recognition (ICR) program

The ICR program recognizes a few conferences presented by international organizations each year and provides physicians with an opportunity to earn *AMA PRA Category 1 Credit*™ at these approved events.

More information is available at www.ama-assn.org/go/internationalcme

Contact Information

For more information on AMA CME programs and activities, visit www.ama-assn.org/go/cme or contact:

AMA CME activities	(312) 464-5196
AMA CME credit processing	(312) 464-4669
Physician's Recognition Award	(312) 464-4669
International Recognition Program	(312) 464-4668
EACCME credit conversion	(312) 464-4669
RCPSC credit conversion	(312) 464-4669
AMA PRA Credit System	(312) 464-4668

For general information, contact:

Continuing Physician Professional Development
American Medical Association
330 N. Wabash Ave.
Chicago, IL 60611-5885
(312) 464-4671
(312) 464-5830 Fax
Email: cme@ama-assn.org

The Joint Commission

An independent, not-for-profit organization, The Joint Commission evaluates, accredits and certifies more than 19,000 health care organizations and programs in the United States. Accreditation by The Joint Commission is recognized nationwide as a symbol of quality that reflects an organization's commitment to meeting certain performance standards.

The Joint Commission develops its standards in consultation with health care experts, practitioners, providers, measurement experts, purchasers, and consumers. The standards focus on an organization's ability to provide safe, high-quality care and on its actual performance.

To earn and maintain accreditation, an organization must undergo an unannounced on-site survey by a team of Joint Commission surveyors at least every three years (laboratories are surveyed every two years). The Joint Commission employs experienced physicians, nurses, health care administrators, medical technologists, psychologists, pharmacists, and other medical professionals to conduct these surveys.

Accreditation Programs

The Joint Commission operates the following accreditation programs, which serve various types of health care organizations:

- Hospital Accreditation Program
- Home Care Accreditation Program
- Ambulatory Care Accreditation Program
- Laboratory Services Accreditation Program
- Long Term Care Accreditation Program
- Behavioral Health Care Accreditation Program
- Critical Access Hospital Accreditation Program
- Office-Based Surgery Accreditation Program

International accreditation services are provided through Joint Commission International, a subsidiary of The Joint Commission.

Certification Programs

The Joint Commission awards Disease-Specific Care Certification, designed to evaluate clinical programs for virtually any chronic disease or condition.

The Joint Commission has developed an advanced level of certification in six clinical areas. These programs must meet additional, clinically specific requirements and expectations. The Joint Commission offers Advanced Certification for the following conditions and procedures:

- Chronic kidney disease
- Chronic obstructive pulmonary disease
- Heart failure
- Inpatient diabetes
- Palliative Care
- Primary stroke center

Certification by The Joint Commission is required by the Centers for Medicare & Medicaid Services (CMS) for hospitals seeking reimbursement for these services:

- Lung volume reduction surgery
- Ventricular assist device

The Joint Commission's Health Care Staffing Services Certification program evaluates a staffing firm's ability to provide qualified and competent clinical staffing services to health care organizations.

Benefits of Accreditation and Certification

Accreditation and certification by The Joint Commission offers the following benefits:

- Strengthens community confidence in the quality and safety of care, treatment, and services
- Provides a competitive edge in the marketplace
- Improves risk management and risk reduction

- Provides education on good practices to improve business operations
- Provides professional advice and counsel, enhancing staff education
- Enhances staff recruitment and development
- Is recognized by select insurers and other third parties
- May fulfill regulatory requirements in select states

Major Initiatives

The Joint Commission works to improve the safety and quality of health care through its Sentinel Event Database and the ORYX initiative. The database permits dissemination of lessons learned from analysis of serious adverse events by accredited organizations and serves as a basis for the annual issuance of National Patient Safety Goals. ORYX measurements supplement and help guide the standards-based survey process by providing a more targeted basis for the regular accreditation survey and for continuously monitoring actual performance and guiding and stimulating continuous improvement in health care organizations.

Established in 2009, the Joint Commission Center for Transforming Healthcare aims to solve health care's most critical safety and quality problems. The Center's participants—the nation's leading hospitals and health systems—use a systematic approach to analyze specific breakdowns in care and discover their underlying causes to develop targeted solutions that solve these problems. The Joint Commission Center for Transforming Healthcare is introducing a new approach to identify, create, and implement consistent safety solutions that address quality and safety challenges facing health care organizations. These challenges—such as health care-associated infections and medication and surgical errors—threaten lives and increase costs. The Center uses Lean Six Sigma and change management tools and methods to identify the most pressing safety problems, measure their impact, discover their causes, develop specific solutions that are targeted to each important cause, and test the solutions in real-life situations.

In March 2002, The Joint Commission, together with the Centers for Medicare and Medicaid Services, launched a national campaign known as Speak Up™ to urge patients to take a role in preventing health care errors by becoming active, involved, and informed participants on the health care team. In 2011, the animated Speak Up video series debuted. Speak Up campaigns have included:

- Help prevent errors in your care
- Help avoid mistakes in your surgery
- Information for living organ donors
- Five things you can do to prevent infection
- Help avoid mistakes with your medicines
- What you should know about research studies
- Planning your follow-up care
- Help prevent medical test mistakes
- Know your rights
- Understanding your doctors and other caregivers
- Diabetes: Five ways to be active in your care at the hospital
- Dialysis: Five ways to be active in your care at the hospital

Consumers can find information about Joint Commission-accredited and -certified health care organizations online through Quality Check™, which is accessible at www.qualitycheck.org. Quality reports that provide detailed performance information about each accredited organization are also available through Quality Check. The Joint Commission issues an annual report that contains aggregate data on the quality and safety-related performance of America's hospitals.

Origins/Governance

The Joint Commission was founded in 1951. Its governing Board of Commissioners consists of 29 individuals whose backgrounds and experience reflect a broad range of professional and lay interests. The board includes practicing physicians, nurses, administrators, quality experts, ethicists, and educators, as well as a labor representative and a consumer advocate. The Board of Commissioners brings to The Joint Commission diverse experience in health care, business, and public policy.

Contact Information

The Joint Commission
One Renaissance Blvd
Oakbrook Terrace, IL 60181
(630) 792-5000
(630) 792-5005 Fax
www.jointcommission.org

National Committee for Quality Assurance (NCQA)

The National Committee for Quality Assurance (NCQA) is a private, not-for-profit organization that assesses and reports on the quality of health care services in multiple areas of the health care system to provide a basis for quality improvement activities and for public reporting of performance. The efforts of NCQA are organized around programs providing accreditation and certification of organizations, including health plans and other entities, and recognition programs for individual clinical practices.

Origins and Scope

The NCQA began evaluating and accrediting managed care organizations in 1991 in response to the need for standardized, objective information about the quality of these organizations. Since then, it has expanded the range of organizations that it accredits or certifies to include managed behavioral health care organizations, credentials verification organizations, physician organizations, and others. NCQA has also developed, in collaboration with organizations such as the American Diabetes Association and American Heart Association/American Stroke Association, recognition programs that evaluate and report on the quality of care at the individual physician level.

Health Plan Accreditation

The NCQA accreditation process is best illustrated by its health plan accreditation program. More than 75% of individuals enrolled in HMOs are in plans currently accredited by NCQA. Organizations seeking NCQA accreditation must report via a Web-based tool (the Interactive Survey System) their adherence to standards that evaluate the health plan's clinical and administrative systems, including efforts to continuously improve the quality of care and service it delivers. In addition, plans are required to report, and are scored on their performance on, a set of clinical quality measures (Health Plan Employer Data and Information Set, or HEDIS®; see next page).

Plans are reviewed against and scored on more than 80 standards and on clinical measures in the following categories:

- Quality improvement
- Credentialing
- Members' rights and responsibilities
- Preventive health services
- Utilization management
- Medical records
- Performance on HEDIS measures (clinical and patient experiences)

NCQA accreditation surveys are conducted by teams of physicians and managed care experts. A national oversight committee of physicians analyzes the team's findings and assigns one of five possible accreditation levels (excellent, commendable, accredited, provisional, or denied) based on the plan's level of compliance with NCQA standards. NCQA's health plan accreditation process is thus unique among accreditation programs in its use of direct measures of clinical performance in scoring of accreditation.

Recognition Programs

NCQA Recognition programs help consumers, employers and health plans identify clinicians who demonstrate that they provide their patients with the evidence-based care they need, when they need it.

Patient-Centered Medical Home (PCMH) recognition highlights primary care practices that meet national standards for patient access, care coordination and evaluation of performance and patient experience. The NCQA medical home program is the most widely adopted medical home model in the country.

A complement to PCMH recognition, Patient-Centered Specialty Practice (PCSP) recognition, highlights practices outside of primary care that coordinate care with their primary care colleagues and each other, provide timely access to care and engage in continuous improvement.

The Diabetes Recognition Program (DRP) highlights clinicians who provide high quality care to diabetic patients. The Heart/Stroke Recognition Program (HSRP) designates physicians who provide evidence-based care to patients with cardiac conditions or who have had a stroke.

NCQA-Recognized practices and clinicians are often eligible for financial incentives. Private commercial health plan pay-for-performance (P4P) programs, as well as multistakeholder initiatives that provide technical assistance and training, often prompt clinicians to seek NCQA Recognition.

Performance Measurement

HEDIS® and related NCQA Clinical Measures

NCQA manages the most widely used set of performance measurements for evaluating quality in ambulatory care, HEDIS®. This measurement set, which includes more than 80 fully specified and standardized measures, is used to evaluate health care quality aggregated at the health plans level. NCQA has also created a companion set of measures for use in reporting at the physician office practice level, including those used in the various physician recognition programs. Nearly all of the physician-level measures have been endorsed by the National Quality Forum (NQF). NCQA has also worked with the AMA-sponsored Physician Consortium on Performance Improvement on developing a broad set of clinical measures for the CMS-sponsored Physician Quality Reporting Incentive program (PQRI).

Work on measurement has led NCQA to develop projects and programs related to distribution and reporting of performance data, ensuring data accuracy, and making sure the performance data are useful to help guide choice.

In summary, NCQA's work in the area of health care evaluation focuses on four key areas: accreditation, recognition programs, data audit oversight, and collection of HEDIS® and related measures. NCQA publicly reports performance data through Quality Compass® (a national database of HEDIS® data and accreditation information) as well as various other evaluation reports for physicians, plans, consumers, and purchasers.

Contact Information

National Committee for Quality Assurance
1100 13th St, NW
Washington, DC 20056
(202) 955-3500
(202) 955-3599 Fax
www.ncqa.org

Administrators in Medicine (AIM)

Administrators in Medicine (AIM), a not-for-profit organization, is the national organization for state medical and osteopathic board executives. Founded in 1984, AIM has the mission of assisting and supporting administrators for medical licensing and regulatory authorities to achieve administrative excellence and ultimately advance public safety. AIM offers education, research, and online services for its membership, both in the US and, increasingly, internationally. AIM provides public outreach through its online search engine along with board Web links on its *AIM DocFinder* website.

Education is the cornerstone of what AIM does as an organization for member board executives. AIM sponsors a variety of educational seminars, including AIM Regional Meetings, where board executives discuss operational issues. Its AIM Institute Educational Workshops—Physician Licensing and Technology—provide an overview of best practices and how to avoid pitfalls. The workshops are presented by board senior staff and experts from the credentialing and technology fields. Its Annual Meeting educational program provides an opportunity to hear from national experts in a variety of fields impacting medical licensure and discipline.

AIM's *State Medical Board Executive Certification Program (JAFEI-CMBE)* offers education, training and group discussion in key areas, including human resources; legislative process; professionalism; communication; policy development; public relations; press relations; personnel management; support services; leadership and strategic planning.

AIM's *State Medical Board Investigator Certification Program (CMBI)* seeks to address the need for highly trained medical board investigators. This specialized training program provides education and resources for individuals conducting investigations for state medical and osteopathic boards. The program includes basic investigation techniques and draws upon recent issues facing boards by presenting the latest investigative techniques to address them.

The AIM DocFinder

The AIM *DocFinder* was the only online physician directory of its kind when it was established in 1996. *DocFinder* contains the licensing background and disciplinary information of physicians and other health care practitioners, in addition to physician profile information from states that have passed physician profile laws. *DocFinder*, which is recognized for its easy-to-use search engine, is the only combined database of all licensing jurisdictions that derives its data directly from and is controlled by state licensing boards. Free of charge to the public, AIM *DocFinder* is available at www.docboard.org.

Appendixes

Appendix A

Boards of Medical Examiners in the United States and Possessions

Alabama State Board of Medical Examiners
848 Washington Ave
P.O. Box 946
Montgomery, AL 36101-0946
www.albme.org

Alaska State Medical Board
Division of Occupational Licensing
550 W Seventh Ave. Suite 1500
Anchorage, AK 99501
www.commerce.state.ak.us/occ/pmed.htm

Arizona Medical Board
9545 E Doubletree Ranch Rd
Scottsdale, AZ 85258-5514
www.azmd.gov

Arkansas State Medical Board
1401 W. Capital, Suite 340
Little Rock, AR 72201-2936
www.armedicalboard.org

Medical Board of California
2005 Evergreen Street
Suite 1200
Sacramento, CA 95815
www.mbc.ca.gov

Colorado Medical Board
1560 Broadway, Ste 1300
Denver, CO 80202-5140
www.dora.state.co.us/medical

State of Connecticut, Department of Health
Physician Licensure Unit
PO Box 340308, 410 Capital Ave, MS 13PHO
Hartford, CT 06134-0308
www.ct.gov/dph

Delaware Board of Medical Licensure and Discipline
861 Silver Lake Blvd, Ste 203
Cannon Building
Dover, DE 19904
www.dpr.delaware.gov

District of Columbia Board of Medicine
Health Professional Licensing Administration
899 North Capitol Street, NE 2nd Fl
Washington, DC 20002
www.hrla.doh.dc.gov

Florida Board of Medicine
Bin # C03
4052 Bald Cypress Way
Tallahassee, FL 32399-3253
www.flboardofmedicine.gov/

Georgia Composite State Board of Medical Examiners
2 Peachtree Street, NW, 36th Floor
Atlanta, GA 30303
http://medicalboard.georgia.gov/

Health Professional Licensing Center
123 Chalan Kareta
South Route 10
Mangilao, GU 96913
www.dphss.guam.gov/

Hawaii Medical Board
335 Merchant St, Rm 301
P.O. Box 3469
Honolulu, HI 96813
http://hawaii.gov/dcca/pvl

Idaho State Board of Medicine
1755 Westgate Dr
Suite 140
Boise, ID 83704
www.bom.idaho.gov

Illinois Medical Licensing Board
Department of Professional Regulation
320 W Washington, 3rd Fl
Springfield, IL 62786
www.idfpr.com

Medical Licensing Board of Indiana
Indiana Professional Licensing Agency
402 W Washington St, Rm W072
Indianapolis, IN 46204
www.in.gov/pla/medical.htm

Iowa Board of Medicine
400 SW 8th St, Suite C
Des Moines, IA 50309-4686
www.medicalboard.iowa.gov

Kansas Board of Healing Arts
800 SW Jackson, Lower Level-Suite A
Topeka, KS 66612
www.ksbha.org

Kentucky Board of Medical Licensure
Hurstbourne Office Park
310 Whittington Pkwy, Ste 1B
Louisville, KY 40222-4916
kbml.ky.gov

Louisiana State Board of Medical Examiners
630 Camp St
PO Box 30250
New Orleans, LA 70190-0250
http://lsbme.la.gov

Maine Board of Licensure in Medicine
137 State House Station
Augusta, ME 04333
www.maine.gov/md

Maryland Board of Physicians
4201 Patterson Ave
Baltimore, MD 21215-0095
www.mbp.state.md.us

Massachusetts Board of Registration in Medicine
200 Harvard Mill Square
Suite 330
Boston, MA 01880
www.massmedboard.org

Michigan Board of Medicine
611 W Ottawa St., 1st Floor
PO Box 30670
Lansing, MI 48933
www.michigan.gov/healthlicense

Minnesota Board of Medical Practice
University Park Plaza
2829 University Ave SE, Ste 500
Minneapolis, MN 55414-3246
www.bmp.state.mn.us

Mississippi State Board of Medical Licensure
1867 Crane Ridge Dr, Ste 200B
Jackson, MS 39216
www.msbml.state.ms.us

Missouri State Board of Registration for the Healing Arts
Division of Professional Registration
3605 Missouri Blvd
Jefferson City, MO 65109
http://pr.mo.gov/healingarts.asp

Montana Board of Medical Examiners
PO Box 200513
301 S Park Ave, 4th Floor
Helena, MT 59620-0513
http://bsd.dli.mt.gov/license/bsd_boards/med_board/board_
page.asp

Nebraska Department of Health and Human Services
Licensure Unit
301 Centennial Mall South, PO Box 94986
Lincoln, NE 68509-4986
http://dhhs.ne.gov/Pages/default.aspx

Nevada State Board of Medical Examiners
1105 Terminal Way, Ste 301
Reno, NV 89502
www.medboard.nv.gov/

New Hampshire Board of Medicine
2 Industrial Park Dr, Ste 8
Concord, NH 03301-8520
www.nh.gov/medicine/

New Jersey State Board of Medical Examiners
PO Box 183
140 E Front Street, 2nd Fl
Trenton, NJ 08625-0183
www.state.nj.us/lps/ca/medical.htm#bme5

New Mexico State Board of Medical Examiners
2055 S Pacheco St
Building 400
Santa Fe, NM 87505
www.nmmb.state.nm.us

New York State Board for Medicine
89 Washington Ave, Rm 306
Albany, NY 12234
www.op.nysed.gov/

North Carolina Medical Board
PO Box 20007
Raleigh, NC 27619
www.ncmedboard.org/

North Dakota State Board of Medical Examiners
418 E Broadway Ave, Ste 12
Bismarck, ND 58501
https://www.ndbomex.org/

State Medical Board of Ohio
30 E Broad St, 3rd Fl
Columbus, OH 43215-6127
www.med.ohio.gov/

Oklahoma State Board of Medical Licensure and
Supervision
101 NE 51st
Oklahoma City, OK 73105
www.okmedicalboard.org/

Oregon Medical Board
1500 SW First Ave
620 Crown Plaza
Portland, OR 97201-5826
www.oregon.gov/omb

Pennsylvania State Board of Medicine
2601 North Third St
PO Box 2649
Harrisburg, PA 17110-2649
www.portal.state.pa.us/portal/server.pt/community/state_bo
ard_of_medicine/12512

Puerto Rico Board of Medical Licensure and Discipline
PO Box 13969
San Juan, PR 00908

Rhode Island Board of Medical Licensure and Discipline
Cannon Bldg
Three Capitol Hill
Providence, RI 02908-5097
www.health.ri.gov/hsr/bmld/

South Carolina Board of Medical Examiners
Department of Labor, Licensing & Regulation
110 Centerview Dr, Ste 202
Columbia, SC 29210-1289
http://llr.state.sc.us/pol/medical/

South Dakota Board of Medical & Osteopathic Examiners
101 N. Main Ave. Ste 301
Sioux Falls, SD 57104
www.sdbmoe.gov/

Tennessee Board of Medical Examiners
227 French Landing #300
Heritage Place, Metro Center
Nashville, TN 37243
http://state.tn.us/health

Texas Medical Board
PO Box 2018
Austin, TX 78768-2018
www.tmb.state.tx.us/

Utah Department of Commerce
Division of Occupational & Professional Licensure
PO Box 146741
Salt Lake City, UT 84114-6741
www.dopl.utah.gov/

Virgin Islands Board of Medical Examiners
Office of the Commissioner, Department of Health
1303 Hospital Ground, Suite 10
St Thomas, VI 00802
http://fsmb.org/fcvs_ssr_virgin_islands.html

Virginia Board of Medicine
9960 Mayland Dr, Suite 300
Henrico, VA 232331463
www.dhp.virginia.gov

Vermont Board of Medical Practice
108 Cherry St.
PO Box 70
Burlington, VT 05402-0070
http://healthvermont.gov/hc/med_board/bmp.aspx

Washington Medical Quality Assurance Commission
Department of Health
PO Box 47866
Olympia, WA 98504-7866
www.doh.wa.gov/

West Virginia Board of Medicine
101 Dee Dr
Suite 103
Charleston, WV 25311
www.wvbom.wv.gov

Wisconsin Medical Examining Board
Department of Safety and Professional Services
PO Box 8935
Madison, WI 53708-8935
http://dsps.wi.gov

Wyoming Board of Medicine
130 Hobbs Ave., Ste 200
Cheyenne, WY 82002
http://wyomedboard.state.wy.us/

Appendix B

Boards of Osteopathic Medical Examiners in the United States and Possessions

Arizona Board of Osteopathic Examiners in Medicine &
Surgery
9535 E Doubletree Ranch Rd
Scottsdale, AZ 85258-5539
www.azdo.gov

Osteopathic Medical Board of California
1300 National Drive, #150
Sacramento, CA 95834
www.ombc.ca.gov

Florida Board of Osteopathic Medicine
Bin #C06
4052 Bald Cypress Way
Tallahassee, FL 32399-1753
www.doh.state.fl.us/mqa/osteopath/

Maine Board of Osteopathic Licensure
142 State House Station
Augusta, ME 04333-0142
www.maine.gov/osteo/

Michigan Board of Osteopathic Medicine and Surgery
611 W Ottawa St
1st floor
Lansing, MI 48933
www.michigan.gov/healthlicense

Nevada State Board of Osteopathic Medicine
901 American Pacific Drive
Unit 180
Henderson, NV 89014
www.bom.nv.gov

New Mexico Board of Osteopathic Medical Examiners
2550 Cerrillos Road
Santa Fe, NM 87505
www.rld.state.nm.us/boards/osteopathy.aspx

Oklahoma State Board of Osteopathic Examiners
4848 N Lincoln Blvd, Ste 100
Oklahoma City, OK 73105-3321
www.osboe.ok.gov

Pennsylvania State Board of Osteopathic Medicine
PO Box 2649
Harrisburg, PA 17101
www.dos.state.pa.us

Tennessee State Board of Osteopathic Examiners
227 French Landing, Suite 300
Heritage Place Metro Center
Nashville, TN 37247
http://health.state.tn.us/

State of Utah Department of Commerce
Division of Occupational & Professional Licensing
PO Box 146741
Salt Lake City, UT 84114-6741
www.dopl.utah.gov/

Vermont Board of Osteopathic Physicians and Surgeons
89 Main Street, 3rd Floor
Montpelier, VT 05620-3402
www.vtprofessionals.org

Washington Board of Osteopathic Medicine & Surgery
Department of Health
PO Box 47852
Olympia, WA 98504-7852
www.doh.wa.gov

West Virginia Board of Osteopathic Medicine
405 Capitol Street
Suite 402
Charleston, WV 25301
https://www.wvbdosteo.org/

Appendix C

Member Organizations of the Federation of Medical Regulatory Authorities of Canada

Fleur-Ange Lefebvre, Executive Director and CEO
Federation of Medical Regulatory Authorities of Canada
103 - 2283 St Laurent Blvd, Ste 103
Ottawa, ON K1G 5A2
(613) 738-0372
Email: info@fmrac.ca
www.fmrac.ca

College of Physicians and Surgeons of Alberta
2700 Telus Plaza South
10020 - 100 Street NW
Edmonton, AB T5J 0N3
(780) 423-4764
www.cpsa.ab.ca

College of Physicians and Surgeons of British Columbia
400 - 858 Beatty St
Vancouver, BC V6B 1C1
(604) 733 7758
www.cpsbc.ca

College of Physicians and Surgeons of Manitoba
1000 - 1661 Portage Ave
Winnipeg, MB R3J 3T7
(204) 774-4344
www.cpsm.mb.ca

College of Physicians and Surgeons of New Brunswick
One Hampton Rd, Ste 300
Rothesay, NB E2E 5K8
(506) 849-5050
www.cpsnb.org

College of Physicians and Surgeons of Newfoundland and Labrador
120 Torbay Road, Suite W100
St. John's, NL A1A 2GB
(709) 726-8546
www.cpsnl.ca

College of Physicians and Surgeons of Nova Scotia
Suite 5005 - 7071 Bayers Rd
Halifax, NS B3L 2C2
(902) 422-5823
www.cpsns.ns.ca

Department of Health and Social Services
Government of Nunavut
Box 390
Kugluktuk, NU X0B 0E0
(867) 982-7655
Email: bharvey@gov.nu.ca

Department of Health and Social Service
Government of the Northwest Territories
Centre Square Tower, 8th Fl, PO Box 1320
Yellowknife, NT X1A 2L9
(867) 920-8058
Email: Samantha_VanGene@gov.nt.ca

College of Physicians and Surgeons of Ontario
80 College St
Toronto, ON M5G 2E2
(416) 967-2600
www.cpso.on.ca

College of Physicians and Surgeons of Prince Edward Island
14 Paramount Drive
Charlottetown, PE C1E 0C7
(902) 566-3861
www.cpspei.ca

College des médecins du Québec
2170 boulevard René Lévésque Ouest
Montréal, QC H3H 2T8
(514) 933-4441
www.cmq.org

College of Physicians and Surgeons of Saskatchewan
500-321A 21st Street East
Saskatoon, SK S7K 0C1
(306) 244-7355
www.quadrant.net/cpss

Yukon Medical Council
PO Box 2703 (c-18)
Whitehorse, Yukon Y1A 2C6
(867) 667-3774
www.yukonmedicalcouncil.ca

Appendix D

Glossary of Medical Licensure Terms

Accreditation Council for Graduate Medical Education (ACGME)

Note: See Chapter 6 for more information.

An accrediting agency with the mission of improving health care by assessing and advancing the quality of resident physicians' education through accreditation. The ACGME establishes national standards for graduate medical education by which it approves and continually assesses educational programs under its aegis. The ACGME accredits GME programs through its 28 review committees (26 Residency Review Committees, or RRCs, the Transitional Year Review Committee, and the Institutional Review Committee). The ACGME has five member organizations:

- American Board of Medical Specialties
- American Hospital Association
- American Medical Association
- Association of American Medical Colleges
- Council of Medical Specialty Societies

Each member organization nominates four individuals to the ACGME's Board of Directors. In addition, the Board includes three public representatives, two resident representatives, and the chair of the Council of Review Committee Chairs; the Board may also include one to four directors at large. A representative for the federal government also serves on the Board in a non-voting capacity.

American Board of Medical Specialties (ABMS®)

Note: See Chapter 6 for more information.

A nonprofit organization of 24 approved medical specialty boards. Its mission is to maintain and improve the quality of medical care by helping its member boards develop and use professional and educational standards for the evaluation and certification of physician specialists. The certification of physicians provides assurance to the public that a physician specialist certified by an ABMS member board has successfully completed an approved educational program and an evaluation process that assesses the knowledge, skills, and experience required to provide quality patient care in that specialty. Medical specialty board

certification is an additional process to receiving a medical degree, completing residency training, and receiving a license to practice medicine.

Bureau of Osteopathic Specialists (BOS)

Note: See Chapter 6 for more information.

A non-profit umbrella organization for 18 medical specialty boards in the United States, the BOS oversees certification of osteopathic physicians (DOs) in the United States. The BOS assists its Member Boards in developing and implementing educational and professional standards to evaluate and certify physician specialists. The BOS is recognized by key health care accreditation organizations as a primary source of physician board certification data on medical specialists for credentialing purposes.

Osteopathic physicians may obtain different types of certification, such as Primary Certification, Certificate of Special Qualifications, Certification of Added Qualifications, and Osteopathic Continuous Certification.

AOA Council on Continuing Medical Education

The Council on Continuing Medical Education (CCME) has been delegated authority by the American Osteopathic Association Board of Trustees to monitor osteopathic CME and to grant or deny Category 1 accreditation status to osteopathic CME sponsors. For more information, see the AOA website at www.osteopathic.org/inside-aoa/accreditation/Pages/cme-sponsor-accreditation.aspx.

Boards and certification

Note: See Chapter 6 for more information.

Each medical specialty (as defined by the ABMS or AOA) has its own unique Board examination process. This process is voluntary and is intended to assure the public that a certified medical specialist has successfully completed an approved educational program and an evaluation including an examination process designed to assess the knowledge, experience, and skills requisite to the provision of high quality patient care in that specialty.

General board certification is the first certification awarded by an ABMS member board or the AOA BOS to approved candidates who meet the requirements for certification in a specified field of medical practice.

Subspecialty board certification is conferred by one or more ABMS member boards in a component of a specialty or subspecialty. It is conferred only to certified medical specialists who have been certified by one or more member boards in an area of general certification.

Some ABMS member boards and the AOA also issue *certificates of added qualifications* or *certificates of special qualifications.* (Source: ABMS)

Also see "Maintenance of Certification" and/or "Osteopathic Continuous Certificaiton"

Clerkship

Note: See page 39 for more information.

Clinical education provided to medical students. Table 13 contains information on clerkship regulations of state medical boards.

Clinical Skills Assessment (CSA)

A 1-day exam, formerly administered by the ECFMG, that required examinees to demonstrate both clinical proficiency and spoken English language proficiency. Step 2 Clinical Skills (Step 2 CS) of the USMLE is the exam currently administered that satisfies the clinical skills requirement for ECFMG Certification.

Also see "Step 2 CS," page 105.

Commission on Osteopathic College Accreditation (COCA)

The Commission on Osteopathic College Accreditation (COCA), of the American Osteopathic Association, is recognized by the United States Department of Education (USDE). Accreditation by COCA signifies that a college of osteopathic medicine has met or exceeded the COCA standards for educational quality with respect to mission, goals, and objectives; governance, administration, and finance; facilities, equipment, and resources, faculty, student admissions, performance, and evaluation; preclinical and clinical curriculum; and research and scholarship activity. For more information, see the AOA website at www.osteopathic.org/inside-aoa/accreditation/predoctoral%20accreditation/Pages/standards-and-

procedures-disclaimer.aspx.

Comprehensive Osteopathic Medical Licensure Examination (COMLEX)

Note: See Chapter 3 for more information.

The three-level Comprehensive Osteopathic Medical Licensure Examination of the United States (COMLEX), administered by the National Board of Osteopathic Medical Examiners (NBOME), is the primary pathway to licensure for osteopathic physicians seeking to practice osteopathic medicine and surgery. A passing score on these examinations indicates that the candidate's medical knowledge and clinical skills have met a national standard. The COMLEX examination sequence is accepted for licensure in all 50 states and a number of international jurisdictions.

The COMLEX examination series is designed to assess the osteopathic medical knowledge and clinical skills considered essential for osteopathic generalist physicians to practice medicine without supervision. The COMLEX examination sequence uses a primary care approach to patient care with the distinctiveness of osteopathic medicine fully integrated throughout the examination.

Comprehensive Osteopathic Medical Variable-Purpose Examination (COMVEX)

The Comprehensive Osteopathic Medical Variable-Purpose Examination (COMVEX) is a post-licensure examination for osteopathic physicians who require reevaluation after initial licensure. COMVEX is a computer-delivered examination administered at professional testing centers nationwide, with at least one testing location in each of the 50 states. The examination uses the same basic design features of the COMLEX and employs the same "Dimensions" to assess the candidate. The examination contains 400 test items using objective type questions such as multiple choice, single best answer, and matching test items.

COMLEX Level 2-Performance Evaluation

The COMLEX Level 2-PE is a one-day examination of clinical skills where each candidate will encounter 12 standardized patients over the course of a seven-hour examination day.

Consistent with NBOME's mission to protect the public, COMLEX Level 2-PE fulfills the public and licensing authority mandate for enhanced patient safety through the documentation of the clinical skills proficiency of graduates from osteopathic medical schools. The Performance Evaluation augments the written COMLEX Level 2-Cognitive Evaluation (CE) of osteopathic medical knowledge by providing an assessment of fundamental clinical skills. These clinical skills are:

- Doctor-patient communication
- Interpersonal skills and professionalism
- Medical history-taking and physical examination skills
- Osteopathic principles and osteopathic manipulative treatment and
- Written communication skills (including synthesis of clinical findings, integrated differential diagnosis and formulation of a diagnostic and treatment plan)

Educational Commission for Foreign Medical Graduates (ECFMG)

Note: See Chapter 4 for more information.

A nonprofit organization that assesses the readiness of graduates of foreign medical schools to enter residency programs in the United States accredited by the Accreditation Council for Graduate Medical Education (ACGME).

ECFMG certification provides assurance to directors of ACGME-accredited residency programs, and to the people of the United States, that graduates of foreign medical schools have met minimum standards of eligibility required to enter such programs. This certification does not guarantee that such graduates will be accepted into these programs in the United States, since the number of applicants frequently exceeds the number of positions available.

ECFMG certification is also a prerequisite required by most states for licensure to practice medicine in the United States and is one of the eligibility requirements to take Step 3 of the United States Medical Licensing Examination (USMLE).

Endorsement, licensure

Note: See page 14 for more information.

A process through which a state issues an unrestricted license to practice medicine to an individual who holds a valid and unrestricted license in another jurisdiction. Licensure endorsement is generally based on documenta-

tion of successfully completing approved examinations, authentication of required core documents, and completion of any additional requirements assessing the applicant's fitness to practice medicine in the new jurisdiction. Previously referred to as "reciprocity."

Fellow

A. A physician in an ACGME-accredited program that is beyond the requirements for eligibility for first board certification in the discipline. Such physicians may also be termed "resident" as well. Other uses of the term "fellow" require modifiers for precision and clarity, e.g., "research fellow."
Also see "Resident or resident physician."

B. A physician who has demonstrated outstanding achievements in medicine, usually within a given medical specialty society. Typical criteria for fellowship in a specialty society include years of membership, years as a practitioner in the specialty, and professional recognition by peers.

Federation Licensing Examination (FLEX)

Note: See page 19 for more information.

Originally introduced in 1968 and subsequently enhanced and modified in 1985, this examination was administered for the last time in December 1993. In 1994, the United States Medical Licensing Examination (USMLE) was fully implemented. Some candidates for licensure may have a combination of scores from FLEX and USMLE. *Also see "United States Medical Licensing Examination."*

Federation of State Medical Boards (FSMB)

Note: See Chapter 3 for more information.

A nonprofit organization whose membership comprises the allopathic, osteopathic, and composite medical licensing boards of all the states, the District of Columbia, Guam, Puerto Rico, and the Virgin Islands. Its primary responsibility is to protect the public through the regulation of physicians and other health care providers. It serves as a liaison, advocate, and information source to the public, health care organizations, and state, national, and international authorities. The FSMB promotes high standards for physician licensure and practice and assists and supports state medical boards collectively and individually in the regulation of medical practice and in their role of public protection.

Fifth Pathway

Note: See page 34 for more information.

Discontinued as of June 30, 2009, the Fifth Pathway was one of several ways for individuals who obtained their undergraduate medical education abroad to enter GME in the United States. The Fifth Pathway was a period of supervised clinical training for students who obtained their premedical education in the United States, received undergraduate medical education abroad, and passed Step 1 of the United States Medical Licensing Examination. After these students successfully completed a year of clinical training sponsored by a US medical school accredited by the Liaison Committee on Medical Education (LCME) and pass USMLE Step 2, they received a Fifth Pathway certificate and became eligible for an ACGME-accredited residency as an international medical graduate.

FLEX Weighted Average (FWA)

Note: See page 19 for more information.

All states currently require a minimum passing score of 75 on each component of the post-1985 two-part FLEX; the resulting number composes the Federation Licensing Examination (FLEX) Weighted Average.

Healthcare Facilities Accreditation Program (HFAP)

The Healthcare Facilities Accreditation Program (HFAP) of the American Osteopathic Association has been providing medical facilities with an objective review of their services since 1945. The program is recognized nationally by the federal government, state governments, insurance carriers, and managed care organizations.

Initial license

Note: See page 97 for more information.

The first ever full and unrestricted license a physician receives in his/her medical career. Some medical boards interpret "initial license" as a physician's first license in their particular states (although the physician could already have been licensed in other states). This publication does not use the term in this sense.

Intern

No longer used by the AMA, AOA, or ACGME. Historically, "intern" was used to designate individuals in the first post-MD or -DO year of hospital training; less commonly, it designated individuals in the first year of any residency program. Since 1975, the AMA's *Graduate Medical Education Directory* and the ACGME have used "resident," "resident physician," or "fellow" to designate all individuals in ACGME-accredited programs. *Also see "Resident or resident physician" and "Fellow."*

International medical graduate (IMG)

A graduate from a medical school outside of the United States and Canada. Formerly referred to as "foreign medical graduate" (FMG).

Liaison Committee on Medical Education (LCME)

The body that accredits educational programs in the United States and Canada leading to the MD degree. The American Osteopathic Association (AOA) accredits educational programs leading to the doctor of osteopathy (DO) degree.

Licensure

The process by which a state or jurisdiction of the United States admits physicians to the practice of medicine. Licensure ensures that practicing physicians have appropriate education and training and that they abide by recognized standards of professional conduct while serving their patients. Candidates for first licensure must complete a rigorous examination designed to assess a physician's ability to apply knowledge, concepts, and principles that are important in health and disease and that constitute the basis of safe and effective patient care. All applicants must submit proof of medical education and training and provide details about their work history. Finally, applicants may have to reveal information regarding past medical history (including the use of habit-forming drugs and emotional or mental illness), arrests, and convictions. *Also see "Limited license" and "Reregistration."*

Limited license

Note: See page 77 for more information.

Issued by state medical boards to resident physicians in graduate medical education (GME) programs within their jurisdictions. Physicians do not receive a full and unrestricted license until completion of GME and fulfillment of other licensure requirements in a given jurisdiction.

Maintenance of Certification

Note: See page 143 for more information.

To better evaluate the competence of physician specialists throughout their careers, ABMS Member Boards are moving from "recertification" to a more comprehensive plan called "maintenance of certification." Where recertification programs evaluate physicians every seven to 10 years, primarily by a written examination, Maintenance of Certification© is an in-depth program that will be continuous and relevant to practice. A key component of this program is the evaluation of physician practice performance, including six core competencies (patient care, medical knowledge, interpersonal and communication skills, professionalism, practice-based learning and improvement, and systems-based practice).

Medical Practice Act

A statute of a US state or jurisdiction that outlines the practice of medicine and the responsibility of the medical board to regulate that practice. The primary responsibility and obligation of a state medical board is to protect the public through proper licensing and regulation of physicians and, in some jurisdictions, other health care professionals. *Also see "Unprofessional conduct."*

National Board of Medical Examiners (NBME)

Note: See Chapter 3 for more information.

A nonprofit, independent organization that prepares and administers medical qualifying examinations, either independently or jointly with other organizations. Legal agencies governing the practice of medicine within each US state or jurisdiction may grant a license without further examination for those physicians who have successfully completed such examinations and met other requirements.

Currently, the NBME administers USMLE Steps 1 and 2 to students and graduates of US and Canadian medical and osteopathic schools accredited by the Liaison Committee on Medical Education or the American Osteopathic Association.

National Board of Osteopathic Medical Examiners (NBOME)

Note: See Chapter 3 for more information.

A not-for-profit corporation serving the public and state licensing agencies by administering examinations testing the medical knowledge of those who seek to practice as osteopathic physicians.

The NBOME examinations have been the primary pathway by which osteopathic physicians have applied for licensure to practice osteopathic medicine. A passing score on these examinations verifies a student's adequacy of medical knowledge for practicing osteopathic medicine.

Osteopathic Continuous Certification (OCC)

The American Osteopathic Association's Bureau of Osteopathic Specialists (BOS) has mandated that each specialty certifying board implement "Osteopathic Continuous Certification" (OCC). OCC will serve as a way in which board-certified DOs can maintain currency and demonstrate competency in their specialty area. The only change to the current osteopathic recertification process is the addition of a Practice Performance Assessment.

Each specialty certifying board is currently developing OCC and will have the OCC process in place and implemented by January 1, 2013. DOs who hold time-limited certificates will be required to participate in the five components of the OCC process to maintain osteopathic board certification. For more information, see the AOA website at www.osteopathic.org/inside-aoa/development/aoa-board-certification/Pages/osteopathic-continuous-certification.aspx.

Osteopathic Post-Doctoral Training Institutions (OPTI)

Osteopathic Postdoctoral Training Institutions (OPTIs) provide an enhanced quality assurance mechanism for postdoctoral training programs approved by the American Osteopathic Association. Partnerships and collaborations between academic medicine, hospitals and other community-based healthcare facilities are an integral part of OPTI.

Part of the OPTI accreditation process includes encouraging clinical medical education research. Research programs are available to osteopathic interns and residents throughout each year of training. These programs are developed in conjunction with guidelines and requirements of osteopathic specialty colleges for residency training programs and the Council on Postdoctoral Training for internship programs. For more information, see the AOA website at www.osteopathic.org/inside-aoa/accreditation/opti-approval/Pages/default.aspx.

Reregistration

Note: See page 65 for more information.

After physicians are licensed in a state or jurisdiction, they must reregister periodically to continue their active status. During this reregistration process, physicians are required to demonstrate that they have maintained acceptable standards of ethics and medical practice and have not engaged in improper conduct. In many states, physicians must also show that they have completed a set number of hours of continuing medical education.

Resident or resident physician

Any individual at any level in an ACGME-accredited GME program, including subspecialty programs. Local usage might refer to these individuals as interns, house officers, house staff, trainees, fellows, or other comparable terminology. Beginning in 2000, the ACGME has used the term "fellow" to denote physicians in subspecialty programs (vs residents in specialty programs) or in GME programs that are beyond the requirements for eligibility for first board certification in the discipline.

Also see "Fellow."

Special Purpose Examination (SPEX)

Note: See page 115 for more information.

This 1-day, computer-administered examination, with approximately 420 multiple-choice questions, assesses primary care medical knowledge and skills. It does not include questions specific to a particular specialty or subspecialty. The SPEX is used to assess physicians who have held a valid, unrestricted license in a US or Canadian jurisdiction who are:

- Required by the state medical board to demonstrate current medical knowledge

- Seeking endorsement licensure some years beyond initial examination
- Seeking license reinstatement after a period of professional inactivity

Physicians holding a valid, unrestricted license may also apply for SPEX, independent of any request or approval from a medical licensing board.

Specialty

A medical specialty is a defined area of medical practice that connotes special knowledge and ability resulting from specialized effort and training in the special field. (Source: ABMS)

Also see "Subspecialty."

Step 2 CS

The Clinical Skills component of USMLE Step 2, in tandem with the Clinical Knowledge component (Step 2 CK), became a part of Step 2 in June 2004. Step 2 assesses whether medical school students and graduates can understand and apply the knowledge, skills, and understanding of clinical science considered essential for the provision of patient care under supervision and includes emphasis on health promotion and disease prevention. The inclusion of Step 2 in the USMLE sequence is intended to ensure that due attention is devoted to principles of clinical sciences and basic patient-centered skills that provide the foundation for safe and competent medical practice.

Subspecialty

A medical subspecialty is an identifiable component of a specialty to which a practicing physician may devote a significant proportion of time. Practice in the subspecialty follows special educational experience in addition to that required for general certification. (*Note:* Two different specialty fields may include two or more similar subspecialty areas, e.g., sports medicine as a subspecialty of emergency medicine and family practice. In these cases the identified subspecialty area might use the same title and equivalent educational standards.) (Source: ABMS)

Also see "Specialty."

Telemedicine

Note: See page 87 for more information.

Telemedicine is the delivery of health care services via electronic means from a health care provider in one location to a patient in another. Applications that fall under this definition include the transfer of medical images, such as pathology slides or radiographs, interactive video consultations between patient and provider or between primary care and specialty care physicians, and mental health consultations.

Unprofessional conduct

Although laws vary from one jurisdiction to the next, the Medical Practice Acts in force in most US jurisdictions would define unprofessional conduct as including:

- Physical abuse of a patient
- Inadequate recordkeeping
- Not recognizing or acting on common symptoms
- Prescribing drugs in excessive amounts or without legitimate reason
- Impaired ability to practice due to addiction or physical or mental illness
- Failing to meet continuing medical education requirements
- Performing duties beyond the scope of a license
- Dishonesty
- Conviction of a felony
- Delegating the practice of medicine to an unlicensed individual

Unprofessional conduct would not include minor disagreements or poor customer service.

United States Medical Licensing Examination (USMLE)

Note: See Chapter 3 for more information.

This three-step examination for US medical licensure provides a common evaluation system for applicants. The USMLE program is governed by a composite committee of representatives from the Federation of State Medical Boards (FSMB), the National Board of Medical Examiners (NBME), the Educational Commission for Foreign Medical Graduates (ECFMG), and the public.

Results of the USMLE are reported to state medical boards for use in granting the initial license to practice medicine. Each medical licensing authority requires, as part of its licensing processes, successful completion of an examination or other certification demonstrating qualification for licensure.

The USMLE replaced FLEX and the certifying examination of the NBME, as well as the Foreign Medical Graduate Examination in the Medical Sciences (FMGEMS), which was formerly used by the ECFMG for certification purposes. Steps 1 and 2 of the USMLE are used as the examination for ECFMG certification. These two steps are also used for promotion and graduation in some US medical schools.

Appendix E

AMA Policy on Medical Licensure

The AMA has a number of policy statements concerning medical licensure. Following is representative AMA policy in this regard, as found in the AMA's Policy Finder, using a search for the term "licensure" (returning 105 results total) in July 2011.

The H prefix indicates that the policy was developed by the AMA House of Delegates; the D prefix indicates that the policy is a directive from the AMA House for the Association to take a specific action.

The number assigned to a policy indicates the topic addressed by the policy. For example, House policies coded between H-255.001 and H-255.999 all relate to the topic of "International Medical Graduates."

Contents

- The Promotion of Quality Telemedicine (H-480.969)
- Evolving Impact of Telemedicine (H-480.974)
- Allocation of Privileges to Use Health Care Technologies (H-480.988)

D-120.000 Drugs: Prescribing and Dispensing

- Concerning Pain Management (D-120.983)

D-130.000 Emergency Medical Services

- All Hazards Disaster Preparedness and Response (D-130.972)
- Emergency Preparedness (D-130.974)

D-160.000 Health Care Delivery

- Licensure and Liability for Senior Physician Volunteers (D-160.991)

D-255.000 International Medical Graduates

- Alternate Licensure Protocols for IMGs (D-255.997)

D-275.000 Licensure and Discipline

- Threat to Medical Licensure (D-275.962)
- Eliminating Disparities in Licensure for IMG Physicians (D-275.966)
- Telemedicine and Medical Licensure (D-275.967)
- Depression and Physician Licensure (D-275.974)
- Arbitrary Exclusion of International Medical Schools Which Impacts Physician Licensure (D-275.976)
- Initial State Licensure (D-275.978)
- Simplifying the State Medical Licensure Process (D-275.980)
- Licensure and Liability for Senior Physician Volunteers (D-275.984)
- Unified Medical License Application (D-275.992)
- Facilitating Credentialing for State Licensure (D-275.994)
- Licensure and Credentialing Issues (D-275.995)
- Creation of AMA Data Bank on Interstate Practice of Medicine (D-275.996)

D-295.000 Medical Education

- Discriminatory Questions on Applications for Medical Licensure (D-295.319)
- Teaching and Evaluating Professionalism in Medical Schools (D-295.954)

D-300.000 Medical Education: Continuing

- Physician Reentry (D-300.984) *(See Table 21)*

D-480.000 Technology

- State Authority and Flexibility in Medical Licensure for Telemedicine (D-480.999)

Guidance for Physicians on Internet Prescribing

H-120.949

Our AMA provides the following guidance for physicians on the appropriate use of the Internet in prescribing medications:

(a) Criteria for an acceptable patient (clinical) encounter and follow-up:
Physicians who prescribe medications via the Internet shall establish, or have established, a valid patient-physician relationship, including, but not limited to, the following components. The physician shall: (i) obtain a reliable medical history and perform a physical examination of the patient, adequate to establish the diagnosis for which the drug is being prescribed and to identify underlying conditions and/or contraindications to the treatment recommended/provided; (ii) have sufficient dialogue with the patient regarding treatment options and the risks and benefits of treatment(s); (iii) as appropriate, follow up with the patient to assess the therapeutic outcome; (iv) maintain a contemporaneous medical record that is readily available to the patient and, subject to the patient's consent, to his or her other health care professionals; and (v) include the electronic prescription information as part of the patient medical record. Exceptions to the above criteria exist in the following specific instances: treatment provided in consultation with another physician who has an ongoing professional relationship with the patient, and who has agreed to supervise the patient's treatment, including use of any prescribed medications; and on-call or cross-coverage situations.

(b) Licensure
Physicians who prescribe medications via the Internet across state lines, without physically being located in the state(s) where the patient (clinical) encounter(s) occurs, must possess appropriate licensure in all jurisdictions where patients reside. An exception to this requirement is when the clinical encounter with the patient, as described in recommendation 1(a) above, occurs in the state where the physician is licensed and his or her practice is located, and the state where the patient resides allows electronic prescriptions from out-of-state prescribers.

(c) Security of patient information
Physicians who prescribe via the Internet should transmit prescriptions over a secure network (i.e., provisions for password protection, encrypted electronic prescriptions, or other reliable authentication techniques [e.g., AMA Internet ID]) in order to protect patient privacy.

(d) Disclosure of identifying information on web sites

Physicians who practice medicine via the Internet, including prescribing, should clearly disclose physician-identifying information on the web site, including (but not necessarily limited to) name, practice location (address and contact information), and all states in which licensure is held. Posting of actual physicians' license numbers (e.g., the DEA number) is unnecessary.

(e) Liability exposure

Physicians should be aware that they may increase their liability exposure by prescribing medications to individuals solely through online interactions (e.g., online questionnaire or online consultation).

(BOT Rep. 7, A-03; Reaffirmed: BOT Rep. 3, I-04; Reaffirmed: Sub. Res. 522, A 05)

Free Clinic Support
H-160.940

The AMA supports: (1) organized efforts to involve volunteer physicians, nurses and other appropriate providers in programs for the delivery of health care to the indigent and uninsured and underinsured through free clinics; and (2) efforts to reduce the barriers faced by physicians volunteering in free clinics, including medical liability coverage under the Federal Tort Claims Act, liability protection under state and federal law, and state licensure provisions for retired physicians.

(Sub. Res. 113, I-96; Reaffirmed: BOT 17, A-04; CMS Rep. 1, A-09)

Supply and Distribution of Health Professionals
H-200.987

1. Licensure, certification and accreditation should not be used for the purpose of regulating the supply of health professionals.

2. Health professions' curricula should emphasize the needs of underserved populations, including the poor, minorities, the chronically ill and disabled, and the geographically isolated. Decisions regarding the financing of health professions education should be based in part on the data and analyses of the national consortium on the supply and distribution of health professionals.

(BOT Rep. NN, A-87; Reaffirmed: Sunset Report, I-97; Reaffirmation A-01; Modified: CME Rep. 2, I-03)

Equality in Licensure and Reciprocity

H-255.982

Our AMA

1. Reaffirms its policy that it is inappropriate to discriminate against any physician because of national origin or geographical location of medical education

2. Continues to recognize the right and responsibility of states and territories to determine the qualifications of individuals applying for licensure to practice medicine within their respective jurisdiction

3. Supports the development and distribution of model legislation to encourage states to amend their Medical Practice Acts to provide that graduates of foreign medical schools shall meet the same requirements for licensure by endorsement as graduates of accredited US and Canadian schools.

(Res. 69, A-89; Rescinded: Sunset Report, A-00; Restored: CME Rep. 3, A-02; Reaffirmed: CME Rep. 7, A-04; Reaffirmed in lieu of Res. 320, A-04)

Graduates of Non-United States Medical Schools
H-255.983

The AMA continues to support the policy that all physicians and medical students should be evaluated for purposes of entry into graduate medical education programs, licensure, and hospital medical staff privileges on the basis of their individual qualifications, skills, and character.

(Sub. Res. 45, A-88; Reaffirmed by Res. 311, A-96; Reaffirmed: CMS Rep. 10, A-03; Reaffirmed: CME Rep. 1, I-03; Reaffirmed: CMF Rep. 7, A-04; Reaffirmed: Sub. Res. 314, A-04)

Report of the Ad Hoc Committee on Foreign Medical Graduates
H-255.988

1. The AMA reaffirms its support of current US visa and immigration requirements applicable to foreign national physicians who are graduates of medical schools other than those in the United States and Canada.

2. The AMA continues to support current regulations governing the issuance of exchange visitor visas to foreign national IMGs, including the requirements for successful completion of the USMLE.

3. The AMA reaffirms its policy that the US and Canada medical schools be accredited by a nongovernmental accrediting body.

4. The AMA continues to support cooperation in the collection and analysis of information on medical schools in nations other than the US and Canada.

5. The AMA supports continued cooperation with the ECFMG and other appropriate organizations to disseminate information to prospective and current students in foreign medical schools.

6. The AMA continues to support working with the ECFMG and other appropriate organizations in developing effective methods to evaluate the clinical skills of IMGs.

7. The AMA strongly supports the policy that the core clinical curriculum of a foreign medical school should be provided by that school and that US hospitals should not provide substitute core clinical experience for students attending a foreign medical school.

8. The AMA continues to support working with the Accreditation Council for Graduate Medical Education (ACGME) and the Federation of State Medical Boards (FSMB) to assure that institutions offering accredited residencies, residency program directors, and US licensing authorities do not deviate from established standards when evaluating graduates of foreign medical schools.

9. The AMA, in cooperation with the ACGME and the FSMB, supports only those modifications in established graduate medical education or licensing standards designed to enhance the quality of medical education and patient care.

10. The AMA continues to support the activities of the ECFMG related to verification of education credentials and testing of IMGs.

11. Special consideration should be given to the limited number of IMGs who are refugees from foreign governments that refuse to provide pertinent information usually required to establish eligibility for residency training or licensure.

12. The AMA reaffirms its existing policy supporting the use of accreditation standards to enhance the quality of patient care and medical education. Also the AMA opposes the use of such standards for purposes of regulating physician manpower.

13. AMA representatives to the ACGME, residency review committees and to the ECFMG should support AMA policy opposing discrimination. In particular, these

AMA representatives should emphasize that AMA policy does not prohibit the appointment of qualified graduates of foreign medical schools to residency training programs.

14. The AMA strongly reaffirms existing policy urging the US licensing authorities to focus on the individual academic and personal achievements when evaluating IMGs for the purposes of licensure. More effective methods for evaluating the quality of the undergraduate medical education of IMGs should be pursued and, when available, the results should be a part of the determination of eligibility for licensure.

15. The AMA reaffirms its support for the requirement that all medical school graduates complete at least one year of graduate medical education in an accredited US program in order to qualify for full and unrestricted licensure.

16. The AMA supports continued monitoring of the effectiveness of the Fifth Pathway program, including to the degree possible any measurable impact of the program on enrollments in Caribbean and Central American medical schools.

17. The AMA reaffirms and supports publicizing existing policy concerning the granting of staff and clinical privileges in hospitals and other health facilities.

18. The AMA reaffirms its support of the participation of all physicians, including graduates of foreign as well as US and Canadian medical schools, in organized medicine.

19. The AMA encourages the constituent medical societies to support qualified IMGs for nominations to AMA committees and councils.

20. The AMA supports studying the feasibility of conducting peer-to-peer membership recruitment efforts aimed at IMGs who are not AMA members.

21. The AMA is committed to using its existing publications to highlight policies and activities of interest to IMGs, stressing the common concerns of all physicians.

22. The AMA supports demonstrating its interests in issues related to IMGs by publicizing its many relevant resources to all physicians, especially to nonmember IMGs.

23. The AMA supports expansion of its efforts to prepare and disseminate information about requirements for

admission to accredited residency programs, the availability of positions, and the problems of becoming licensed and entering full and unrestricted medical practice in the US that face IMGs. This information should be addressed to college students, high school and college advisors, and students in foreign medical schools.

24. The AMA continues to recognize the common aims and goals of all physicians, particularly those practicing in the US, and supports making every effort to include all physicians who are permanent residents of the US in the mainstream of American medicine.

25. The AMA is committed to identifying and publicizing resources within the AMA that will respond to inquiries from IMGs.

26. The AMA is committed to providing leadership to promote the international exchange of medical knowledge as well as cultural understanding between the US and other nations.

27. The AMA urges institutions that sponsor exchange visitor programs in medical education, clinical medicine and public health to tailor programs for the individual visiting scholar that will meet the needs of the scholar, the institution, and the nation to which he will return.

28. The AMA is committed to informing foreign national IMGs that the availability of training and practice opportunities in the US is limited by the availability of fiscal and human resources to maintain the quality of medical education and patient care in the US.

(BOT Rep. Z, A-86; Reaffirmed: Res. 312, I-93; Modified: CME Rep. 2, A-03)

Discrimination Against Physicians
H-255.992

Our AMA:

1. Believes that the quality of a physician's medical education is an appropriate consideration in the recruitment and licensure of physicians and discrimination against physicians on the basis of the country in which they completed their medical education is inappropriate

2. Affirms that the residency application process should be free of discrimination, including discrimination arising from the electronic submission of applications.

(Sub. Res. 44, A-85; Reaffirmed: CLRPD Rep. 2, I-95; Appended: Sub. Res. 305 and Reaffirmation A-00)

Physician Exemption from Medical School Standards and Performance Evaluation Requirements
H-255.994

1. The AMA recommends to medical licensing boards that those physicians who are foreign medical graduates currently duly licensed by any licensing jurisdiction in the US should not be denied endorsement of their licenses, or denied admission to reexamination when this is required by law, solely because they are unable to provide documentation of graduation from a school meeting "equivalent standards and performance evaluation requirements" to those of programs accredited by the Liaison Committee on Medical Education.

2. The AMA encourages licensing boards, in reviewing applications for licensure endorsement, to take into account a physician's ethical standards and his or her having practiced medicine of an acceptable quality.

(Sub. Res. 108, A-83; Reaffirmed: CLRPD Rep. 1, I-93; Reaffirmed: CME Rep. 2, A-05)

International Medical Graduates
H-255.995

The AMA believes that reduced requirements for licensure should not be applied under any circumstances to graduates of foreign medical schools.

(Res. 23, A-82; Reaffirmed: CLRPD Rep. A, I-92; Modified: CME Rep. 5, A-04)

Licensure for Physicians Not Engaged in Direct Patient Care
H-275.921

Our AMA: (1) opposes laws, regulations, and policies that would limit the ability of a physician to obtain or renew an unrestricted state or territorial medical license based solely on the fact that the physician is engaged exclusively in medical practice which does not include direct patient care; (2) advocates that the Federation of State Medical Boards support provision of unrestricted state or territorial medical licenses to physicians engaged in medical practice that does not include direct patient care; (3) urges constituent state and territorial medical societies to advocate with their respective medical boards to establish policy that will facilitate provision of unrestricted state or territorial medical licenses to physicians in medical practice that does not include direct patient care; and (4) opposes activities by medical licensure boards to create separate categories of medical licensure solely on the basis of the predominant professional activity of the practicing physician.

(Res. 923, I-10)

Short-Term Physician Volunteer Opportunities Within the United States
H-275.922

Our AMA encourages the Federation of State Medical Boards to develop a process among the various state licensure boards that would make it possible for a physician who holds an unrestricted license in one state/district/territory to participate in short-term (less than 90 day) physician volunteerism in another state/district/territory in which the physician volunteer does not hold an unrestricted license.

(Sub. Res. 915, I-10)

Maintenance of Certification / Maintenance of Licensure
H-275.923

Our AMA will: 1. Continue to work with the Federation of State Medical Boards (FSMB) to establish and assess maintenance of licensure (MOL) principles with the AMA to assess the impact of MOC and MOL on the practicing physician and the FSMB to study the impact on licensing boards. 2. Recommend that the American Board of Medical Specialties (ABMS) not introduce additional assessment modalities that have not been validated to show improvement in physician performance and/or patient safety. 3. Encourage rigorous evaluation of the impact on physicians of future proposed changes to the MOC and MOL processes including cost, staffing, and time. 4. Review all AMA policies regarding medical licensure (Appendix A); determine if each policy should be reaffirmed, expanded, consolidated or is no longer relevant; and in collaboration with other stakeholders, update the policies with the view of developing AMA Principles of Maintenance of Licensure in a report to the HOD at the 2010 Annual Meeting. 5. Urge the National Alliance for Physician Competence (NAPC) to include a broader range of practicing physicians and additional stakeholders to participate in discussions of definitions and assessments of physician competence. 6. Continue to participate in the NAPC forums. 7. Encourage members of our House of Delegates to increase their awareness of and participation in the proposed changes to physician self-regulation through their specialty organizations and other professional membership groups. 8. Continue to support and promote the AMA Physician's Recognition Award (PRA) Credit

system as one of the three major CME credit systems that comprise the foundation for post graduate medical education in the US, including the Performance Improvement CME (PICME) format; and continue to develop relationships and agreements that may lead to standards, accepted by all US licensing boards, specialty boards, hospital credentialing bodies, and other entities requiring evidence of physician CME. 9. Collaborate with the American Osteopathic Association and its eighteen specialty boards in implementation of the recommendations in CME Report 16-A-09, Maintenance of Certification / Maintenance of Licensure.

(CME Rep. 16, A-09)

Arbitrary Exclusion of International Medical Schools Which Impacts Physician Licensure
H-275.928

Our AMA opposes the practice by state medical boards of creating arbitrary and non criterion-based lists of approved or unapproved international medical schools.

(Res. 310, A-05)

Additions to United States Medical Licensure Examination and Comprehensive Osteopathic Medical Licensure Examination
H-275.929

Our AMA opposes additions to the United States Medical Licensing Examination and Comprehensive Osteopathic Medical Licensure Examination that lack predictive validity for future performance as a physician.

(Res. 308, A-04)

Internal Medicine Board Certification Report—Interim Report
H-275.932

Our AMA opposes the use of recertification or Maintenance of Certification (MOC) as a condition of employment, licensure or reimbursement.

(CME Rep. 7, A-02)

Alternatives to the Federation of State Medical Boards' Recommendations on Licensure
H-275.934

Our AMA adopts the following principles:

1. Ideally, all medical students should successfully complete Steps 1 and 2 of the United States Medical Licensing Examination (USMLE) or Levels 1 and 2 of the Comprehensive Osteopathic Medical Licensing Examination (COMLEX-USA) prior to entry into residency training. At a minimum, individuals entering residency training must have successfully completed Step 1 of the USMLE or Level 1 of COMLEX-USA. There should be provision made for students who have not completed Step 2 of the USMLE or Level 2 of the COMLEX-USA to do so during the first year of residency training.

2. All applicants for full and unrestricted licensure, whether graduates of US medical schools or international medical graduates, must have completed one year of accredited graduate medical education (GME) in the US, have passed all licensing examinations (USMLE or COMLEX-USA), and must be certified by their residency program director as ready to advance to the next year of GME and to obtain a full and unrestricted license to practice medicine. The candidate for licensure should have had education that provided exposure to general medical content.

3. There should be a training permit/educational license for all resident physicians who do not yet have a full and unrestricted license to practice medicine. To be eligible for an initial training permit/educational license, the resident must have completed Step 1 of the USMLE or Level 1 of COMLEX-USA.

4. Residency program directors shall report only those actions to state medical licensing boards that are reported for all licensed physicians.

5. Residency program directors should receive training to ensure that they understand the process for taking disciplinary action against resident physicians, and are aware of procedures for dismissal of residents and for due process. This requirement for residency program directors should be enforced through Accreditation Council for Graduate Medical Education accreditation requirements.

6. There should be no reporting of actions against medical students to state medical licensing boards.

7. Medical schools are responsible for identifying and remediating and/or disciplining medical student unprofessional behavior, problems with substance abuse, and other behavioral problems. as well as gaps in student knowledge and skills.

8. The Dean's Letter of Evaluation should be strengthened and standardized, to serve as a better source of information to residency programs about applicants.

(CME Rep. 8, A-99; Reaffirmed: CME Rep. 4, I-01)

**Licensure of IMGs
H-275.935**

Our AMA asks the Federation of State Medical Boards to ask all the state licensing boards to adopt a uniform standard governing the allowed number of administrations of the licensure examinations.

(Res. 314, A-99)

**Mechanisms to Measure Physician Competency
H-275.936**

Our AMA (1) reviews and proposes improvements for assuring continued physician competence, including but not limited to performance indicators, board certification and recertification, professional experience, continuing medical education, and teaching experience; and (2) opposes the development and/or use of "Medical Competency Examination" and establishment of oversight boards for current state medical boards as proposed in the fall 1998 Report on Professional Licensure of the Pew Health Professions Commission, as an additional measure of physician competency.

(Res. 320, I-98; Amended: Res. 817, A-99; Reaffirmed: CME Rep. 7, A-02; Reaffirmed: CME Rep. 7, A-07)

**USMLE Part III and Licensure
H-275.938**

Our AMA will lobby the Federation of State Medical Boards to discourage states from linking mandatory application for licensure with application to take the USMLE Part III.

(Res. 325, A-98)

**Out-of-State Residents in Training and State Licensing Board Requirements for Temporary Licenses
H-275.941**

The AMA will work with the Federation of State Medical Boards (FSMB) to facilitate a timely process so that residents in a training program can meet the licensure requirements to avail themselves of opportunities for educational experiences in states other than that of their primary program location.

(Sub. Res. 301, A-97; Reaffirmed: CME Rep. 2, A-07)

Self-Incriminating Questions on Applications for Licensure and Specialty Boards
H-275.945

The AMA will:

1. Encourage the Federation of State Medical Boards and its constituent members to develop uniform definitions and nomenclature for use in licensing and disciplinary proceedings to better facilitate the sharing of information

2. Seek clarification of the application of the Americans with Disabilities Act to the actions of medical licensing and medical specialty boards

3. Until the applicability and scope of the Americans with Disabilities Act are clarified, will encourage the American Board of Medical Specialties and the Federation of State Medical Boards and their constituent members to advise physicians of the rationale behind inquiries on mental illness, substance abuse or physical disabilities in materials used in the licensure, reregistration, and certification processes when such questions are asked.

(BOT Rep. 1, I-933; CME Rep. 10 - I-94; Reaffirmed: CME Rep. 2, A-04)

Board Certification
H-275.950

Our AMA

1. Reaffirms its opposition to the use of board certification as a requirement for licensure or reimbursement

2. Seeks an amendment to the new Medicaid rules that would delete the use of board certification as a requirement for reimbursement and would address the exclusion of internal medicine, emergency medicine, and other specialties.

(Res. 143, A-92; ; Reaffirmed by Res. 108, A-98; Reaffirmation A-00)

Mandatory Acceptance of Patient's Group Plan
H-275.951

It is the policy of the AMA that the sole purpose of medical licensure is to assure the competence of physicians to practice medicine.

(Sub. Res. 111, I-91; Modified: Sunset Report, I-01)

The Grading Policy for Medical Licensure Examinations
H-275.953

(1) The AMA's representatives to the ACGME are instructed to promote the principle that selection of residents should be based on a broad variety of evaluative criteria, and to propose that the ACGME General Requirements state clearly that residency program directors must not use NBME or USMLE ranked passing scores as a screening criterion for residency selection. (2) The AMA adopts the following policy on NBME or USMLE examination scoring: (a) Students receive "pass/fail" scores as soon as they are available. (If students fail the examinations, they may request their numerical scores immediately.) (b) Numerical scores are reported to the state licensing authorities upon request by the applicant for licensure. At this time, the applicant may request a copy of his or her numerical scores. (c) Scores are reported in pass/fail format for each student to the medical school. The school also receives a frequency distribution of numerical scores for the aggregate of their students.

(CME Rep. G, I-90; Reaffirmed by Res. 310, A-98; Reaffirmed: CME Rep. 3, A-04)

Physician Licensure Legislation
H-275.955

Our AMA (1) reaffirms its policies opposing discrimination against physicians on the basis of being a graduate of a foreign medical school and supports state and territory responsibility for admitting physicians to practice; and (2) reaffirms earlier policy urging licensing jurisdictions to adopt laws and rules facilitating the movement of physicians between states, to move toward uniformity in requirements for the endorsement of licenses to practice medicine, and to base endorsement of medical licenses on an assessment of competence rather than on passing a written examination of cognitive knowledge.

(CME Rep. B, A-90; Reaffirmation A-00

Demonstration of Clinical Competence
H-275.956

It is the policy of the AMA to

1. Support continued efforts to develop and validate methods for assessment of clinical skills

2. Continue its participation in the development and testing of methods for clinical skills assessment

3. Recognize that clinical skills assessment is best performed using a rigorous and consistent examination administered by medical schools and should not be used for licensure of graduates of Liaison Committee on Medical Education (LCME)- and American Osteopathic Association (AOA)-accredited medical schools or of Educational Commission for Foreign Medical Graduates (ECFMG)-certified physicians.

(CME Rep. E, A-90, Reaffirmed. CME Rep. 5, A-00; Modified: Sub. Res. 821, I-02; Modified: CME Rep. 1, I-03)

Changing the Grading Policy for Medical Licensure Examinations (H-275.957)

Our AMA is concerned about the potential for inappropriate use of numerical scores of licensing examinations, particularly as a significant criterion in appointment to residency training programs. Past studies show some residency programs inappropriately use USMLE examination scores in screening their applicants. Our AMA supports the development of mechanisms to ensure confidentiality of the results of licensure exams, and that these results are used only in an appropriate fashion.

(BOT Rep. GGG, A-90; Reaffirmed: Sunset Report, I-00)

Proposed Single Examination for Licensure
H-275.962

Our AMA:

1. Endorses the concept of a single examination for medical licensure

2. Urges the NBME and the FSMB to place responsibility for developing Steps I and II of the new single examination for licensure with the faculty of US medical schools working through the NBME

3. Continues its vigorous support of the LCME and its accreditation of medical schools and supports monitoring the impact of a single examination on the effectiveness of the LCME

4. Urges the NBME and the FSMB to establish a high standard for passing the examination

5. Strongly recommends and supports actively pursuing efforts to assure that the standard for passing be criterion-based; that is, that passing the examination indicate a degree of knowledge acceptable for practicing medicine

6. Urges that appointing graduates of LCME-accredited medical schools to accredited residency training not be dependent on their passing Steps I and II or the single examination for licensure.

(CME Rep. B, I-89; Reaffirmed: Sunset Report, A-00)

Mandatory Medicare Assignment or Determination of Fee Levels
H-275.963

Our AMA supports federal legislation that would prohibit states from enacting legislation to require that acceptance of Medicare assignment or the Medicare allowance of reimbursement be a condition of medical licensure, or used in determinations of unprofessional conduct, or made effectively mandatory in any other fashion.

(Sub Res. 75, A-89; Reaffirmed: Sunset Report, A-00)

Licensure Confidentiality
H-275.970

The AMA

1. Encourages specialty boards, hospitals, and other organizations involved in credentialing, as well as state licensing boards, to take all necessary steps to assure the confidentiality of information contained on application forms for credentials

2. Encourages boards to include in application forms only requests for information that can reasonably be related to medical practice

3. Encourages state licensing boards to exclude from license application forms information that refers to psychoanalysis, counseling, or psychotherapy required or undertaken as part of medical training

4. Encourages state medical societies and specialty societies to join with the AMA in efforts to change statutes and regulations to provide needed confidentiality for information collected by licensing boards

5. Encourages state licensing boards to require that, if an applicant has had psychiatric treatment, the physician who has provided the treatment submit to the board an official statement that the applicant's current state of health does not interfere with his or her ability to practice medicine.

(CME Rep. B, A-88; Reaffirmed: BOT Rep. 1, I-933; CME Rep. 10 - I-94; Reaffirmed: CME Rep. 2, A-04)

State Control of Qualifications for Medical Licensure
H-275.973

1. The AMA firmly opposes the imposition of federally mandated restrictions on the ability of individual states to determine the qualifications of physician candidates for licensure by endorsement.

2. The AMA actively opposes the enactment of any legislation introduced in Congress that promotes these objectives.

(Res. 84, I-87; Reaffirmed: Sunset Report, I-97; Reaffirmed: CME Rep. 2, A-07)

Qualifications of Health Professionals
H-275.975

(1) Private certifying organizations should be encouraged to continue certification programs for all health professionals and to communicate to the public the qualifications and standards they require for certification. Decisions concerning recertification should be made by the certifying organizations. (2) Working with state licensing and certifying boards, health care professions should use the results of quality assurance activities to ensure that substandard practitioner behavior is dealt with in a professional and timely manner. Licensure and disciplinary boards, in cooperation with their respective professional and occupational associations, should be encouraged to work to identify "deficient" health care professionals.

(BOT Rep. NN, A-87; Reaffirmed: Sunset Report, I-97; Reaffirmed: CME Rep. 2, A-07)

Boundaries of Practice for Health Professionals
H-275.976

(1) The health professional who coordinates an individual's health care has an ethical responsibility to ensure that the services required by an individual patient are provided by a professional whose basic competence and current performance are suited to render those services safely and effectively. In addition, patients also have a responsibility for maintaining coordination and continuity of their own health care. (2) As a supplement to strengthen state licensure of health professionals, standard-setting and self-regulatory competency assurance programs should be conducted by health professions associations, certifying and accrediting agencies, and health care facilities.

(BOT Rep. NN, A-87; Reaffirmed: Sunset Report, I-97

Medical Licensure
H-275.978

The AMA:

1. Urges directors of accredited residency training programs to certify the clinical competence of graduates of foreign medical schools after completion of the first year of residency training; however, program directors must not provide certification until they are satisfied that the resident is clinically competent

2. Encourages licensing boards to require a certificate of competence for full and unrestricted licensure

3. Urges licensing boards to review the details of application for initial licensure to assure that procedures are not unnecessarily cumbersome and that inappropriate information is not required. Accurate identification of documents and applicants is critical. It is recommended that boards continue to work cooperatively with the Federation of State Medical Boards to these ends

4. Will continue to provide information to licensing boards and other health organizations in an effort to prevent the use of fraudulent credentials for entry to medical practice

5. Urges those licensing boards that have not done so to develop regulations permitting the issuance of special purpose licenses. It is recommended that these regulations permit special purpose licensure with the minimum of educational requirements consistent with protecting the health, safety and welfare of the public

6. Urges licensing boards, specialty boards, hospitals and their medical staffs, and other organizations that evaluate physician competence to inquire only into conditions which impair a physician's current ability to practice medicine (BOT Rep. I-93-13; CME Rep. 10 - I-94)

7. Urges licensing boards to maintain strict confidentiality of reported information

8. Urges that the evaluation of information collected by licensing boards be undertaken only by persons experienced in medical licensure and competent to make judgments about physician competence. It is recommended that decisions concerning medical competence and discipline be made with the participation of physician members of the board

9. Recommends that if confidential information is improperly released by a licensing board about a physician, the board take appropriate and immediate steps to correct any adverse consequences to the physician

10. Urges all physicians to participate in continuing medical education as a professional obligation

11. Urges licensing boards not to require mandatory reporting of continuing medical education as part of the process of reregistering the license to practice medicine

12. Opposes the use of written cognitive examinations of medical knowledge at the time of reregistration except when there is reason to believe that a physician's knowledge of medicine is deficient

13. Supports working with the Federation of State Medical Boards to develop mechanisms to evaluate the competence of physicians who do not have hospital privileges and who are not subject to peer review

14. Believes that licensing laws should relate only to requirements for admission to the practice of medicine and to assuring the continuing competence of physicians, and opposes efforts to achieve a variety of socioeconomic objectives through medical licensure regulation

15. Urges licensing jurisdictions to pass laws and adopt regulations facilitating the movement of licensed physicians between licensing jurisdictions; licensing jurisdictions should limit physician movement only for reasons related to protecting the health, safety and welfare of the public

16. Encourages the Federation of State Medical Boards and the individual medical licensing boards to continue to pursue the development of uniformity in the acceptance of examination scores on the Federation Licensing Examination and in other requirements for endorsement of medical licenses

17. Urges licensing boards not to place time limits on the acceptability of National Board certification or on scores on the United State Medical Licensing Examination for endorsement of licenses

18. Urges licensing boards to base endorsement on an assessment of physician competence and not on passing a written examination of cognitive ability, except in those instances when information collected by a licensing board indicates need for such an examination

19. Urges licensing boards to accept an initial license provided by another board to a graduate of a US medical school as proof of completion of acceptable medical education

20. Urges that documentation of graduation from a foreign medical school be maintained by boards providing an initial license, and that the documentation be provided on request to other licensing boards for review in connection with an application for licensure by endorsement

21. Urges licensing boards to consider the completion of specialty training and evidence of competent and honorable practice of medicine in reviewing applications for licensure by endorsement.

(CME Rep. A, A-87; Modified: Sunset Report, I-97; Reaffirmation A-04)

Medicare Reporting of Adverse Incidents in Hospitals to State Agencies
H-275.979

The AMA opposes the sharing of information generated through the Medicare utilization process or other institutional review with state licensure bodies until hospital quality assurance committees have been notified and given a reasonable time to respond.

(Res. 118, I-86; Reaffirmed: Sunset Report, I-96; Reaffirmed: CME Rep. 2, A-06)

Legislative Action
H-275.984

The AMA

1. Vigorously opposes legislation which mandates that, as a condition of licensure, physicians who treat Medicare beneficiaries must agree to charge or collect from Medicare beneficiaries no more than the Medicare allowed amount

2. Strongly affirms the policy that medical licensure should be determined by educational qualifications, professional competence, ethics and other appropriate factors necessary to assure professional character and fitness to practice

3. Opposes any law that compels either acceptance of Medicare assignment or acceptance of the Medicare allowed amount as payment in full as a condition of state licensure.

(Sub. Res. 117, I-85; Modified by CLRPD Rep. 2, I-95; Reaffirmed: BOT Rep. 12, A-05)

Graduate Medical Education Requirement for Medical Licensure
H-275.985

The AMA reaffirms its policy that all applicants for full and unrestricted licensure should be required to provide evidence of satisfactory completion of at least one year of an accredited program of graduate medical education in the US.

(CME Rep. E, I-85; Reaffirmed by CLRPD Rep. 2, I-95; Reaffirmed: CME Rep. 2, A-05)

Physician Participation in Third Party Payer Programs
H-275.994

The AMA opposes state laws making a physician's licensure contingent upon his providing services to Medicaid beneficiaries or any other specific category of patients.

(CMS Rep. N, A-81; Reaffirmed: CLRPD Rep. F, I-91; Reaffirmed by Res. 108, A-98)

Physician Competence
H-275.996

Our AMA:

1. Urges the American Board of Medical Specialties and its constituent boards to reconsider their positions regarding recertification as a mandatory requirement rather than as a voluntarily sought and achieved validation of excellence

2. Urges the Federation of State Medical Boards and its constituent state boards to reconsider and reverse their position urging and accepting specialty board certification as evidence of continuing competence for the purpose of re-registration of licensure

3. Favors continued efforts to improve voluntary continuing medical education programs, to maintain the peer review process within the profession, and to develop better techniques for establishing the necessary patient care data base.

(CME Rep. J, A-80; Reaffirmed: CLRPD Rep. B, I-90; Reaffirmed: Sunset Report, I-00; Reaffirmed: CME Rep. 7, A-02; Reaffirmed: CME Rep. 7, A-07)

Licensure by Specialty
H-275.997

Experience with licensure by specialty is too limited to determine what the long-range effects will be in the provision of timely, safe and comprehensive medical care. However, the AMA does not consider licensure by specialty to be desirable even in unusual cases.

(CME Rep. F, A-80; Reaffirmed: CLRPD Rep. B, I-90; Reaffirmed: Sunset Report, I-00)

Recommendations for Future Directions for Medical Education
H-295.995

(Note: Portion relevant to medical licensure excerpted below.)

The AMA supports the following recommendations relating to the future directions for medical education:

27. The AMA recommends to state licensing authorities that they require individual applicants, to be eligible to be licensed to practice medicine, to possess the degree of Doctor of Medicine or its equivalent from a school

or program that meets the standards of the LCME or accredited by the American Osteopathic Association, or to demonstrate as individuals, comparable academic and personal achievements. All applicants for full and unrestricted licensure should provide evidence of the satisfactory completion of at least one year of an accredited program of graduate medical education in the US. Satisfactory completion should be based upon an assessment of the applicant's knowledge, problem-solving ability, and clinical skills in the general field of medicine. The AMA recommends to legislatures and governmental regulatory authorities that they not impose requirements for licensure that are so specific that they restrict the responsibility of medical educators to determine the content of undergraduate and graduate medical education.

30. US citizens should have access to factual information on the requirements for licensure and for reciprocity in the various jurisdictions, prerequisites for entry into graduate medical education programs, and other factors that should be considered before deciding to undertake the study of medicine in schools not accredited by the LCME.

(CME Rep. B, A-82; Amended: CI RPD Rep. A, I-92; Res. 331, I-95; Reaffirmed by Res. 322, A-97; Reaffirmation I-03; Modified: CME Rep. 7, A-05; Modified: CME Rep. 2, I-05)

Content-Specific CME Mandated for Licensure H-300.953

1. The AMA, state medical societies, specialty societies, and other medical organizations should reaffirm that the medical profession alone has the responsibility for setting standards and determining curricula in continuing medical education.

2. State medical societies should establish avenues of communication with groups concerned with medical issues, so that these groups know that they have a place to go for discussion of issues and responding to problems.

3. State medical societies should periodically invite the various medical groups from within the state to discuss issues and priorities.

4. State medical societies in states which already have a content-specific CME requirement should consider appropriate ways of rescinding or amending the mandate.

(CME Rep. 6, A-96; Reaffirmed: CME Rep. 2, A-06)

Uniform Standards for Continuing Medical Education H-300.969

The AMA (1) will continue its efforts to develop uniform standards for continuing medical education; and (2) will solicit input from all state medical associations, medical licensure boards, and national specialty organizations concerning the development of the most appropriate uniform standards for continuing medical education.

(Res. 313, A-92; Reaffirmed: CME Rep. 2, A-03; Reaffirmed in lieu of Res. 901, I-05)

Post-Licensure Assessment as a Condition for Physician Participation in Medicare H-330.950

The AMA opposes proposals for periodic post-licensure assessment as a condition for physician participation in the Medicare program or other health-related entitlement program.

(Res. 231, I 93; Reaffirmed: BOT Rep. 28, A-03)

Resident Physician Licenses H-405.966

The AMA supports the option of limited educational licenses in all states for resident physicians to provide care within their residency programs; and supports reduced licensure fees for resident physicians for participation solely in graduate medical education training programs when full medical licensure is required by a state.

(Sub. Res. 312, A-96; Reaffirmed: CME Rep. 2, A-06)

The Promotion of Quality Telemedicine H-480.969

1. It is the policy of the AMA that medical boards of states and territories should require a full and unrestricted license in that state for the practice of telemedicine, unless there are other appropriate state-based licensing methods, with no differentiation by specialty, for physicians who wish to practice telemedicine in that state or territory. This license category should adhere to the following principles:
(a) application to situations where there is a telemedical transmission of individual patient data from the patient's state that results in either (i) provision of a written or otherwise documented medical opinion used for diagnosis or treatment or (ii) rendering of treatment to a patient within the board's state;

(b) exemption from such a licensure requirement for traditional informal physician-to-physician consultations ("curbside consultations") that are provided without expectation of compensation;

(c) exemption from such a licensure requirement for telemedicine practiced across state lines in the event of an emergent or urgent circumstance, the definition of which for the purposes of telemedicine should show substantial deference to the judgment of the attending and consulting physicians as well as to the views of the patient; and

(d) application requirements that are non-burdensome, issued in an expeditious manner, have fees no higher than necessary to cover the reasonable costs of administering this process, and that utilize principles of reciprocity with the licensure requirements of the state in which the physician in question practices.

2. The AMA urges the FSMB and individual states to recognize that a physician practicing certain forms of telemedicine (e.g., teleradiology) must sometimes perform necessary functions in the licensing state (e.g., interaction with patients, technologists, and other physicians) and that the interstate telemedicine approach adopted must accommodate these essential quality-related functions.

3. The AMA urges national medical specialty societies to develop and implement practice parameters for telemedicine in conformance with Policy 410.973 (which identifies practice parameters as "educational tools"); Policy 410.987 (which identifies practice parameters as "strategies for patient management that are designed to assist physicians in clinical decision making," and states that a practice parameter developed by a particular specialty or specialties should not preclude the performance of the procedures or treatments addressed in that practice parameter by physicians who are not formally credentialed in that specialty or specialties); and Policy 410.996 (which states that physician groups representing all appropriate specialties and practice settings should be involved in developing practice parameters, particularly those which cross lines of disciplines or specialties).

(CME/CMS Rep., A-96; Amended: CME Rep. 7, A-99)

Evolving Impact of Telemedicine
H-480.974

Our AMA:

1. Will evaluate relevant federal legislation related to telemedicine;

2. Urges CMS and other concerned entities involved in telemedicine to fund demonstration projects to evaluate the effect of care delivered by physicians using telemedicine-related technology on costs, quality, and the physician-patient relationship;

3. Urges medical specialty societies involved in telemedicine to develop appropriate practice parameters to address the various applications of telemedicine and to guide quality assessment and liability issues related to telemedicine; (Reaffirmed by CME/CMS Rep. A-96)

4. Encourages the CPT Editorial Board to develop CPT codes or modifiers for telemedical services;

5. Will work with CMS and other payers to develop and test, through these demonstration projects, appropriate reimbursement mechanisms;

6. Will develop a means of providing appropriate continuing medical education credit, acceptable toward the Physician's Recognition Award, for educational consultations using telemedicine; and

7. Will work with the Federation of State Medical Boards and the state and territorial licensing boards to develop licensure guidelines for telemedicine practiced across state boundaries.

(CMS/CME Rep., A-94; Reaffirmation A-01)

Allocation of Privileges to Use Health Care Technologies H-480.988

The AMA (1) affirms the need for the Association and specialty societies to enhance their leadership role in providing guidance on the training, experience and knowledge necessary for the application of specific health care technologies; (2) urges physicians to continue to ensure that, for every patient, technologies will be utilized in the safest and most effective manner by health care professionals; and (3) asserts that licensure of physicians by states must be based on scientific and clinical criteria.

(BOT Rep. F, I-88; Reaffirmed: CME Rep. 8, I-93; Reaffirmed: CME Rep. 2, A-05)

Concerning Pain Management
D-120.983

Our AMA will communicate to the President, the Secretary of the Department of Health and Human Services, and the Attorney General, its strong opposition to the inappropriate use of 21 Code of Federal Regulations Section 1306.04 or any other rationale that would involve placement of licensure restrictions on physicians who use opioid analgesics and other pain-reducing medications appropriately to treat patients with pain. To assist our AMA in opposing harassment of physicians, state medical and specialty societies will be requested to submit, to the AMA Office of General Counsel, examples of physicians who allegedly have been harassed by DEA agents for appropriate prescribing of controlled substances for pain management.

(Sub. Res. 213, A-03)

All Hazards Disaster Preparedness and Response D-130.972

Our AMA will work with: (1) subject matter experts at the national level to quickly produce a provider manual on state licensure and medical liability coverage for physicians during disasters; (2) appropriate medical, public health, disaster response and relief organizations to improve plans, protocols, and policies regarding the provision of health care in mass evacuation shelters; and (3) appropriate state and local organizations to develop templates for private practice/office continuity plans in CD-ROM or web-based format that can be stored in state medical association offices on a server in the event of a disaster.

(Res. 420, A-06)

Emergency Preparedness D-130.974

Our AMA will: (1) call for each state and local public health jurisdiction to develop and periodically update, with public and professional input, a comprehensive Public Health Disaster Plan specific to their locations. The plan should: (a) provide for special populations such as children and the disabled; (b) provide for anticipated public health needs of the affected and stranded communities including disparate, hospitalized and institutionalized populations; (c) provide for appropriate coordination and assignment of volunteer physicians; and (d) be deposited in a timely manner with the Federal Emergency Management Agency, the Public Health Service, the Department of Health and Human Services, the Department of Homeland Security and other appropriate federal agencies; (2) continually refine and more actively advocate its three courses, Core, Basic and Advanced Disaster Life Support, and other equivalent courses for training hospital medical and nursing staffs and public health physicians and nurses so they are better prepared to handle mass casualty situations; (3) work with and through the Federation of State Medical

Boards, its member boards and state, district and territorial governments to implement a clearinghouse for volunteer physicians (MDs and DOs) that would validate licensure in any state, district or territory to provide medical services in another distressed jurisdiction where a federal emergency has been declared; (4) support national legislation that gives qualified physician volunteers (MDs and DOs), automatic medical liability immunity in the event of a declared national disaster or federal emergency; and (5) report back at the 2006 Annual Meeting with an update on AMA disaster relief activities.

(Sub. Res. 803, I-05; Reaffirmation A-06; Reaffirmed: BOT Rep. 2, A-07)

Licensure and Liability for Senior Physician Volunteers D-160.991

Our AMA

1. And its Senior Physician Group will inform physicians about federal and state-based charitable immunity laws that protect physicians wishing to volunteer their services in free medical clinics and other venues

2. Will work with organizations representing free clinics to promote opportunities for physicians who wish to volunteer.

(BOT Rep. 17, A-04)

Alternate Licensure Protocols for IMGs D-255.997

Our AMA will actively support the Florida Medical Association in pursuing legislation that would require the Florida Department of Health to prevent and negate separate criteria for International Medical Graduates to become licensed as Florida physicians.

(Res. 311, A-00)

Threat to Medical Licensure D-275.962

Our AMA will develop model legislation to ensure that medical licensure is independent of participation in any health insurance program.

(Res. 717, A-10; Reaffirmation I-10)

Eliminating Disparities in Licensure for IMG Physicians

D-275.966

Our AMA will advocate and assist the state medical societies to seek legislative action eliminating any disparity in the years of graduate medical education training required for full and unrestricted licensure between IMG and LCME graduates.

(Res. 327, A-08)

Telemedicine and Medical Licensure
D-275.967

Our AMA will work with the Federation of State Medical Boards to study how guidelines regulating medical licenses are affected by telemedicine and medical technological innovations that allow for physicians to practice outside their states of licensure.

(Res. 317, A-08)

Depression and Physician Licensure
D-275.974

Our AMA will

1. Recommend that physicians who have major depression and seek treatment not have their medical licenses and credentials routinely challenged but instead have decisions about their licensure and credentialing and recredentialing be based on professional performance

2. Make this resolution known to the various state medical licensing boards and to hospitals and health plans involved in physician credentialing and recredentialing.

(Res. 319, A-05)

Arbitrary Exclusion of International Medical Schools Which Impacts Physician Licensure
D-275.976

Our AMA will, in close consultation with its IMG Section, work with the Federation of State Medical Boards in its current efforts to study methods to evaluate international medical schools for licensure of their graduates.

(Res. 310, A-05)

Initial State Licensure

D-275.978

Our AMA will work with the Federation of State Medical Boards, state medical societies, state medical boards, and state legislatures, to eliminate the additional graduate medical education requirements imposed on IMGs for an unrestricted license, in the earnest hope of implementing AMA Policy H-275.985.

(Res. 831, I-04)

Simplifying the State Medical Licensure Process
D-275.980

Our AMA Board of Trustees will assign appropriate individuals from within the AMA to work with the Federation of State Medical Boards and keep the AMA membership apprised of the FSMB's actions on developing a standardized medical licensure application, and the individuals assigned by the AMA Board of Trustees regarding the FSMB's work on standardized medical licensure application will report back to the AMA on a yearly basis beginning at the 2005 Annual Meeting, until decided by the Board of Trustees that this is no longer necessary.

(Res. 324, A-04)

Licensure and Liability for Senior Physician Volunteers
D-275.984

Our AMA (1) and its Senior Physician Group will inform physicians about special state licensing regulations for volunteer physicians; and (2) will support and work with state medical licensing boards and other appropriate agencies, including the sharing of model state legislation, to establish special reduced-fee volunteer medical license for those who wish to volunteer their services to the uninsured or indigent.

(BOT Rep. 17, A-04)

Unified Medical License Application
D-275.992

Our AMA will request the Federation of State Medical Boards to examine the issue of a standardized medical licensure application form for those data elements that are common to all medical licensure applications.

(Res. 308, I-01)

Facilitating Credentialing for State Licensure
D-275.994

Our AMA will:

1. Encourage the Federation of State Medical Boards to urge its Portability Committee to complete its work on developing mechanisms for greater reciprocity between state licensing jurisdictions as soon as possible

2. Work with the Federation of State Medical Boards and the Association of State Medical Board Executive Directors to encourage the increased standardization of credentials requirements for licensure, and to increase the number of reciprocal relationships among all licensing jurisdictions

3. Encourage the Federation of State Medical Boards and its licensing jurisdictions to widely disseminate information about the Federation's Credentials Verification Service, especially when physicians apply for a new medical license.

(Res. 302, A-01)

Licensure and Credentialing Issues
D-275.995

Our AMA will:

1. Support recognition of the Federation of State Medical Boards' (FSMB) Credentials Verification Service by all licensing jurisdictions

2. Work jointly with the FSMB to take measures to encourage increased standardization of credentials requirements, and improved portability by increased use of reciprocal relationships among all licensing jurisdictions

3. Communicate, either directly by letter or through its publications, to all hospitals and licensure boards that the Joint Commission on Accreditation of Healthcare Organizations encourages recognition of both the Educational Commission for Foreign Medical Graduates' Certification Verification Service and the AMA's Masterfile as primary source verification of medical school credential; and

4. Encourage the National Commission on Quality Assurance (NCQA) and all other organizations to accept the Federation of State Medical Boards' Credentials

Verification Service, the Educational Commission for Foreign Medical Graduates' Certification Verification Service, and the AMA Masterfile as primary source verification of credentials.

(Res. 303, I-00; Reaffirmation A-04)

Creation of AMA Data Bank on Interstate Practice of Medicine
D-275.996

Our AMA will: (1) continue to study interstate practice of medicine issues as they relate to the quality of care available to patients; (2) explore the provision of information on physician licensure, including telemedicine, to members and others through the World Wide Web and other media; and (3) continue to make information on state legal parameters on the practice of medicine, including telemedicine, available for members and others.

(BOT Rep. 6, I-99; Reaffirmed: CLRPD Rep. 1, A-09)

Discriminatory Questions on Applications for Medical Licensure
D-295.319

Our American Medical Association will work with the Federation of State Medical Boards and other appropriate stakeholders to develop model language for medical licensure applications which is non discriminatory and which does not create barriers to appropriate diagnosis and treatment of psychiatric disorders, consistent with the responsibility of state medical boards to protect the public health.

(Res. 925, I-09)

Teaching and Evaluating Professionalism in Medical Schools
D-295.954

Our AMA will: (1) strongly urge the Liaison Committee on Medical Education (LCME) to promptly create and enforce uniform accreditation standards that require all LCME-accredited medical schools to evaluate professional behavior regularly as part of medical education; (2) strongly urge the LCME to develop standards for professional behavior with outcome assessments at least every eight years, examining teaching and evaluation of the competencies at LCME-accredited medical schools; (3) recognize that evaluation of professionalism is best performed by medical schools and should not be used in evaluation for licensure of graduates of LCME accredited medical schools; (4) continue its efforts to teach and evaluate professionalism during medical education; and (5) actively oppose, by all available means, any attempt by the National Board of Medical Examiners and/or the Federation of State Medical Boards to add separate, fee-based examinations of behaviors of professionalism to the United States Medical Licensing Examinations.

(Res. 304, A-05)

Physician Reentry
D-300.984

Note: See Table 25

State Authority and Flexibility in Medical Licensure for Telemedicine
D-480.999

Our AMA will:

1. Develop a policy regarding the practice of medicine as it relates to the prescribing of prescription-only pharmaceuticals or other therapies via the Internet

2. Continue its opposition to a single national federalized system of medical licensure.

(CME Rep. 7, A-99)